Computational Hydraulics

Other books by C A Brebbia published by Butterworths

'*Finite element techniques for fluid flow*,' 3rd edn (with J J Connor).

'*Boundary element techniques in engineering*' (with S Walker).

'*New developments in Boundary Element Methods*,' Proc of 2nd Int. Conference in B.E. Methods, Southampton 1980 (ed C A Brebbia).

'*Dynamic analysis of Offshore Structures*' (with S Walker).

Computational Hydraulics

C. A. Brebbia, Dipl.Ing, PhD,
Reader in Computational Mechanics, University of Southampton

and

A. J. Ferrante, Dipl.Ing, PhD,
*President of ISC and Professor of Civil
Engineering, COPPE, U. Federal of Rio de Janeiro*

Butterworths
London · Boston · Sydney · Wellington · Toronto · Durban

First published 1983

© Butterworth & Co (Publishers) Ltd 1983

British Library Cataloguing in Publication Data

Brebbia, C.A.
    Computational hydraulics.
    1. Hydraulic engineering—Data processing
    I. Title II. Ferrante, A.J.
    627′.028′54   TC157.8

    ISBN 0-408-01153-X
        0-408-01322 2 Pbk

Typeset in Great Britain by Mid County Press, London SW15
Printed by Thomson Litho Ltd, East Kilbride, Scotland

D
627. 0285'4
BRE

Preface

The advent of modern computers has had a profound effect in all branches of engineering, but has been more marked in structural and stress analysis applications rather than in hydraulics. This is undoubtedly due to the initial difficulties in modelling many of the complex problems frequently found in hydraulic sciences. The recent development of numerical methods and the capabilities of modern machines has changed this situation and many problems which were, up to recently, considered unsuited for numerical solution can now be solved without difficulty.

Although computer codes are now available for the solution of hydraulic problems, a text does not exist which introduces both students and practicing engineers to computational methods. Hence this text has been written to present in an introductory but modern way computational techniques to hydraulic and fluid flow engineers. The book is the product of several years' experience in teaching and research at undergraduate and post-graduate level and can be used to offer a self-contained course on Computational Hydraulics for final year or M.Sc. Engineering students.

The book combines classical hydraulics with new methods such as finite elements and boundary elements, which are both presented in a matrix formulation. The finite element method is now a well-known technique with many practical applications in hydraulics and fluid flow as described in *Finite Element Techniques for Fluid Flow, 3rd edn*, by J. J. Connor and C. A. Brebbia published by Butterworths. The boundary element method is more recent but it is presented here as an extension of the basic concepts of classical potential theory (see also *Boundary Element Techniques in Engineering* by C. A. Brebbia and S. Walker, published by Butterworths).

The most interesting feature of the book is the integrated treatment given to the theoretical and computing aspects of numerical methods. The format which has been highly successful with structural engineers, presents a series of complete computer programs, for linear and non-linear pipe network analysis, depth flow computations, finite and boundary elements for Laplace equations. The programs which are written in standard FORTRAN are self-contained and easy to implement in any computer.

The authors hope that this book will make practising hydraulic engineers more aware of modern computer techniques and be useful in teaching them to the next generation.

C. A. Brebbia and A. J. Ferrante

This book is dedicated to my former students
at University of California, Irvine.

Carlos Brebbia

Contents

List of Programs

Program for linear analysis of pipe networks
1   Main program
2   Data input (INPUT)
3   Computation of the half-bandwidth (BAND)
4   Assembling of the system matrix (ASSEM)
5   Computation of the element matrix (STIFF)
6   Addition of an element matrix to the system matrix (ELASS)
7   Introduction of boundary conditions (BOUND)
8   Solution of the system of equations (SLBSI)
9   Evaluation of results (RESUL)
10 Result output (OUTPT)

Program for non-linear analysis of pipe networks
11 Main program
12 Data input (INPUT)
13 Evaluation of the initial element coefficient (INCOE)
14 Computation of the element matrix (STIFF)
15 Multiplication of a symmetric banded matrix by a vector (MULTI)
16 Evaluation of results (RESUL)

Program for computation of depth of flow
17 Main program for testing subroutine CHDEP
18 Evaluation for depth of flow for channel

Finite element program for the solution of the Laplace equation
19 Main program
20 Input program (INPUT)
21 Computation of the element matrices (STIFF)
22 Routine for calculating the nodal variables' derivatives (RESUL)
23 Output program (OUTPT)

Boundary element program for the solution of the Laplace equation
24 Main program
25 Input program (INPUT)
26 Assembling of the total system of equations and introduction of the
     boundary conditions (ASBOU)
27 Computation of the off-diagonal terms of the **H** and **G** matrices
     (OFFDGT)
28 Computation of the diagonal terms of matrix **H** (DIAGT)
29 Solution of the system of equations: non-positive-definite case (SLNPD)
30 Computation of internal results (RESUL)
31 Output of the results (OUTPT)

Note. A computer tape containing copies of these programs is available from:
                   Computational Mechanics Centre
                   Ashurst Lodge,
                   Ashurst, Hants SO4 2AA,
                   England

Chapter 1

Properties of fluids

1.1 Introduction

All physical matter is found in nature either as a solid, a liquid or a gas. These forms of matter have chemically stable thermodynamic phases. Depending on parameters such as temperature, pressure, etc., a given substance may adopt any of the three basic forms of matter.

A solid is a substance that does not flow perceptibly under moderate stress, and has a well defined shape and volume.

A liquid is a substance characterised by the free movement of its molecules, but without tendency to separate. A liquid has a definite volume but more or less readily takes the shape of its container. When placed in an open container a liquid will be bound by a free surface. A liquid is slightly compressible.

A gas is a substance that has neither an independent shape nor a volume, but which will tend to expand indefinitely. When placed in a closed container, a gas will tend to fill all the available space. A gas is highly compressible.

Due to their similar behaviour under dynamic conditions, both liquids and gases are known as fluids.

All fluids have a certain amount of viscosity and they deform continuously under a shearing stress. Viscosity is a measure of the resistance to deformation of the fluid and generates internal viscous forces.

In practice there are many fluid problems where viscous forces are negligible compared with other acting forces. In such cases it is consistent to assume that the fluid has a null viscosity. These fluids are called inviscid fluids.

When a fluid is inviscid tangential stresses cannot be applied to a fluid layer by other layers or by solid walls. Two adjacent layers of an inviscid fluid can move with different velocities, without any interaction derived from internal friction. Thus, any layer of an inviscid fluid can be replaced by a solid contour having the same shape, without the movement of the other layers being altered.

Under the assumption of zero viscosity the flow of a fluid in a pipe will present the distribution shown in Figure 1.1(a). For a real fluid, however, the actual velocity field will show a parabolic distribution, as indicated in Figure 1.1(b), where the fluid tends not to slip along the solid surface of the pipe. In spite of this obvious drawback, the behaviour of many fluids can be accurately

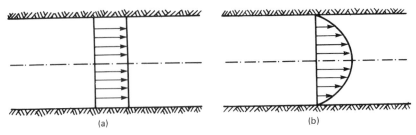

Figure 1.1 Velocity distributions for (a) inviscid and (b) viscous fluids

described as inviscid. These fluids are sometimes called ideal fluids, as opposed to real fluids, which have non-zero viscosity.

Another property of fluids which is sometimes neglected is compressibility, or the ability of a substance to change volume when subjected to direct pressure. Liquids, in particular, are usually considered to be incompressible substances.

1.2 Basic definitions

Mass, denoted by *M*, is the quantity of matter; it is a function of the internal structure, and the dimensions of a substance. In the SI system the unit used to define mass is the kilogram, kg.

Density, denoted by ρ, is defined as the mass per unit volume of a substance. In the SI system, as mass is defined in kg and volume in cubic metres, m^3, density is defined in kilograms per cubic metre, i.e.

$$\rho \left[\frac{kg}{m^3} \right] \tag{1.1}$$

Densities of different liquids are given in Table 1.1. From the previous definitions it follows that the total mass *M* can be expressed as the product of the density ρ times the volume *V*,

$$M \, [kg] = \rho \left[\frac{kg}{m^3} \right] V \, [m^3] \tag{1.2}$$

A mass will be at rest or under uniform motion, unless acted upon by a *force*.

TABLE 1.1. **Density of various liquids** (After Hodgman, C. (Ed.), *Handbook of Chemistry and Physics*, 37th edn, Chemical Rubber Publishing Co., Cleveland (1955).)

Liquid		Temperature (°C)	Density (10^{-3} kg/m³)
Alcohol	Ethyl	20	0.792
	Methyl	20	0.791
Glycerin		0	1.260
Gasoline			0.66–0.69
Mercury			13.6
Sea water		15	1.025
Water		4	1.00

Thus, to put in motion a mass which is at rest, or to change the nature of the motion of a moving mass the application of a force is required. The *weight*, W, of an object is the force applied to that object by the action of *gravity*. In the SI system the acceleration due to gravity, denoted by g, is equal to

$$g = 9.81 \text{ m s}^{-2} \tag{1.3}$$

where the unit of time is the second, s. Then the weight of a mass is equal to the product of the acceleration of gravity times the mass:

$$W = gM = g\rho V \tag{1.4}$$

A dimensional analysis of expression (1.4) will show that, in the SI system, weight is defined by kilograms times metres, divided by square seconds, i.e.

$$W\left[\frac{\text{m kg}}{\text{s}^2}\right] \tag{1.5}$$

That unit is called a newton, with symbol N, and,

$$1 \text{ N} = 1 \text{ newton} = 1 \text{ m kg s}^{-2} \tag{1.6}$$

When using grams, g, and centimetres, cm, i.e. the c.g.s. system, rather than kilograms and metres, the unit for force is the dyne, dyn, given by

$$1 \text{ dyn} = 1 \text{ g cm s}^{-2} = 10^{-5} \text{ N} \tag{1.7}$$

Pressure, denoted by p, is a force per unit area. From its definition it follows that

$$\text{pressure} = \frac{\text{force}}{\text{unit area}} \left[\frac{\text{N}}{\text{m}^2} \text{ or } \frac{\text{kg}}{\text{m s}^2}\right] \tag{1.8}$$

To define *velocity* let us consider a fluid particle, that is the fluid contained in an infinitesimal volume, which is at a position P at initial time t_0. As shown in Figure 1.2, the particle position can be defined by vector $\vec{r}$, which goes from the reference origin O to the particle position P. At time t_1 the particle has moved to a new position, P', which is now identified by vector $\vec{r}'$, going from points O to P'. The difference between the initial position P and the final position P' is given by the vector $\Delta \vec{r}$, also shown in Figure 1.2.

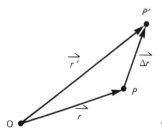

Figure 1.2 Position of particle

The velocity $\vec{v}$ of the particle is defined by the limit of the quotient of $\Delta \vec{r}$ divided by Δt, with Δt equal to $t_1 - t_0$, when t_1 tends to t_0, or $t_1 \to t_0$,

$$\vec{v} = \lim_{t_1 \to t_0} \left(\frac{\Delta \vec{r}}{\Delta t}\right) = \frac{d\vec{r}}{dt} \tag{1.9}$$

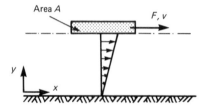

Figure 1.3 Fluid deformation

Thus, the velocity is equal to the derivative of the position vector $\vec{r}$ with regard to time. Therefore, in the SI system, the velocity will be defined in metres per second. Clearly, the velocity of a system of particles is a function of position and time.

The *viscosity* of a fluid, as suggested in the introduction of this chapter, is a measure of the resistance of the fluid to deformation caused by shearing stresses. Although in practice a null viscosity situation is sometimes accepted, all real fluids have some viscosity. In order to clarify further the meaning of a non-null viscosity let us consider the case shown in Figure 1.3, which indicates a fluid filling the space between two parallel plates. It is assumed that the only part of the upper body in contact with the fluid is the face of area A. When a horizontal force F is applied to the upper body, the body starts to move with a certain velocity v_A. This velocity is transmitted to the fluid, for real fluids, in such a way that at face A the fluid velocity is equal to v_A and decreases linearly in the vertical direction, until it becomes zero at the bottom plate. The relationship between the shearing stress τ, at surface A, and the velocity v at any horizontal layer in the fluid is given by Newton's viscosity law,

$$\tau = \mu \frac{dv}{dy} \tag{1.10}$$

where μ is called dynamic viscosity, and is equal to the ratio of the shear stress to the velocity gradient. Clearly, the shear stress will be null for a stationary fluid, which accounts for μ being called 'dynamic' viscosity.

Fluids for which the dynamic viscosity μ is a constant are called Newtonian fluids. For ideal fluids the dynamic viscosity is equal to zero. For solids the shear stress is independent of the velocity gradient. These cases are illustrated in Figure 1.4.

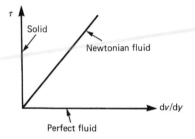

Figure 1.4 Newtonian fluids

Dimensionally, the viscosity is expressed as

$$\mu = \frac{\text{shear stress}}{\text{velocity gradient}} \left[\frac{N}{m^2} s \text{ or } \frac{kg}{m \, s} \right] \tag{1.11}$$

Normally the dynamic viscosity is expressed in poises, symbol P, such that,

$$1 \text{ poise} = 1 \left[\frac{\text{dyn s}}{\text{cm}^2} \right] = 10^{-1} \left[\frac{N \, s}{m^2} \right] = 1 \left[\frac{kg}{m \, s} \right] \tag{1.12}$$

or in centipoises, such that

$$1 \text{ centipoise} = 10^{-2} \left[\frac{\text{dyn s}}{\text{cm}^2} \right] = 10^{-3} \left[\frac{kg}{m \, s} \right] \tag{1.13}$$

It is frequent in some cases to divide the dynamic viscosity μ by the density ρ. The result is called the kinematic viscosity, v, given by

$$v = \frac{\mu}{\rho} \left[\frac{N \, s \, m}{kg} \text{ or } \frac{m^2}{s} \right] \tag{1.14}$$

Values of dynamic viscosity for some fluids are given in Table 1.2 and Figures 1.5(a) and (b).

The dynamic viscosity of water at 20°C is around 1.005 centipoise (cP) and its density is approximately 1 g cm^{-3}. The viscosity of dry air is approximately equal to 18.5×10^{-3} cP and its density at 20°C is approximately equal to 1.20×10^{-3} g cm^{-3}. Their kinematic viscosities are,

TABLE 1.2. Viscosity for different fluids (After Hodgman, C. (Ed.), *Handbook of Chemistry and Physics*, 37th edn, Chemical Rubber Publishing Co., Cleveland (1955).)

Liquid	Temperature (°C)	Viscosity (cP)
Water	0	1.7921
	20	1.0050
	40	0.6560
	70	0.461
	100	0.2838
Ethyl alcohol	0	1.773
	20	1.200
	40	0.834
	70	0.504
Glycerin	0	12 110
	20	1 490
Lead (liquid)	350	2.58
Mercury	0	1.685
	20	1.554
	70	1.331
Methyl alcohol (methanol)	0	0.82
	20	0.597
	40	0.456
Machine oil:	15.6	113.8
light	37.8	34.2
	100	4.9
heavy	15.6	660.6
	37.8	127.4
Sucrose	100	2.8×10^6
(cane sugar)	124.6	1.9×10^5

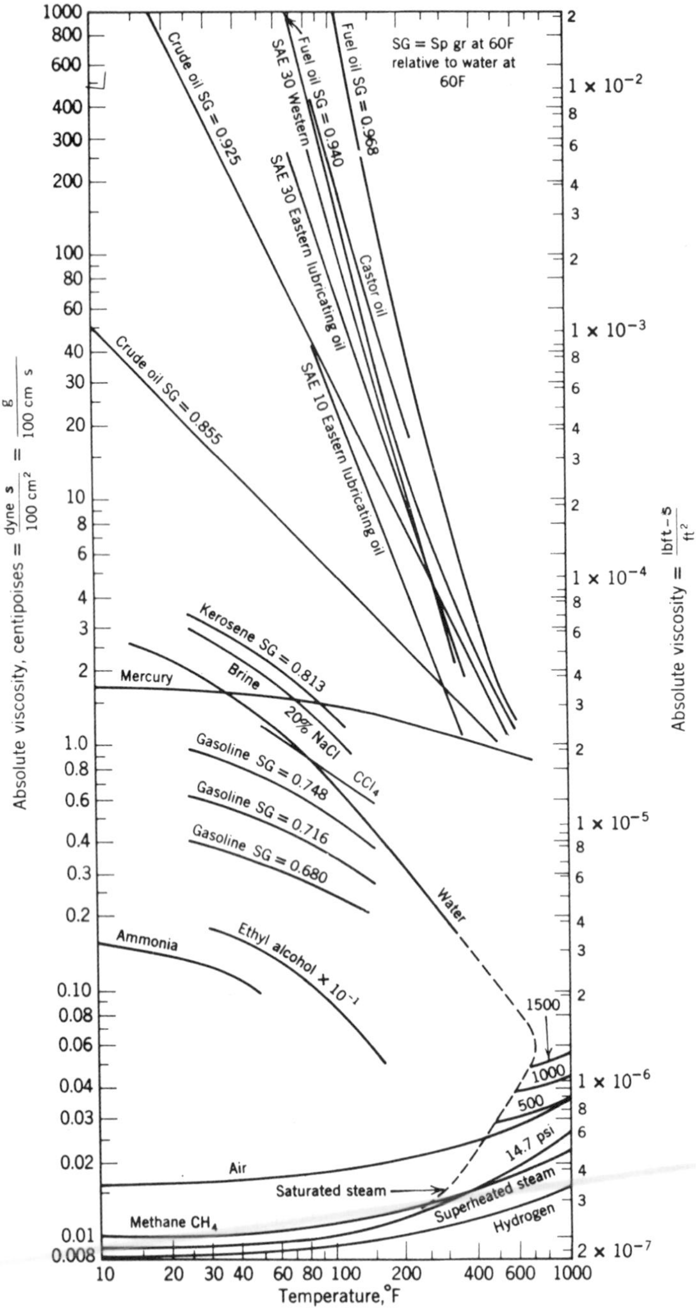

Figure 1.5 (a) Dynamic viscosity of common fluids as a function of temperature (from Fox, R. W. and McDonald, A. J., *Introduction to Fluid Mechanics*, Wiley, New York (1973).

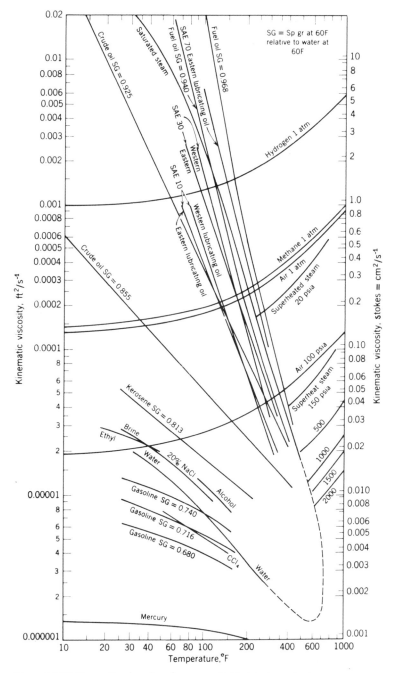

Figure 1.5 (b) Kinematic viscosity of common fluids (at atmospheric pressure) as a function of temperature (from Fox, R. W. and McDonald, A. J., *Introduction to Fluid Mechanics*, Wiley, New York (1973).)

$$v_{\text{water}} = \frac{1.005}{1.00} \, cP \, g^{-1} \, cm^3 = 1.005 \times 10^{-2} \, cm^2 \, s^{-1}$$

$$v_{\text{air}} = \frac{18.5 \times 10^{-3}}{1.20 \times 10^{-3}} \, cP \, g^{-1} \, cm^3 = 15.4 \times 10^{-2} \, cm^2 \, s^{-1} \tag{1.15}$$

Hence, the kinematic viscosity of air is approximately 15 times that of water.

1.3 Hydrostatic pressure

The atmosphere exerts a pressure over the surface of the earth equal to 760 mm of Hg at sea level. This pressure reduces to around 210 mm at 10 000 m and 9.5 mm at 30 000 m,

$$760 \, mm \, of \, Hg = 1.013 \times 10^6 \, dyn \, cm^{-2} = 1.013 \times 10^{-3} \, N \, m^{-2}$$

$$= 1.013 \times 10 \, N \, cm^{-2} \tag{1.16}$$

Hydrostatic pressures are the pressures existing in a stationary fluid. These pressures act normally to the surface under consideration and are independent of the viscosity. The pressure at a given point, for incompressible liquids, is defined in terms of pressure above the atmospheric pressure as indicated in Figure 1.6. The pressure at point P is due to the weight of the liquid column h.

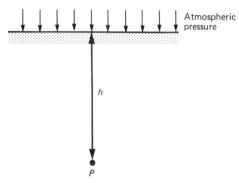

Figure 1.6 Pressure at a point inside a liquid

Hence, the pressure at P is

$$p = \gamma h \left[\frac{N}{m^2} \right] \tag{1.17}$$

where γ is the specific weight of the fluid, given by

$$\gamma = g\rho \left[\frac{kg}{m^2 \, s^2} \quad or \quad \frac{N}{m^3} \right] \tag{1.18}$$

where g is the acceleration due to gravity and ρ is the density. The atmospheric pressure does not need to be taken into account as it acts on all points on the horizontal free surface of the liquid.

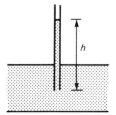

Figure 1.7 Piezometer

The hydrostatic pressure at any point can be measured with a piezometer or manometer. The piezometer shown in Figure 1.7 is simply a sufficiently long tube connected to the liquid in question. The liquid rises up the tube until its pressure equilibrates the atmospheric pressure. The pressure in the mass of liquid is represented by the height of the column. Piezometers can only be used when the pressures are moderate; otherwise, a very long tube would be required!

In order to avoid having a long tube, one can use a manometer, shown in Figure 1.8, where the tube has been bent in a U shape and is partially filled with an immiscible liquid. Mercury is generally used for this purpose because of its large specific weight (13.6 times that of water). The pressure p is now given by

$$p = \gamma_m h_m - \gamma y \qquad (1.19)$$

where h_m is the difference in mercury levels in the two branches of the manometer, y is the height, defined in Figure 1.7, and γ_m is the specific weight of the mercury.

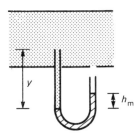

Figure 1.8 Manometer

Sometimes, we prefer to use a *differential* manometer, indicated in Figure 1.9, to measure differences in pressure rather than absolute values. In this case a manometric fluid is also used. Normally this is mercury but, if the difference produced is small, a liquid with less specific weight would be preferred.

The difference in pressure is

$$\Delta p = p_1 - p_2 = \gamma_m h_m + \gamma(y_2 - y_1) \qquad (1.20)$$

Note that for a horizontal pipe,

$$\Delta p = h_m(\gamma_m - \gamma) \qquad (1.21)$$

The Bourdon manometer, shown in Figure 1.10, consists of a closed tube that tends to straighten with pressure rise. This movement is simplified by a mechanism, and one can read the pressure directly on a calibrated scale. These

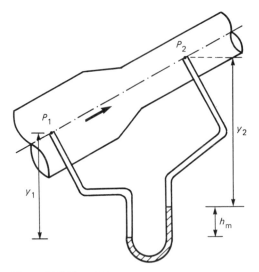

Figure 1.9 Differential manometer

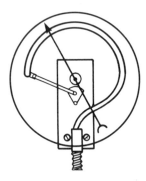

Figure 1.10 Bourdon manometer

manometers are calibrated against other types of manometer and consequently are less precise.

1.4 Hydrostatic pressure forces on submerged bodies

Let us consider first the case of a plane surface submerged in a liquid and inclined at a given angle α, as indicated in Figure 1.11. The centre of gravity of the plate is denoted by G. The centre of pressure P is underneath G due to the linear variation of the hydrostatic pressure with depth.

For a differential element of area $d\Gamma$ the pressure is

$$dP = p\,d\Gamma = \gamma y\,d\Gamma = \gamma \xi \sin \alpha\,d\Gamma \tag{1.22}$$

The total pressure force is thus

$$P = \sin \alpha \int \gamma \xi\,d\Gamma = \gamma \sin \alpha \int \xi\,d\Gamma$$
$$= \gamma \sin \alpha \Gamma \xi_G \tag{1.23}$$

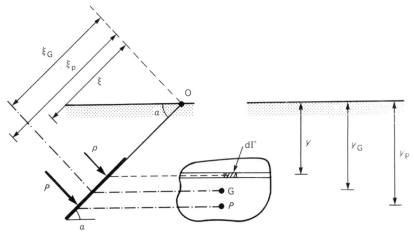

Figure 1.11 Pressure forces on a submerged plate

where Γ is the area of the plate. The moment is

$$\xi \, dP = p\xi \, d\Gamma = \gamma \xi^2 \sin \alpha \, d\Gamma$$

In order to determine the pressure centre, we need to take moments. If we take them with respect to O, for instance,

$$\int \xi \, dP = P\xi_P = \gamma \sin \alpha \int \xi^2 \, d\Gamma \tag{1.24}$$

Note that $\int \xi^2 \, d\Gamma$ is the moment of inertia I_0 of the plate with respect to the axis passing through O.

We also know that according to Steiner's theorem I_0 is given by

$$I_0 = I_G + \Gamma \xi_G^2 \tag{1.25}$$

where I_G is the moment of inertia of the section with respect to an axis passing through the centre of gravity G. The previous expression can also be written as,

$$I_0 = \Gamma r_G^2 + \Gamma \xi_G^2 \tag{1.26}$$

where r_G is the radius of *gyration*.

Hence,

$$P\xi_P = \gamma \sin \alpha \, \Gamma (r_G^2 + \xi_G^2)$$

and (from expression (1.23)),

$$\xi_P = \frac{\gamma \sin \alpha \, \Gamma (r_G^2 + \xi_G^2)}{\gamma \sin \alpha \, \Gamma \xi_G} \tag{1.27}$$

$$\xi_P = \frac{r_G^2}{\xi_G} + \xi_G \tag{1.28}$$

or,

$$y_P = \left(\frac{r_G^2}{\xi_G}\right) \sin \alpha + y_G \tag{1.29}$$

The centre of pressure is at a depth $(r_G^2/\xi_G)\sin\alpha$ under the centre of gravity.

On a curved surface, forces $p\,d\Gamma$ on individual differential elements will have different directions and hence the simplest way of determining the pressure forces is to decompose them in the vertical and horizontal directions and then superimpose their resultants.

Considering Figure 1.12, we can find the vertical pressure forces P_V, which are given by the weight of the water above the surface, and the horizontal component P_H, given by the trapezoidal distribution of pressures from h_1 to h_2.

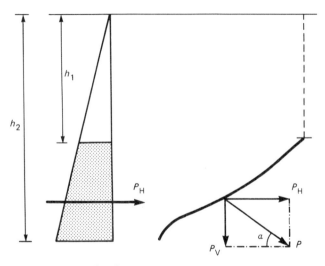

Figure 1.12 Curved surface

The resultant is

$$P^2 = P_H^2 + P_V^2 \tag{1.30}$$

and the angle α is given by

$$\tan \alpha = P_V/P_H \tag{1.31}$$

These considerations can be applied when designing gates in hydraulic structures. The most common gates are radial ones, shown in Figure 1.13(a), and the *drum* gate shown in Figure 1.13(b). Notice that the convex curvature is towards the water to reduce the moments on the supports.

Radial gates are useful to control small as well as large volumes of water. *Drum* gates are used in large spillways. Notice that the water always has access to the flotation chamber.

In both cases, the pressure forces are calculated by decomposing the pressure into horizontal and vertical components as indicated in Figure 1.14.

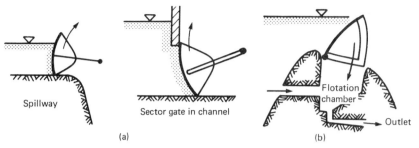

Figure 1.13 (a) Radial gates; (b) 'drum' gate

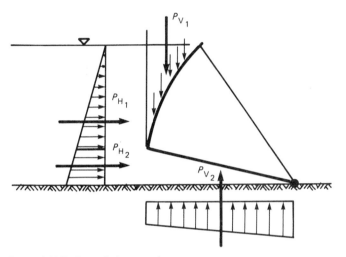

Figure 1.14 Hydrostatic forces acting on a gate

1.5 Buoyancy

Because the pressure in a fluid increases with depth, the fluid will exert an upward force, called buoyancy, on a body that is partially or wholly submerged. This effect is known as Archimedes Principle, which states that the force exerted on the body is equal to the weight of the liquid displaced by the body. The centre of gravity of the displaced fluid is called the centre of buoyancy.

The buoyancy force has a vertical component only because the horizontal pressure forces will always equilibrate.

The hydrostatic position of a floating body depends on its shape and mass. The stability of the body is determined by the position which it adopts when it is disturbed from its position of hydrostatic equilibrium. Figure 1.15 illustrates the transverse section of a ship in hydrostatic equilibrium. The centre of gravity of the ship is at G and itw weight is W. The equilibrium condition is $W = B$, where B is the booyancy force acting on the centre of buoyancy CB. The centre of buoyancy is usually below the centre of gravity.

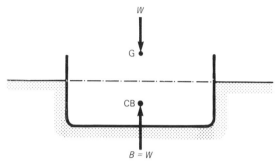

Figure 1.15 Ship in hydrostatic equilibrium

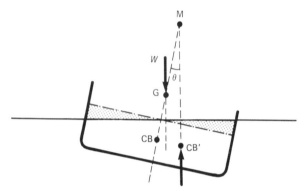

Figure 1.16 Ship in an inclined position

Let us now consider what will happen if the ship is inclined by a small angle θ as indicated in Figure 1.16. If the positions of the masses in the ship are not changed, the centre of gravity G will remain in its original position, but the centre of buoyancy will pass to B' because of the new distribution of pressures on the ship's hull. The total force, $B \equiv W$, is the same because the triangular area which is now above the water level is compensated by the area which is now under it.

The intersection of the vertical line passing through CB' and the line of symmetry, is called the metacentre, M, and it is evident that its relative position with respect to G will determine *stability*. If M is under G, the moment produced by W will tend to increase the θ angle. Otherwise the position will be *stable*. The distance from G to M is the metacentric height and gives an idea of the stability.

Bibliography

ROUSE, H. and INCE, S. *History of Hydraulics*, Iowa Institute of Hydraulic Research, University of Iowa (1957)

HODGMAN, C. (Ed.), *Handbook of Chemistry and Physics* 37th edn, Chemical Rubber Publishing Co., Cleveland (1955)

BOLZ, R.E. and TUVE, G.L. *Handbook of Tables for Applied Engineering Science*, Chemical Rubber Publishing Co., Cleveland (1973)

Chapter 2

Basic concepts of fluids in movement

2.1 Introduction

The basic concepts of fluid dynamics will be reviewed in this chapter, in order to study their application for the solution of engineering problems. For this the fluid is considered to be incompressible.

Two types of fluid flows are found in practice, known as *turbulent* flows and *laminar* flows. In turbulent flows the fluid particles follow irregular paths and the velocities, at a given point, change with time. The instantaneous velocity v can be decomposed into a constant mean velocity component $\bar{v}$, and a variable velocity component v', such that

$$v = \bar{v} + v' \tag{2.1}$$

The distribution of velocities between two plates, for turbulent flow, is depicted in Figure 2.1(a). The particles are subjected not only to axial but also to transverse velocities.

For laminar flow between two plates, the fluid particles, not being subjected to transverse velocities, follow rectilinear paths (Figure 2.1(b)). If a colour dye is injected as a tracer the result will be a thin rectilinear line for laminar flow, while for turbulent flow the colour will be rapidly dispersed in the fluid.

Laminar flows exist for low velocity and high viscosity fluids. The theory describing laminar flow is mathematically very well developed. That is not the case for turbulent flow, however, which is still a largely unknown area for research.

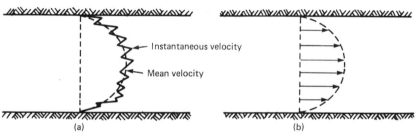

Figure 2.1 (a) Turbulent and (b) laminar flow

Flows can also be classified as rotational or irrotational. In a rotational flow the fluid particles will possess a non-zero angular velocity, while for irrotational flows that velocity component will be null. In Figure 2.2 we illustrate both types of flow, by defining an infinitesimal particle of dimension $dx\,dy$, and studying the rotation of the axes. Figure 2.2(a) shows a flow where velocities in the horizontal direction are constant for any given height, but there is a vertical velocity gradient. Because of this the particle will rotate, having a non-zero angular velocity, and producing a rotational flow. Figure 2.2(b) shows a flow with a uniform distribution of velocities in the x and y directions. Since there is no velocity gradient the particle will not rotate and irrotational flow is produced.

Figure 2.3 shows the case of a flow in a circular conduit. This is interesting because the flow will be rotational or irrotational depending on the distribution of the velocities. If the velocities are proportional to the radius, the particle rotates in the clockwise direction, and the flow will be rotational. On the other hand, if the distribution of velocities is inversely proportional to the radius, the rotation of one axis will be compensated by the rotation of the other one, and the flow will be irrotational.

In practice, because of their viscosity, all fluids have some rotationality. In many cases, however, real flows can be treated as inviscid, and therefore as irrotational, without giving rise to large errors.

Another important distinction is between *stationary* and *non-stationary* flows. A flow will be stationary when its characteristics are constant with time,

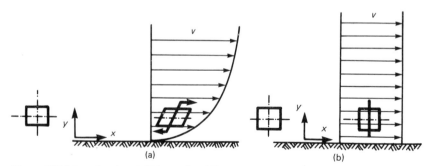

Figure 2.2 (a) Rotational and (b) irrotational flow

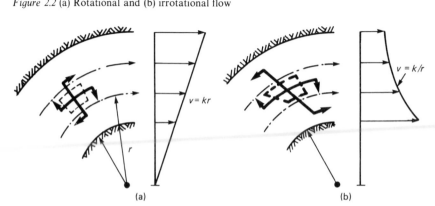

Figure 2.3 Flow in a circular channel: (a) rotational; (b) irrotational (from Webber, N., *Fluid Mechanics for Civil Engineers*, E. & F. N. Spon, London 1965).

at any given point. Non-stationary flows will occur when the flow characteristics vary with time. These types of flow are also known as *steady* and *unsteady*.

2.2 Pathlines and streamlines

The curve described by a given particle during its motion is called a *pathline*, and shows how the particle is moving at each instant. Pathlines can be traced using dyes, for either steady or unsteady laminar flow.

Streamlines are lines drawn such that their tangents at any point are in the direction of the particle velocity. They may alter with time for unsteady flow or may be the same at all times for steady flow. The streamlines show the flow directions at each instant. Since the streamlines are tangential to the velocity vector at every point, there cannot be flow across a streamline.

It is also possible to define a *streakline* as the line joining all particles passing through the same fixed point in the fluid.

For a steady flow a particle located in a streamline will remain in the same streamline, and particles passing through the same fixed point in space will also be on the same streamline. Thus, for steady motion the streamlines, pathlines and streaklines coincide, while for unsteady motion they will generally be different.

A *stream tube* is defined as the tube formed by an envelope of streamlines, as indicated in Figure 2.4. From the previous discussion it is clear that the stream tube will behave as an actual tube in the case of steady flow, because there is no flow in directions normal to the streamlines.

A stream tube with an infinitesimally small cross-section is called a *stream filament*.

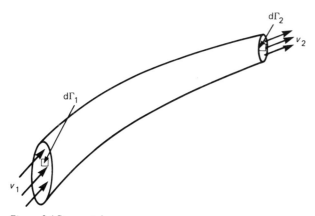

Figure 2.4 Stream tube

2.3 Continuity equation

The idea of the stream tube allows one to formulate the continuity equation in a simple way. Considering the stream tube of Figure 2.4, and assuming the fluid to be incompressible, conservation of mass requires that the quantity of fluid which flows in at one end flows out at the other. This condition can be written as

$$\int_{\Gamma_1} v_1 \, d\Gamma_1 = \int_{\Gamma_2} v_2 \, d\Gamma_2 \tag{2.2}$$

where $d\Gamma_1$ and $d\Gamma_2$ are the surface differentials, and v_1 and v_2 are the velocities, at ends 1 and 2 respectively. Integration of this equation gives the total flux:

$$Q = V_1\Gamma_1 = V_2\Gamma_2 \tag{2.3}$$

where V_1 and V_2 are the mean velocities, and Γ_1 and Γ_2 are the areas, at ends 1 and 2, respectively. Then, for a stream tube, the continuity equation means that

$$Q = V\Gamma = \text{constant} \tag{2.4}$$

for any section Γ, having a mean velocity V.

According to the previous expression the velocity is inversely proportional to the area of the section under consideration. Thus, streamlines tend to approach each other more closely in areas of larger velocity.

2.4 Bernouilli's equation

Figure 2.5 shows a stream filament. The length of a differential element of the stream filament is ds, and the area of the cross-section is $d\Gamma$. The weight of that differential element will be $\gamma \, ds \, d\Gamma$, where γ is the specific weight of the fluid. The pressure acting on the left-hand side area is equal to p, and on the right-

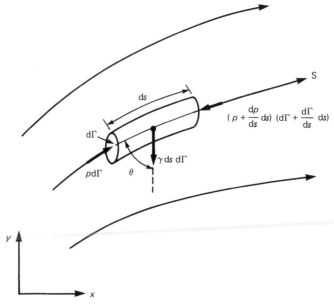

Figure 2.5 Forces acting on a stream filament

hand side area is equal to $p+(\mathrm{d}p/\mathrm{d}s)\,\mathrm{d}s$. Making use of Newton's law, which states that force is the product of mass and acceleration, the condition for equilibrium in the direction of s is expressed by

$$-\gamma\,\mathrm{d}s\,\mathrm{d}\Gamma\cos\theta+p\,\mathrm{d}\Gamma-\left(p+\frac{\mathrm{d}p}{\mathrm{d}s}\,\mathrm{d}s\right)\mathrm{d}\Gamma=\rho\,\mathrm{d}s\,\mathrm{d}\Gamma\frac{\mathrm{D}v}{\mathrm{D}t}$$

(2.5)

which reduces to

$$-\gamma\cos\theta-\left(\frac{\mathrm{d}p}{\mathrm{d}s}\right)=\rho\,\frac{\mathrm{D}v}{\mathrm{D}t}$$

(2.6)

where ρ is the fluid density and t is time. From Figure 2.5 it follows that

$$\cos\theta=\mathrm{d}y/\mathrm{d}s$$

(2.7)

where y is the vertical coordinate. For steady flow,*

$$\frac{\mathrm{D}v}{\mathrm{D}t}=v\,\frac{\mathrm{d}v}{\mathrm{d}s}$$

(2.8)

Substituting equations (2.7) and (2.8) into equation (2.6) gives,

$$\gamma\,\frac{\mathrm{d}y}{\mathrm{d}s}+\frac{\mathrm{d}p}{\mathrm{d}s}+\rho v\,\frac{\mathrm{d}v}{\mathrm{d}s}=0$$

(2.9)

or

$$\frac{\mathrm{d}}{\mathrm{d}s}\left(y+\frac{p}{\gamma}+\frac{v^2}{2g}\right)=0$$

(2.10)

where g is the acceleration due to gravity.

Integrating along a streamline S for a fluid of constant density, gives

$$y+\frac{p}{\gamma}+\frac{v^2}{2g}=\text{constant}$$

(2.11)

* *Acceleration of a Fluid Particle.* Notice that the acceleration of a fluid particle $(\mathrm{D}v/\mathrm{D}t)$ is a function of the velocity v and this velocity is function of position and time. This is due to two reasons: (i) the particle moves from one position to another with different velocity at the same instance of time; (ii) during the time taken by the particle to move to the new position the velocity at the final position will be changing. Hence any δv is given by adding the increase due to the change of position say at δs distance, for the particle and the increase due to the δt time increment, i.e.

$$\delta v(t,s)=\frac{\delta v}{\delta s}\,\delta s+\frac{\delta v}{\delta t}\,\delta t$$

Hence for the limit $\delta t\to0$,

$$\lim_{\delta t\to0}\left(\frac{\delta v}{\delta t}\right)=\frac{\mathrm{D}v}{\mathrm{D}t}=\lim_{\delta t\to0}\left(\frac{\delta v}{\delta s}\frac{\delta s}{\delta t}+\frac{\delta v}{\delta t}\right)$$

$$=v\,\frac{\delta v}{\delta s}+\frac{\delta v}{\delta t}$$

The derivative $\mathrm{D}v/\mathrm{D}t$ is called the material or total derivative and is explained in more detail in section 6.1.

This is a form of Bernouilli's equation. Note that the terms in equation (2.11) have the dimension of length; hence they are called:

y: head or elevation associated with potential energy (gravitational or potential energy/weight);

p/γ: pressure head or elevation ('pressure' energy/weight);

$v^2/2g$: term due to the kinetic energy; sometimes called velocity head (kinetic energy/weight).

The sum of the three terms gives the total elevation and is sometimes indicated by *h*.

In spite of the dimension involved, Bernouilli's equation is an equation of motion because it has been obtained from Newton's law. It is valid for steady flow and was deduced for inviscid and constant-density fluids. The constant is generally the same only over a streamline.

2.5 Applications of Bernouilli's equation

2.5.1 Pipes and channels

Let us consider how equation (2.11) can be interpreted for the pipe and channel shown in Figure 2.6. In each case two sections with elevations y_1 and y_2 will be considered. The pressure at each end is usually found by a manometer reading, in the case of a pipe, or simply by knowing the position of the free surface, in the case of a channel. The velocity heads are $v_1^2/2g$ and $v_2^2/2g$ for the two sections. Bernouilli's equation implies that the energies for sections 1 and 2 are the same.

In practice this constant-energy principle is not valid as there is always loss of energy due to friction, turbulence, or other causes. This loss, called 'head loss', is represented in Figure 2.6 by the difference between the dot-dashed horizontal line and the dot-dashed inclined line representing the sum of energies. The latter is called the total energy line.

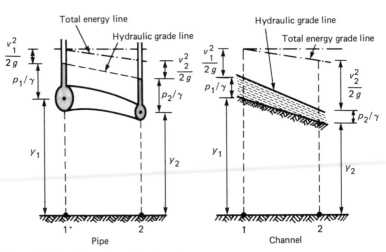

Figure 2.6 Flow in a pipe and a channel

2.5.2 Stagnation pressure

Consider a cylindrical obstruction as shown in Figure 2.7. The divergency of the streamlines indicates a reduction in the velocity and an increase in the pressure. Note that the centre streamline, by symmetry, will touch the cylinder at S. This streamline will divide into two parts at S, and consequently the tangent is normal to the original streamline, which implies that the velocity of the flow is zero there. This point is called the point of stagnation, and the corresponding pressure is the stagnant pressure, p_s. Applying Bernouilli's equation at O and S, we can write,

$$\frac{p_0}{\gamma} + \frac{v_0^2}{2g} = \frac{p_s}{\gamma} \tag{2.12}$$

hence $p_s = p_0 + \frac{1}{2}\rho v_0^2$ (2.13)

where p_0 and v_0 are the pressure and velocity in the fluid before the obstruction.

Points of stagnation will appear if the streamline suddenly changes direction with an interior angle of less than 180°. For instance, in Figure 2.8, a point of stagnation will appear at S.

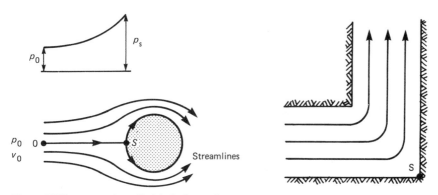

Figure 2.7 Flow around a cylindrical obstruction   *Figure 2.8* Streamlines and stagnation point

Problem 2.1
A submarine, submerged in sea water, travels at 20 km h^{-1}. Calculate the pressure at the front stagnation point situated 10 m below the sea surface. Consider that the density of sea water is equal to 1026 kg m^{-3}.

The stagnation pressure is given by

$$p_s = p_0 + \frac{1}{2}\rho v_0^2$$

or, in this case,

$$p_s = \gamma H + \frac{1}{2}\rho v_0^2$$

where H is the depth of the stagnation point. Then,

$$p_s = 1206 \times 9.81 \times 10 + \tfrac{1}{2} \times 1026\left(\frac{20 \times 1000}{3600}\right)^2$$

or

$$p_s = 116.5 \times 10^3 \text{ N m}^{-2} = 116.5 \text{ kN m}^{-2}$$

2.5.3 The Pitot tube

The stagnation principle is the foundation of Pitot's tube, which is an instrument designed to measure fluid velocities. Its simple version is a tube curved at 90°, open at both ends, as shown in Figure 2.9. One extreme is immersed in the fluid and faces in the direction of the current; the other is open to the atmosphere. A stagnation point will exist in the submerged branch, and the pressure inside it exceeds that of the surrounding fluid by the velocity head $v^2/2g$, which is represented by the height of the liquid forced up the vertical part of the tube. Therefore

$$h = \frac{v^2}{2g} = \frac{\Delta p}{\gamma} \quad \text{(stagnation pressure)} \tag{2.14}$$

One could calculate v using this formula. Unfortunately the difference of level is usually very small.

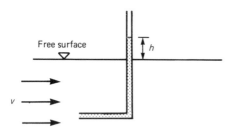

Figure 2.9 Simple Pitot tube (free surface flow)

Notice that for an open stream channel flow, the Δp stagnation pressure represents the difference between the stagnation and static heads, the latter represented by the depth. For enclosed flow, however, h will represent the stagnation pressure only, and so the static pressure needs to be measured separately.

We can measure the static pressure by another tube on the boundary of the flow as indicated in Figure 2.10, where tube A is recording the static pressure and B the stagnation pressure in a pipe of small diameter.

The two tubes are usually combined into one instrument, known as the Pitot static tube, shown in Figure 2.11. Due to its form, this tube produces very little alteration in the flow. The two tubes are connected to a manometer that gives the difference in pressure $\Delta p = p_s - p$. Then,

$$v = \sqrt{2g\,\Delta p/\gamma} = \sqrt{2\,\Delta p/\rho} \tag{2.15}$$

In general, a correction coefficient C, which is very near one, is used to take shape factors and other effects into consideration. This coefficient is obtained

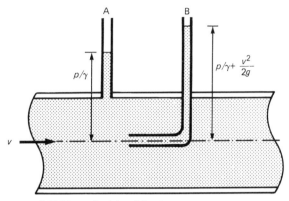

Figure 2.10 Pitot tube (closed flow)

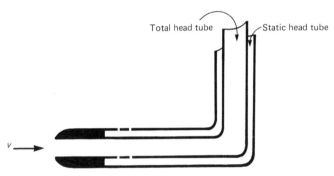

Figure 2.11 Pitot tube

from calibration and finally we obtain

$$v = C\sqrt{2\,\Delta p/\rho} \tag{2.16}$$

2.5.4 Venturi meter

The Venturi meter is used to measure the rate of flow in a fluid. The meter consists of a tube with shape as shown in Figure 2.12. It gives a greater velocity at the throat than at the inlet, and consequently produces a difference in pressure which enables the rate of flow to be calculated.

Along a streamline, one has

$$\frac{v_2^2}{2g} + \frac{p_2}{\gamma} + y_2 = \frac{v_1^2}{2g} + \frac{p_1}{\gamma} + y_1 \tag{2.17}$$

where the subscripts 1, 2 refer to quantities at points 1, 2 in Figure 2.12. For continuity, and considering fluids with constant density, the ratio between areas Ω_1 and Ω_2 must be

$$\frac{v_2}{v_1} = \frac{\Omega_1}{\Omega_2} \tag{2.18}$$

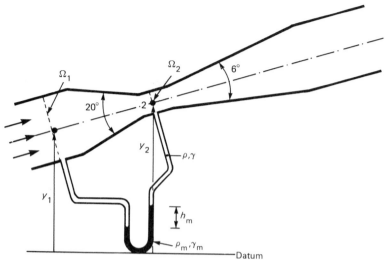

Figure 2.12 Venturi meter

Hence, substituting v_2 into equation (2.17), gives

$$v_1 = \left(\frac{2g[(p_1/\gamma + y_1) - (p_2/\gamma + y_2)]}{(\Omega_1/\Omega_2)^2 - 1}\right)^{1/2} \tag{2.19}$$

The change in piezometric head h is given by the differential manometer shown in Figure 2.12, and is defined by the expression

$$h = \left[\left(\frac{p_1}{\gamma} + y_1\right) - \left(\frac{p_2}{\gamma} + y_2\right)\right] \tag{2.20}$$

Note that the ratio of the piezometric head h to h_m can be obtained from,

$$\Delta p = p_1 - p_2 = (\gamma_m - \gamma)h_m + \gamma(y_2 - y_1)$$

thus

$$(p_1 + \gamma y_1) - (p_2 + \gamma y_2) = (\gamma_m - \gamma)h_m$$

which gives,

$$h_m = \left(\frac{\gamma}{\gamma_m - \gamma}\right)\left[\left(\frac{p_1}{\gamma} + y_1\right) - \left(\frac{p_2}{\gamma} + y_2\right)\right]$$

$$= \left(\frac{\gamma}{\gamma_m - \gamma}\right)h$$

Hence,

$$h_m = \left(\frac{\gamma}{\gamma_m - \gamma}\right)h$$

The discharge is simply

$$Q = \Omega_1 v_1 = \Omega_1 \left(\frac{2gh}{(\Omega_1/\Omega_2)^2 - 1} \right)^{1/2}$$
(2.21)

Due to frictional effects, pressure p_2 is slightly less than the corresponding pressure for an inviscid flow, and hence the head h is greater. To account for this discrepancy, a coefficient of discharge C, which is around 0.97–0.98, is introduced. This coefficient also accounts for non-uniformity in the velocity profiles at sections 1 and 2, so that

$$Q = C\Omega_1 \left(\frac{2gh}{(\Omega_1/\Omega_2)^2 - 1} \right)^{1/2}$$
(2.22)

The diverging part of the meter has a small angle to gradually reduce the velocity to its original value. Sometimes, however, this is not done in the nozzle and orifice type Venturi meters, illustrated in Figures 2.13 and 2.14. The dissipation of energy for these two meters is much larger than for the previous one, but they are popular due to their reduced cost.

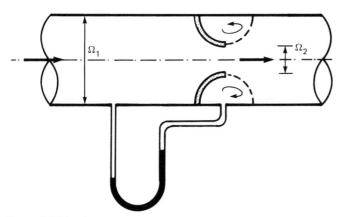

Figure 2.13 Nozzle meter

Problem 2.2
Considering the Venturi tube shown in Figure 2.12 derive an expression relating the volume rate of flow with the manometer reading.

Application of Bernouilli's equation gives

$$\frac{p_1}{\gamma} + \frac{v_1^2}{2g} + y_1 = \frac{p_2}{\gamma} + \frac{v_2^2}{2g} + y_2$$
(a)

This expression can also be written in the form

$$p_1 - p_2 + \rho g(y_1 - y_2) = \tfrac{1}{2}\rho(v_2^2 - v_1^2)$$
(b)

For circular tubes, the continuity equation

$$Q = v_1\Omega_1 = v_2\Omega_2$$
(c)

can also be written in the form

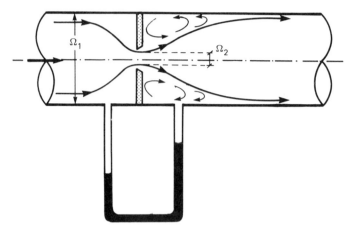

Figure 2.14 Orifice meter

$$v_1 D_1^2 = v_2 D_2^2 = 4Q/\pi \tag{d}$$

where D_1 and D_2 are the diameters at sections 1 and 2, respectively. From the manometer

$$p_1 + h_m l_m g - (y_2 - y_1 - h_m g)\rho g = p_2 \tag{e}$$

or

$$p_1 - p_2 + \rho g(y_1 - y_2) = h_m g(\rho_m - \rho) \tag{f}$$

Finally, combining equations (b), (d) and (f) gives

$$Q = \frac{\pi D_2^2}{4} \left(\frac{2h_m g(\rho_m/\rho - 1)}{1 - (D_2/D_1)^4} \right)^{1/2} \tag{g}$$

2.5.5 Orifices

Another application of Bernouilli's equation is in the study of flow through orifices such as in the case shown in Figure 2.15. The reservoir and the free surface are assumed to be large by comparison with the dimensions of the orifice.

The jet of fluid coming from the orifice will be subject to gravity. The streamlines will continue to converge beyond the orifice until they are parallel

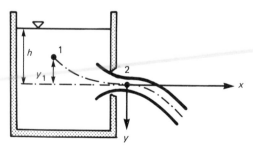

Figure 2.15 Flow through an orifice

at point 2 where the section reaches a minimum area, which is called the 'vena contracta'. Frictional effects will ensure parallel streamlines for a short distance, and afterwards the streamlines may diverge again.

Bernouilli's equation can be applied between two points on a particular streamline, like points 1 and 2 in Figure 2.15. This gives,

$$\frac{p_1}{\gamma} + \frac{v_1^2}{2g} + y_1 = \frac{p_a}{\gamma} + \frac{v_2^2}{2g} + 0 \tag{2.23}$$

where p_a is atmospheric pressure.

If the container is large and point 1 is far from the orifice, one can take the velocity v_1, to be approximately equal to zero. At that point we find hydrostatic conditions only, such that

$$p_1 = \gamma(h - y_1) + p_a \tag{2.24}$$

Equation (2.23) now gives,

$$h = \frac{v_2^2}{2g}$$

and so

$$v_2 = \sqrt{2gh} \tag{2.25}$$

In practice, a velocity coefficient c_v, approximately equal to 0.97, is introduced because of energy losses due to viscosity, such that

$$v_c = c_v \sqrt{2gh} \tag{2.26}$$

where v_c is the velocity at the vena contracta.

One can also find the shape of the jet by working with coordinates x and y in Figure 2.15, with origin in the 'vena contracta' section. Due to gravitational effects, one has the following velocities:

$u = v_2$, velocity in x direction

$v = gt$, velocity in y direction $\tag{2.27}$

The coordinates are obtained by integration:

$x = ut$

$y = \frac{1}{2}gt^2 \tag{2.28}$

where t is the time taken for the particle to go from point 2 to the point under consideration. One can eliminate time t from equations (2.28), which gives,

$$y = \frac{g}{2v_2^2} x^2 = \frac{1}{4h} x^2 \tag{2.29}$$

This equation shows that the trajectory of the particle is parabolic. Notice that if the coordinates x, y are known at any point on the jet one can determine the velocity of discharge and consequently the flow rate.

2.6 The momentum equation for steady flow

Consider a small fluid element in a stream tube. During a time interval δt, the mass of fluid will be

$$\rho \, \delta Q \, \delta t \qquad\qquad (2.30)$$

Newton's second law states that the net force acting on a body in a given direction is equal to the rate of increase of momentum in that direction. If we apply Newton's law, expressed as force = mass × acceleration the increase of the resulting force in the x direction will be

$$\delta F_x = \rho \, \delta Q \, \delta t \, \frac{\delta v_x}{\delta t} \qquad\qquad (2.31)$$

or,

$$\delta F_x = \rho \, \delta Q[(v_x)_2 - (v_x)_1] \qquad\qquad (2.32)$$

where $(v_x)_2$ and $(v_x)_1$ are the components of velocities in the x direction at outlet and inlet, respectively (see Figure 2.16).

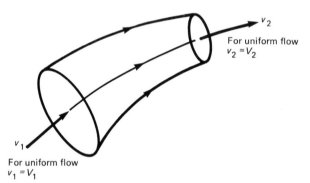

For uniform flow
$v_2 = V_2$

For uniform flow
$v_1 = V_1$

Figure 2.16 Diagram for momentum equation

For a uniform velocity distribution at inlet and outlet, one can write

$$F_x = \rho Q[(V_x)_1 - (V_x)_2] \qquad\qquad (2.33)$$

and similarly for y and z, such that

$$F_y = \rho Q[(V_y)_1 - (V_y)_2] \qquad\qquad (2.34)$$

$$F_z = \rho Q[(V_z)_1 - (V_z)_2] \qquad\qquad (2.35)$$

Note that the quantity ρQ is the rate of mass flow. For uniform flow (Figure 2.16) one can write:

$$\rho Q = \rho \Omega_1 V_1 = \rho \Omega_2 V_2 \qquad\qquad (2.36)$$

where Ω_1 and Ω_2 are the cross-sectional areas of the stream tube.

The momentum equation is of great importance in fluids as it allows forces and velocities to be related in a simple way, without having to consider complex transformation of internal energy.

2.7 Applications of the momentum equation

In many cases the momentum equation is used in combination with the continuity equation and Bernouilli's equation to study complex flow problems. It can be used in problems for which there is a sudden change in velocity or flow direction, as in hydraulic pumps, hydraulic machineries, etc.

2.7.1 Nozzle

Assume that we have a nozzle in a tube, which produces a water jet discharging in the atmosphere. In such a case one needs to know the reaction force R produced by the contraction.

Noting that the forces acting on the system (Figure 2.17(a)) are the hydrostatic forces $p_1\Omega_1$ and $p_2\Omega_2$ at points 1 and 2, respectively, and the reaction R_x due to the walls acting on the fluid, one can write the momentum equation as,

$$\text{force} = p_1\Omega_1 - p_2\Omega_2 - R_x = \rho Q(V_2 - V_1) \tag{2.37}$$

If the discharge is into the atmosphere, such that pressure p_2 can be taken to be zero, the previous expression gives

$$R_x = p_1\Omega_1 - \rho Q(V_2 - V_1) \tag{2.38}$$

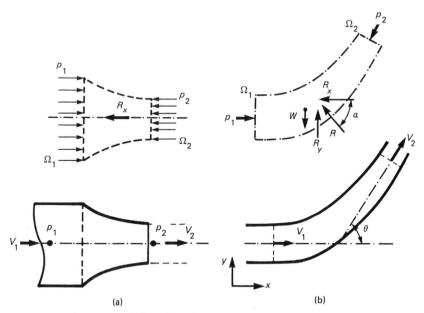

(a)   (b)

Figure 2.17 (a) Jet nozzle; (b) bend in a pipe

2.7.2 Change of velocity and direction

Now consider the flow around a pipe bend as shown in Figure 2.17(b). Applying the momentum equation in two directions, one finds the following expressions:

(a) in direction x

$$p_1\Omega_1 - p_2\Omega_2 \cos\theta - R_x = \rho Q(V_2 \cos\theta - V_1) \qquad (2.39)$$

(b) in direction y

$$R_y - W - p_2\Omega_2 \sin\theta = \rho Q V_2 \sin\theta \qquad (2.40)$$

where W is the weight of the fluid between sections 1 and 2.

One can obtain the reactions R_x and R_y from expressions (2.39) and (2.40), and then calculate the total resultant reaction R as

$$R = \sqrt{R_x^2 + R_y^2} \qquad (2.41)$$

Note that the direction of the reaction R is given by

$$\tan\alpha = R_y / R_x \qquad (2.42)$$

2.8 Flow along a curvilinear path

We now consider the forces acting on a fluid moving along a curvilinear path for the two particular cases corresponding to movement with free vortex and movement with forced vortex.

The forces acting on an elementary volume moving along a curvilinear path are shown in Figure 2.18, where v is the velocity, F is the centrifugal force, v^2/r

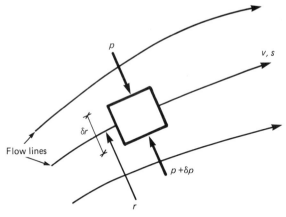

Figure 2.18 Fluid moving along a curvilinear path:

$$\delta s/r = \delta v_n/v \rightarrow \partial v_n/\partial s = v/r$$

$$\frac{1}{\rho}\frac{\partial}{\partial n}(p + \gamma h) = v\frac{\partial v_n}{\partial s} = \frac{v^2}{r}$$

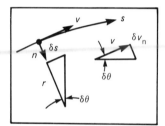

Figure 2.19

is the radial acceleration due to curvature, and δV is the elementary volume equal to $\delta\Omega\ \delta r$. Hence the force F is equal to

$$F = \rho\ \delta\Omega\ \delta r\left(\frac{v^2}{r}\right) \tag{2.43}$$

This force has to be equilibrated by the pressure difference, such that

$$F = \delta p\ \delta\Omega \tag{2.44}$$

Then, in the direction normal to the flow, we have

$$\delta p\ \delta\Omega = \rho\ \delta r\left(\frac{v^2}{r}\right)\delta\Omega \tag{2.45}$$

or

$$\frac{dp}{dr} = \rho\left(\frac{v^2}{r}\right) \tag{2.46}$$

Note that if the flow lines are straight, r will be equal to infinity and dp/dr will be equal to zero, which is correct.

2.8.1 Free vortex

A free vortex in an ideal fluid will remain in movement without any addition of external energy. It can be originated by some small perturbation effect, such as the one due to the movement of the earth.

In a free vortex, shown in Figure 2.20, the flow lines are circular and concentric. As there is no exchange of energy with the exterior, the energy is constant along the flow lines and in all the parts of the same horizontal plane. Hence

$$\frac{p}{\gamma} + \frac{v^2}{2g} = \text{constant} \tag{2.47}$$

Differentiating with respect to r, gives

$$\frac{dp}{dr} = -\rho v\frac{dv}{dr} \tag{2.48}$$

Hence, equating equations (2.46) and (2.48), one finds

$$\frac{v^2}{r} = -v\frac{dv}{dr} \tag{2.49}$$

or

$$\frac{dv}{v} + \frac{dr}{r} = 0$$

Integrating, this last expression gives,

$$\ln v + \ln r = \text{constant} \tag{2.50}$$

or,

$$\ln(vr) = \text{constant} \tag{2.51}$$

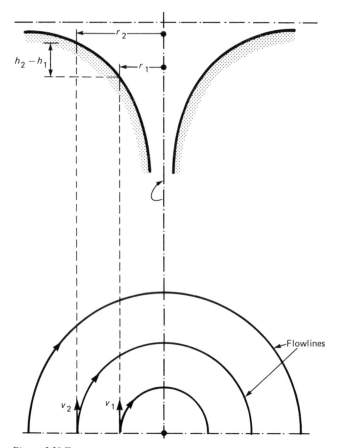

Figure 2.20 Free vortex

or,

$$vr = \text{constant}$$

This result indicates that in a free vortex the velocity is inversely proportional to the radius. In principle the velocity would tend to infinity when the radius tends to zero, but this is impossible in practice, when dealing with real fluids.

One can now determine the pressure distribution by applying Bernouilli's equation for the case in which the radi r_1 and r_2 are equal, obtaining

$$\frac{p_1}{\gamma} + \frac{v_1^2}{2g} = \frac{p_2}{\gamma} + \frac{v_2^2}{2g} \tag{2.52}$$

or

$$\frac{p_2 - p_1}{\gamma} = \frac{v_1^2}{2g}\left[1 - \left(\frac{r_1}{r_2}\right)^2\right] \tag{2.53}$$

Hence the variation of the pressure with the radius is hyperbolic. On the surface both pressures p_1 and p_2 are equal to the atmospheric pressure p_a, but we have a difference in head, such that

$$\Delta h = h_2 - h_1 = \frac{v_1^2}{2g}\left[1 - \left(\frac{r_1}{r_2}\right)^2\right]$$

The profile of the free surface is an asymptotic curve, where for r_2 equal to infinity,

$$\Delta h = v_1^2/2g \tag{2.54}$$

and for r_2 equal to zero,

$$\Delta h = -\infty \tag{2.55}$$

In an ideal fluid a free vortex will remain unaltered without any addition of external energy, and can be originated by some small perturbation effect.

2.8.2 Forced vortex

A forced vortex is produced and maintained by the application of an external force. Consider for instance the case of a cylindrical container partially filled with a liquid and rotating with respect to its vertical axis. The fluid will rotate with the same angular velocity as the container; as shown in Figure 2.21. Strictly speaking the forced vortex is only possible with a real fluid, that is a fluid with non-null viscosity. Since the angular velocity ω is the same throughout the fluid, the velocity

$$v = \omega r \tag{2.56}$$

increases with radius. Notice that this is contrary to what happens in the case of a free vortex.

The pressure gradient is

$$\frac{dp}{dr} = \rho\left(\frac{v^2}{r}\right) = \rho\omega^2 r \tag{2.57}$$

Integrating one obtains,

$$\int dp = \rho\omega^2 \int r\,dr \tag{2.58}$$

or,

$$p = \rho\frac{\omega^2 r^2}{2} + \text{constant} \tag{2.59}$$

Assuming that the pressure p is equal to p_0 when the radius r is zero, we can eliminate the constant and write

$$\frac{p - p_0}{\rho g} = \frac{\omega^2 r^2}{2g} \tag{2.60}$$

In this expression one can multiply both terms by g to obtain heads in units of length.

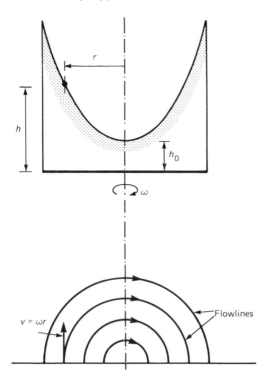

Figure 2.21 Forced vortex

This equation defines a parabolic pressure distribution for a horizontal section. The free surface is given by

$$h - h_0 = \omega^2 r^2 / 2g$$

which is the expression for a paraboloid.

Substituting the velocity v for ωr in equation (2.60), it is evident that an increase in pressure head from p_1/γ to p_2/γ is related to an increase in the kinetic head from $v_1^2/2g$ to $v_2^2/2g$. Producing a forced kinetic head will give rise to a pressure head. One can use this principle in the centrifugal pump. In this case, the water enters at low pressure and velocity at the centre and is expelled at high pressure and velocity at the perimeter.

2.9 Behaviour of real fluids

In practice, although the ideal fluid assumption is often acceptable, there are a number of effects which cause real fluids to behave differently. The more important of these effects are reviewed in what follows.

2.9.1 Turbulence

In many cases, pressures and velocities fluctuate through the fluid, producing vorticity and losses of energy. To analyse this type of flow, one requires knowledge of the time-dependent variation of velocities and pressures, which is only possible using statistical approaches. To date a complete treatment of turbulent flow has defeated analysis, although some simple approximations can give reasonable results in many cases.

Boussinesq proposed the following expression for shear forces produced by turbulence:

$$\tau = \eta \frac{dv}{dy} \tag{2.61}$$

This expression is similar to that used in laminar flow, but η is now the turbulent or 'eddy' viscosity and depends on the turbulence rather than on the fluid properties.

Hence the total shear in a turbulent flow is given by

$$\tau = \mu \frac{dv}{dy} + \eta \frac{dv}{dy} \tag{2.62}$$

where μ is a measure of the fluid viscosity and η of the turbulent viscosity. In many cases, the dynamic viscosity μ can be neglected by comparison with η. An exception is the case of the boundary layer where one does not have normal fluctuations, and the molecular viscosity is dominant.

Prandtl introduced the idea of 'mixing length' in turbulence. The mixing length is the distance that one particle can travel with reference to another particle running in parallel before there is an interchange of momentum between the two particles. This interchange of momentum occurs to reduce the relative velocity of the faster particle; the longer the 'mixing length' the larger is the degree of turbulence.

If we look at Figure 2.22 and consider two different flow layers, 'aa' and 'bb', with instantaneous velocities v and $v + \delta v$, the distance between the two layers

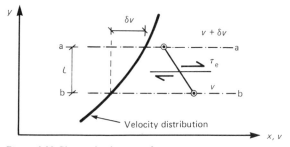

Figure 2.22 Change in the rate of momentum

is the 'mixing length', l. If the particle moves from 'aa' to 'bb' and the length l is small,

$$\delta v = l \left(\frac{dv}{dy} \right) \tag{2.63}$$

The instantaneous random components of velocities in the two directions can be called v'_x and v'_y.

The mass per unit surface per unit time that is transported from 'aa' to 'bb' is equal to $\rho v'_y$. The velocity variation in the x direction is δv. This is also equal to the random component v'_x. By Newton's second law the change in momentum is

$$\tau_e = (\rho v'_y)\, \delta v = \rho v'_y v'_x \tag{2.64}$$

This stress is called the Reynolds stress.

Prandtl assumed that the v'_y velocity component is of the same order as the component v'_x. He then assumed that both can be considered equal to δv, that is,

$$\tau_e \simeq \rho l^2 \left(\frac{dv}{dy}\right)^2 \tag{2.65}$$

where l is the mixing length.

Note that if ζ is approximately equal to τ_e the eddy viscosity η in Boussinesq's equation is given by

$$\eta = \rho l^2 \left(\frac{dv}{dy}\right) \tag{2.66}$$

2.9.2 Modification to Bernouilli's equation

Modifications to Bernouilli's equation are needed to account for the rotational characteristics of real fluids and the fact that usually one only knows the mean velocities at any given section.

(a) *Coefficient for the kinematic head.* If the kinematic head is expressed as a function of the mean velocity, one may need a dimensionless coefficient α to take account of the distribution of velocity. This coefficient can be obtained as

$$\alpha = \frac{\int v^2\, dQ}{V^2 Q} = \frac{\int v^3\, d\Omega}{V^3 \Omega} \tag{2.67}$$

where dQ and $d\Omega$ are the discharge and section of the elementary tube, respectively. In general, the cube of the mean velocity is less than the mean of v^3; hence α can be as high as 2 for laminar flow in pipes, but for turbulent flow will vary from 1 to 1.1. Because of this the α coefficient is generally taken to be equal to one, but it should be determined carefully when the kinetic energy is important.

(b) *Energy losses.* These are due to a series of complex factors, including friction, turbulence, etc.

(c) *Interchange of energy with the external medium.* Energy inputs are normally due to external factors, such as happens with pumps. Energy can also be removed from the system as is the case in turbines.

In order to account for these interchanges of energy the Bernouilli equation should be written as,

$$y_1 + \frac{p_1}{\gamma} + \alpha_1 \frac{V_1^2}{2g} = y^2 + \frac{p_2}{\gamma} + \alpha_2 \frac{V_2^2}{2g} + h - E \tag{2.68}$$

where E is the added energy head.

2.9.3 Cavitation

When the velocity increases, the pressure will decrease in the liquid until it is less than the vaporisation pressure. When this happens, the fluid becomes a gas or, in the case of water, it is transformed into vapour. Bubbles are created which can be carried by the current until they reach a region where the pressure is such that they can condense. This condensation is very rapid and produces an 'implosion', called cavitation. Cavitation is considered detrimental because it changes the characteristics of the flow affecting its efficiency; it results in instabilities including noise and vibrations, and the bubbles produce a continuous bombardment of the surfaces causing erosion. Structural failure can occur due to cavitation.

Cavitation is produced by regions of low pressure, and it is necessary to design components carefully to avoid its occurrence.

2.9.4 Boundary layers

Real fluids are viscous, and the effects of viscosity are greatest near the boundaries of the fluids. In contrast to ideal or inviscid fluids, they do not 'slip' at a solid boundary where there is no relative motion between fluid and solid, and therefore the velocity at the boundary is zero.

The region close to a boundary in which the velocity varies from zero to its full value is called the 'boundary layer': this is depicted in Figure 2.23. The fluid outside the boundary layer is relatively unaffected by the reduction of velocity close to the solid surface. The study of many problems can therefore be considered divided into two parts: (a) the boundary layer itself in which a large velocity gradient exists, giving rise to large shear stresses; (b) the fluid outside the boundary layer in which viscous forces are negligible by comparison with inertia or other forces.

The type of fluid flow occurring in the boundary layer may be turbulent or laminar, depending largely on the relative values of viscosity and inertia. Turbulent flows are characterised by random components of velocity in all directions, including components perpendicular to the main flow.

As the particles of the flow cannot pass through an impermeable solid surface, these perpendicular components are reduced to zero and hence, near the solid surface, the flow must be laminar. This region is sometimes called the

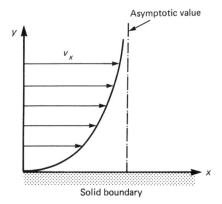

Figure 2.23 Boundary layer

laminar sublayer and, although very thin, it cannot be ignored in problems such as heat transfer.

2.9.5 Separation

Another interesting effect in real fluids is the separation effect which occurs over curved surfaces, shown in Figure 2.24. If the flow is inviscid, the streamlines will converge towards the top, to diverge afterwards, with the consequent variation in pressure and velocity, as indicated in Figure 2.24. In the case of a real fluid, however, one needs to consider the effect of the boundary layer. Towards the left of the diagram, the flow acceleration compensates for the effects of viscosity, but towards the right, the negative

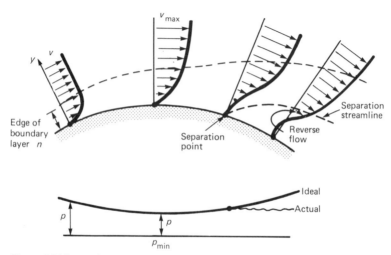

Figure 2.24 Separation on a convex surface

pressure gradient together with the viscosity reduces the energy of the particles near the surface, increasing in this way the thickness of the boundary layer until the deceleration is such that a flow inversion occurs. At this point, the main flow loses contact with the surface. This is called 'separation point', and coincides with the occurrence of a low value of pressure. For this reason, separation and cavitation are usually associated phenomena. At the point of separation

$$dv_x/dy = 0 \tag{2.69}$$

(Note that this is equivalent to shear at the wall being zero.)

The region after separation has a reverse flow with eddies which tend to dissipate energy. For turbulent flow, the separation point tends to move downstream of the separation point for laminar flow. This is due to the fact that the velocity gradient is smaller in laminar than in turbulent flow, resulting in smaller forces needed to invert the flow.

Eddies produced behind an obstruction generate a 'wake' region in which the pressure is largely constant (see Figure 2.25). The wake for a cylinder, for

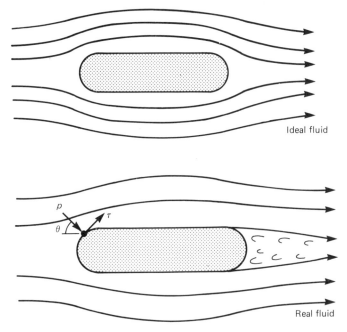

Figure 2.25 Flow around an obstruction

instance, presents first a series of symmetric vortices, but when the velocity of the main flow increases an alternating 'vortex street' appears. This generates lateral forces and oscillation of the cylindrical obstruction. This phenomenon is important in bridges, piles, cables, etc., as it can cause failure of the system.

If the velocity of the main flow increases further, the turbulence also increases, and the vortices become less well defined, tending again to be symmetric, with the separation point moving downstream and the wake becoming narrower.

2.9.6 Drag

A fluid flow exerts a force against a body submerged in the current. This force has a component in the direction of the fluid flow called drag.

For an ideal fluid the drag is zero, as the pressure forces are in perfect equilibrium around the body. This paradox is due to the fact that the viscosity is zero and therefore drag cannot exist. The drag forces can be computed by integrating the pressure and shear components around the body. These can be expressed as

$$dF = p \cos \theta \, d\Gamma + \tau \sin \theta \, d\Gamma \tag{2.70}$$

Integrating around the body gives

$$F = \int p \cos \theta \, d\Gamma + \int \tau \sin \theta \, d\Gamma \tag{2.71}$$

Then,

$$F = F_p + F_s \tag{2.72}$$

Note that these forces are resisted by the *pressure* or *form drag* and the *skin friction* or *viscosity drag*. Usually, form drag is the more important and sometimes aerodynamic profiles are adopted to diminish it.

The drag coefficient is defined as the ratio between the actual forces F and the dynamic force, i.e.

$$C_D = \frac{F}{\frac{1}{2}\rho V^2 \Omega} \tag{2.73}$$

where Ω is the cross-sectional area of the body, and C_D depends on the shape of the body.

Values of C_D are usually obtained by laboratory experiments.

2.10 Dimensionless numbers

Dimensionless numbers allow us to correlate the behaviour of fluids in experiments of different dimensions and properties, provided that they have the same parametric ratios. The type of ratio or dimensionless number used will depend on the forces which are predominant in the fluid: (i) pressure forces; (ii) gravity; (iii) viscosity; and (iv) surface tension.

2.10.1 Pressure forces

When pressure forces are the dominant forces, the results are related to the Euler number, which is obtained by consideration of Bernouilli's equation.

We consider the application of Bernouilli's equation between two sections, giving

$$\frac{p_1 - p_2}{\gamma} = \frac{v_2^2 - v_1^2}{2g} \tag{2.74}$$

Then

$$\frac{\Delta p}{\rho v_2^2 / 2} = 1 - \left(\frac{v_1}{v_2}\right)^2 \tag{2.75}$$

Note that the first term, sometimes called the pressure coefficient C_p, is similar to the drag coefficient C_D previously derived. It represents a ratio of pressure to inertia forces.

Inverting the equation (2.75) and taking the square root, one can write

$$E = \frac{V}{(2\Delta p/\rho)^{1/2}} \tag{2.76}$$

where E is the Euler number.

2.10.2 Gravity forces

The forces due to gravity are related to the ratio between gravity forces and inertia forces by the Froude number F, given by

$$F = \frac{V}{(gL)^{1/2}} \tag{2.77}$$

where V is velocity and L is a characteristic dimension such as depth.

2.10.3 Viscosity

These forces appear in real fluids and are related to the ratio between inertia and viscosity by the Reynolds number Re, given by

$$Re = \frac{\rho L V}{\mu} = \frac{LV}{v} \tag{2.78}$$

where v is the kinematic viscosity, equal to μ/ρ. Note that equation (2.78) implies that the viscosity is negligible when the section is large or the velocity is high. For pipes if Re less than 2000 the flow is still laminar, but above this it becomes turbulent.

2.10.4 Surface tension

Surface tension forces occur at the surface separating two liquids. These are usually small forces but can be significant if the dimensions are small.

The forces due to surface tension can be represented by σL where σ is the tension per unit length. The ratio between inertia forces and tension forces is given by

$$\frac{\rho L^2 V^2}{\sigma L} = \frac{\rho L V^2}{\sigma} \tag{2.79}$$

Hence, we can define a number, called Weber's number, given by

$$W = \frac{V}{(\sigma/\rho L)^{1/2}} \tag{2.80}$$

to relate those two types of forces. Note that this number indicates that the surface tension can be large when V and L are small.

Bibliography

FOX, R.W. and McDONALD, A.J. *Introduction to Fluid Mechanics*, Wiley, New York (1973)
MASSEY, B.S. *Mechanics of Fluids*, 2nd edn, Van Nostrand Reinhold, London (1970)
STREETER, V.L. *Handbook of Fluid Dynamics*, McGraw-Hill, New York (1961)
WEBBER, N.B., *Fluid Mechanics for Civil Engineers*, E. & F.N. Spon Ltd, London (1965)

Exercises

2.1 The flow of water between the piers shown in Figure 2.26 is such that the water depth upstream is 2.5 m and between piers is 2.10 m. Assuming that the river bed is horizontal and the friction negligible, calculate the flow. The piers are 1.0 m wide and at a distance of 10 m from centre to centre.

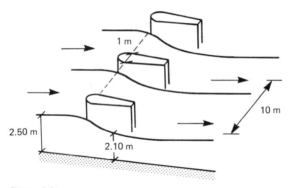

Figure 2.26

2.2   A submarine travels at $10 \, \text{km} \, \text{h}^{-1}$ under the sea. Calculate the pressure at the stagnation point in the front of the submarine. Assume that the point is situated 20 m below sea level.

2.3   Consider the Venturi meter shown in Figure 2.27 and find the volume

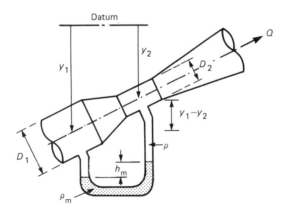

Figure 2.27

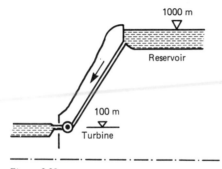

Figure 2.28

rate of flow Q assuming that $D_1 = 30$ mm, $D_2 = 10$ mm, $h_m = 12$ mm, ρ_m is the density of mercury and ρ is the density of water at 20°C.

2.4 Calculate the Reynolds number for a fluid of density 900 kg m^{-3} and viscosity 0.040 N s m^{-2}, flowing in a 100 mm diameter pipe at a rate of 5 litre s^{-1}.

2.5 Consider a Pelton turbine as shown in Figure 2.28. Assume that the discharge Q is 50 m^3 s^{-1} and the total loss of head due to friction in the pipe, turbine, etc. is 10 m. Calculate the power produced by the turbine.

CHAPTER 3

Pipe flow

3.1 Introduction

In this chapter flow in closed pipes will be discussed. Some of the concepts presented here will be applied in network analysis (Chapter 4). We will deduce an expression for laminar flow in circular pipes, starting from the basic momentum equation of the fluid. This equation is sometimes called Poiseuille's equation and will be deduced from simple equilibrium considerations.

Consider the pipe segment shown in Figure 3.1. Notice that the fluid will flow from a region of higher pressure to another of lower pressure. Consider a cylinder of fluid of arbitrary radius r and length δx. Due to viscosity a shear stress τ will exist over the surface of this cylinder such that

shear force = force due to pressure

or

$$\tau(2\pi r)\,\delta x = \delta p \pi r^2 \tag{3.1}$$

Hence

$$\tau = \frac{\delta p}{\delta x}\frac{r}{2} \tag{3.2}$$

or, in the limit,

$$\tau = \left(\frac{\partial p}{\partial x}\right)\frac{r}{2} \tag{3.3}$$

Notice that this equation implies a linear distribution of shear across the diameter of the pipe as shown in Figure 3.2 varying from $\tau = 0$ at the centre to a maximum value τ_0 on the wall.

If the fluid is Newtonian we can assume that the shear stress is related to the velocity as follows,

$$\tau = \mu \frac{\partial v}{\partial r} \tag{3.4}$$

44

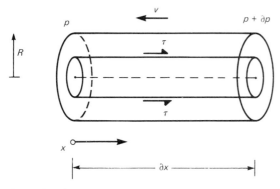

Figure 3.1 Pipe

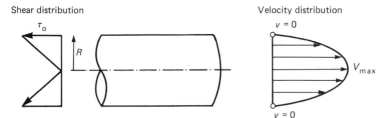

Shear distribution

Velocity distribution

Figure 3.2 Shear stress and velocity distribution

where μ is the dynamic viscosity. From equations (3.3) and (3.4) one obtains

$$\frac{r}{2}\left(\frac{\partial p}{\partial x}\right) = \mu\frac{\partial v}{\partial r} \tag{3.5}$$

Integrating with respect to r,

$$v = \int \frac{r}{2\mu}\left(\frac{\partial p}{\partial x}\right)dr \tag{3.6}$$

This gives,

$$v = \frac{r^2}{4\mu}\left(\frac{\partial p}{\partial x}\right) + C \tag{3.7}$$

Where C is a constant deduced by the condition that $v=0$ at $r=R$. Hence,

$$v = -\frac{R^2}{4\mu}\left(\frac{\partial p}{\partial x}\right)\left[1 - \left(\frac{r}{R}\right)^2\right] \tag{3.8}$$

Notice that the distribution of velocity is parabolic across the diameter. The maximum velocity, which occurs at $r=0$, is

$$V_{max} = -\frac{R^2}{4\mu}\left(\frac{\partial p}{\partial x}\right) \tag{3.9}$$

The average value is given by,

$$V = \frac{\int_0^R v \, d\Omega}{\Omega} = \frac{\text{volumetric flow rate}}{\text{cross-section}} \tag{3.10}$$

where $\Omega = \pi R^2$ is the cross-section of the pipe. Hence $d\Omega = 2\pi r \, dr$ and so

$$V = \frac{1}{\pi R^2} \int_0^R 2\pi r \left(\frac{1}{4\mu}\right)\left(\frac{\partial p}{\partial x}\right)(r^2 - R^2) \, dr \tag{3.11}$$

which gives,

$$V = -\frac{R^2}{8\mu}\left(\frac{\partial p}{\partial x}\right) = \frac{V_{max}}{2} \tag{3.12}$$

Notice that we can now compute the head losses due to frictional forces. From equation (3.12),

$$\Delta p = -\frac{8\mu V}{R^2} \Delta x \tag{3.13}$$

Hence the head loss for a pipe of length L becomes

$$h_f = \frac{\Delta p}{\rho g} = \frac{8\mu V}{\rho g R^2} L = \frac{32\mu V}{\rho g D^2} L \tag{3.14}$$

where $D \, (= 2R)$ is the diameter of the pipe. Note that the frictional slope (h_f/L) is proportional to the mean velocity.

The flow is only laminar for the case of a viscous fluid in small-diameter ducts; otherwise, it is turbulent. The above relationships are valid for laminar flow and have to be modified to take into account turbulence; to do this we have to rely on experimental data.

When the flow becomes turbulent, the velocity profile becomes more 'blunt' (Figure 3.3) for the same average velocity. This profile can be expressed by an empirical equation:

$$\frac{v}{V_{max}} = \left(1 - \frac{r}{R}\right)^{1/n} \tag{3.15}$$

where n varies with Re, i.e.

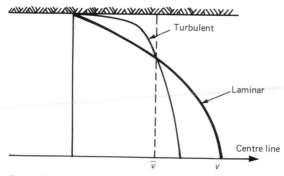

Figure 3.3 Velocity profiles for laminar and turbulent flow

$$n = \begin{cases} 6 & \text{for } Re = 4 \times 10^3 \\ 7 & \text{for } Re = 1.1 \times 10^5 \\ 10 & \text{for } Re = 3.2 \times 10^6 \end{cases}$$

3.2 Turbulent flow: Darcy–Weisbach formula

The equation known as the Darcy–Weisbach formula expresses the loss of head in pipes as given by

$$h_f = \lambda \frac{V^2}{D} \left(\frac{L}{2g} \right) \tag{3.16}$$

where λ is a friction coefficient. This equation applies to turbulent flow.

Note that this formula differs from equation (3.14) in that the head losses are proportional to V^2 instead of V and inversely proportional to D instead of D^2.

The formula was obtained experimentally and can be explained by looking at equation (3.3) at the pipe wall, i.e.

$$\frac{\partial p}{\partial x} \simeq \frac{\Delta p}{\Delta L} = \frac{4}{D} \tau_0 \tag{3.17}$$

Experimental evidence indicated that τ_0 was proportional to V raised to a power near 2 (actually a bit less). If we assume,

$$\tau_0 = c V^2 \tag{3.18}$$

equation (3.17) becomes,

$$\frac{\Delta p}{\rho g} = \frac{4c}{D \rho g} V^2 L \tag{3.19}$$

comparing this equation with equation (3.16) we have $\lambda = 8c/\rho$ and so

$$\frac{\Delta p}{\rho g} = \lambda \frac{V^2}{D} \left(\frac{L}{2g} \right) \tag{3.20}$$

Experiments by Osborne Reynolds determined that when the velocity increases, the flow changes from laminar to turbulent as shown in Figure 3.4 where head losses are plotted against velocity. For laminar flow, losses are proportional to V; for turbulent flow the law was given as V^n. This simple expression is not fully correct as we will see.

It is also interesting to point out that head losses in turbulent flow were shown to be much greater than for laminar flow due to the greater losses of energy associated with the random movements of turbulent flow than for the latter. Results in the transition region shown in Figure 3.4 were affected by the pipe diameter. Because of this, Reynolds tried to determine the factors which influence the nature of the flow and found what is now known as the Reynolds number, Re. He started by considering that only three variables will influence the behaviour of the fluid in the pipe: μ, the viscosity of the fluid; ρ, the density of the fluid; and D, the diameter of the pipe. The only way these variables can be combined to produce the dimension of velocity is in the form

$$\mu/\rho D \tag{3.21}$$

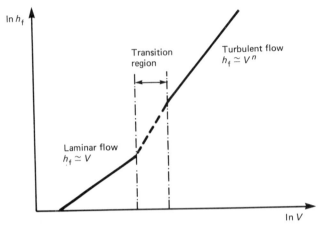

Figure 3.4 Velocity versus head loss

He then divided all critical velocities found in the experiments by this expression and obtained a dimensionless ratio which was around 2000 for circular pipes. (He reasoned that rugosity would not greatly influence laminar flow and the critical velocity although it would be important in the turbulent region.) Reynolds asserted that if $Re\,(=\rho DV/\mu)$ was less than 2000, the flow was laminar, but for $Re>2000$ the flow could become turbulent.

The *transition* region (Figure 3.4) is an unstable zone and, depending on perturbations, we may have there laminar or turbulent flow. Hence we will accept that

laminar flow	$Re<2000$	
transition region	$2000<Re<4000$	(3.22)
turbulent flow	$Re>4000$	

Note that for laminar flow Poiseuille's equation will be valid, and hence the λ value for laminar flow can be deduced by comparing equation (3.14),

$$h_f = \frac{32\mu V}{\rho g D^2} L \qquad (3.14)$$

with equation (3.16),

$$h_f = \lambda \frac{V^2}{2gD} L \qquad (3.16)$$

Hence,

$$\frac{32\mu V}{\rho g D^2} = \lambda \frac{V^2}{2gD} \qquad (3.25)$$

and so

$$\lambda = 64 \frac{\nu}{DV} = \frac{64}{Re} \qquad (3.24)$$

3.3 Effect of rugosity in turbulent flow

Blasius investigated the effect of rugosity on turbulent flow and determined that for smooth walls viscosity effects are dominant, and the friction coefficient λ depends only on the Re number. If the roughness increases, however, the flow is influenced by a roughness coefficient as well as by Re number.

For the case of smooth pipes, and for $4000 < Re < 10^5$, Blasius presented the following expression for λ in the Darcy–Weisbach formula:

$$\lambda = \frac{0.316}{Re^{0.25}} \tag{3.25}$$

Note that if one substitutes this value in the Darcy–Weisbach formula, one obtains,

$$h_f = 0.316 \left(\frac{v}{DV} \right)^{0.25} \left(\frac{\Delta L V^2}{2gD} \right) \tag{3.26}$$

or

$$h_f = c V^{1.75} \tag{3.27}$$

where c is a constant. The formula has been confirmed experimentally for values of Re in the range $4000 < Re < 10^5$. For values of $Re > 10^5$, the exponent of V has to be changed (i.e. we need a larger value) for theoretical predictions to agree with experimental results.

In 1930 Nikuradse obtained experimental results for smooth pipes (Figure 3.5) and measured velocities in the transverse section; this work was important

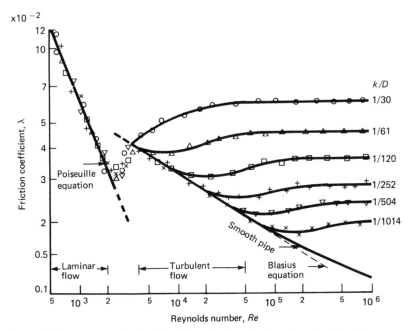

Figure 3.5 λ–Re curves obtained by Nikuradse (from Webber, N., *Fluid Mechanics for Civil Engineers*, E. & F. N. Spon, London (1965).)

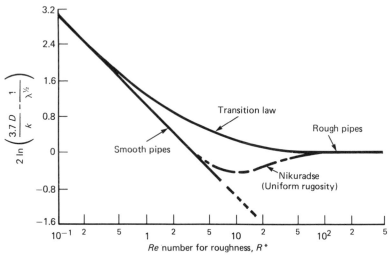

Figure 3.6 Comparison of curves in the transition region for uniform rugosity and the rugosity in real pipes — see text for relationships in various regions. (From Webber, N., *Fluid Mechanics for Civil Engineers*, E. & F. N. Spon, London (1965).)

in the development of a theory of turbulence for pipe flow.

He also studied the effect of roughness by experimenting with sand grains fixed to the internal surfaces of the pipes. He defined k as the height of the grains and a roughness factor given by k/D, where k/D varied between $1/130$ and $1/1014$. The results are shown in Figure 3.5. Notice that the laminar part is not affected by the roughness and that above a certain Re number the friction factor λ is independent of Re and depends only on the roughness of the pipe. This means that the head loss h_f is proportional to V^n:

$$h_f = cV^n \tag{3.28}$$

The importance of Nikuradse's results is that they permitted Prandtl and Karman to establish their turbulence formulae for smooth and rough pipes. The main problem was that it is difficult to relate his results to the pipe roughness in reality.

The formulae of Prandtl and Karman were obtained using the general equation of turbulence (cf. equation (2.65)), i.e.

$$\tau = \rho l^2 \left(\frac{dv}{dy}\right)^2 \tag{3.29}$$

(where l is the mixing length) in the case of pipes by applying two hypotheses:

(i)   That the shear stress τ is constant over the section and has a value equal to the shear stress at the wall. In support of this, it was observed that the larger variation of velocity occurs in the laminar boundary layer next to the wall.

(ii) The mixing length is a linear function of the distance from the wall. This is based on the experimental observation that turbulence increases with distance from the wall.

These two hypotheses allow the development of a new formula for *smooth* pipes with,

$$\frac{1}{\lambda^{1/2}} = 2 \ln \left(\frac{Re\lambda^{1/2}}{2.51} \right) \tag{3.30}$$

For *rough* pipes, the relationship is given by,

$$\frac{1}{\lambda^{1/2}} = 2 \ln \left(3.7 \frac{D}{k} \right) \tag{3.31}$$

Their limits of applicability are given in Figure 3.6 where R^* is the Re number for roughness given by

$$R^* = Re \left(\frac{\lambda}{8} \right)^{1/2} \frac{k}{D} \tag{3.32}$$

Finally, Colebrook and White deduced the following law to cover the transition region (Figure 3.6):

$$\frac{1}{\lambda^{1/2}} = -2 \ln \left(\frac{k}{3.7D} + \frac{2.51}{Re\lambda^{1/2}} \right) \tag{3.33}$$

For $R^* = 0.3$ we approach the smooth pipe limit and for $R^* = 60$ the rough pipe.

The engineer can now obtain the λ coefficient for a wide range of Re numbers and different roughnesses. Table 3.1 presents some experimental results showing the effective roughness k to be expected in different pipes. The results are also graphically presented in Figure 3.7.

TABLE 3.1. Value of effective roughness for pipes of different materials (From Webber (1965), see bibliography)

Type of pipe	Effective roughness (cm)
Copper, lead, tin, glass, asbestos cement, plastic	smooth
Cast iron coated with bitumen	0.003
Cast iron coated with concrete	0.003
Steel without coating	0.003
Steel with coating	0.006
Cast iron with tin coating	0.0150
Cast iron coated	0.0150
Cast iron uncoated	0.03
Centrifugated concrete	0.06
Rough concrete	0.30

Moody published a simplified general diagram (Figure 3.8) showing the relationship between λ, Re and k/D.

3.4 Empirical formulae

Empirical formulae of exponential type are frequently used in engineering to estimate head losses in pipes. They have the form,

$$V = aD^n S_f^m \tag{3.34}$$

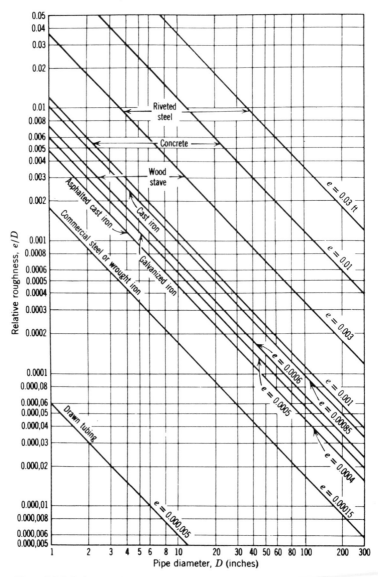

Figure 3.7 Relative rugosity values for pipes of common engineering materials. (From Moody, L. F., Friction factors for pipe flow, *Trans. ASME* 66.8, November, 671–84 (1944).)

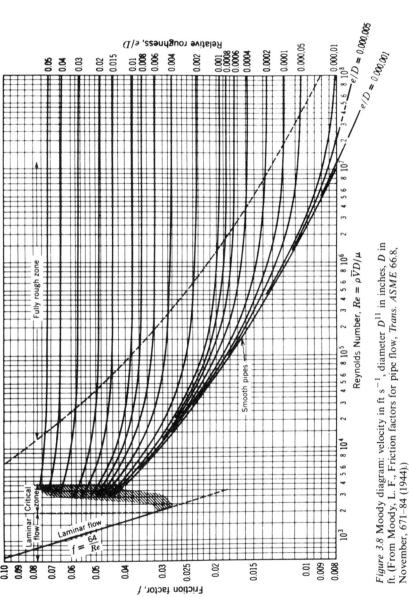

Figure 3.8 Moody diagram: velocity in ft s^{-1}, diameter D^{11} in inches, D in ft. (From Moody, L. F., Friction factors for pipe flow, *Trans. ASME* 66.8, November, 671–84 (1944).)

where S_f is the friction gradient, equal to h_f/L. The values of a, n, and m are obtained from experiments.

To understand the terms in equation (3.34) consider the Darcy–Weisbach formula, which can be written in the form

$$S_f = \frac{h_f}{L} = \frac{\lambda V^2}{2gD} \tag{3.35}$$

Substituting this into equation (3.34), we have,

$$V = aD^n \left(\frac{\lambda V^2}{2gD}\right)^m \tag{3.36}$$

which gives

$$\lambda = 2g \frac{D^{1-n/m}}{a^{1/m} V^{2-1/m}} \tag{3.37}$$

where a is a coefficient that depends on the roughness and viscosity. Equation (3.37) is a very general formula, and we can now specialise it to find several empirical formulae.

3.4.1   The Blasius formula

This is valid for $4000 < Re < 10^5$ and smooth pipes, and can be expressed as

$$S_f = \frac{0.316}{R^{0.25}} \frac{V^2}{2gD}$$

$$= 0.316 \left(\frac{\nu}{DV}\right)^{0.25} \frac{V^2}{2gD} \tag{3.38}$$

3.4.2 The Hazen–Williams formula

This formula applies for the *transition* region, and is given by

$$S_f = \frac{h_f}{L} = \frac{6.285}{D^m} \left(\frac{V}{c}\right)^n \tag{3.39}$$

Note that the number 6.285 is valid only for the SI system.

The value of c depends upon the roughness; i.e.

$$c = \begin{cases} 140 & \text{extremely smooth pipes; asbestos–cement} \\ 130 & \text{very smooth pipes; cement, new cast iron} \\ 120 & \text{wood stove; new welded steel} \\ 110 & \text{vitrified clay; new riveted steel} \\ 100 & \text{cast iron, old} \\ 95 & \text{riveted steel, old} \\ 60\text{–}80 & \text{old pipes} \end{cases}$$

$n = 1.852$ and $m = 1.166$. Note that

$$V = 0.3545 c S_f^{0.54} D^{0.63} \tag{3.40}$$

3.4.3 Manning formula

Sometimes the Manning formula is used in turbulent regions of rough pipes, although the formula is more generally applied in canals.

For this case, we have (in SI units)

$$V = \frac{1}{N} \rho^{2/3} S_f^{1/2} \tag{3.41}$$

where ρ is the hydraulic radius ($=D/4$ for a circular pipe) and N is a roughness factor. Hence

$$V = \frac{1}{N} 0.397 D^{0.66} S_f^{0.50} \tag{3.42}$$

Note that N will vary according to the roughness of the pipe (see Table 3.2).

TABLE 3.2. **Average values of the Manning roughness factor for various materials**

Boundary material	Manning N
Planed wood	0.012
Unplaned wood	0.013
Finished concrete	0.012
Unfinished concrete	0.014
Cast iron	0.015
Brick	0.016
Riveted steel	0.018
Corrugated metal	0.022
Rubble	0.025
Earth	0.025
Earth, with stones or weeds	0.035
Gravel	0.029

From equation (3.37) and noticing that

$$a = 0.397/N \quad n = 0.666 \quad n = 0.50$$

$$\left(\frac{2g}{a^{1/m}}\right) = 124.5 N^2$$

$$1 - n/m = -1/3 \quad 2 - 1/m = 0$$

we can write:

$$\lambda = 124.5 \frac{N^2}{D^{1/3}} \tag{3.43}$$

Note that the Re dependency has been lost as $m = 0.5$. This means that Manning's formula appears in the λ–Re diagram as a series of lines parallel to the Re axis.

3.5 Summary of formulae

Table 3.3 presents a summary of the formulae presented in this chapter.

TABLE 3.3. **Formulae for friction losses in pipes** (after Webber, N. '*Fluid Mechanics for Civil Engineers*', E. & F.N. Spon, London (1965))

Name	Formula	Equation number	Re limits	R* limits
Poiseuille	$h_f = \dfrac{32\nu VL}{gD^2} \qquad \lambda = \dfrac{64}{Re}$	14	<2000	no limit
Darcy–Weisbach	$h_f = \dfrac{\lambda LV^2}{2gD}$	16	universal	
Blasius	$\lambda = \dfrac{0.316}{Re^{0.25}}$	25	4000–10^5	<0.3
Smooth law (Karman–Prandtl)	$\dfrac{1}{\lambda^{1/2}} = 2\ln\left(\dfrac{Re\lambda^{1/2}}{2.51}\right)$	30	>4000	<0.3
Rough law (Karman–Prandtl)	$\dfrac{1}{\lambda^{1/2}} = 2\ln\left(\dfrac{3.7D}{k}\right)$	31	>4000	>60.0
Transition law (Colebrook–White)	$\dfrac{1}{\lambda^{1/2}} = 2\ln\left(\dfrac{k}{3.7D} + \dfrac{2.51}{Re\lambda^{1/2}}\right)$	33	>4000	no limit
Exponential (Hazen–Williams)	$V = 0.35456D^{0.63}S_f^{0.54}$	40	>4000	0.3–60
Exponential (Manning)	$V = \dfrac{0.497}{N}D^{2/3}S_f^{1/2}$, λ eq. (43)	42	>4000	>40

Bibliography

COLEBROOK, C.F. 'Turbulent flow in pipes, with particular reference to the transition region between the smooth and rough pipe laws', *J. Inst. Civ. Engrs*, **11**, 133 (1938–39)

FOX, R.W. and McDONALD, A.T. *Introduction to Fluid Mechanics*, Wiley, New York (1973)

MOODY, L.F. 'Friction factors for pipe flow', *Trans. ASME* 66.8, November, 671–84 (1944)

NIKURADSE, J. 'Strömungsgesetze in Rauhen Rohren', *VDI-Forschungsh.* No. 361 (1933). Translated in *N A C A Tech. Memo* 1292

PRANDTL, L. *Essentials of Fluid Dynamics*, Blackie, London (1952)

REYNOLDS, O. 'An experimental investigation of the circumstances which determine whether the motion of water shall be direct or devious and of the law of resistance in parallel channels', *Phil. Trans. R. Soc. London*, **174**, Part III (1883)

ROBERTSON, J.A. and CROWE, C.T. *Engineering Fluid Mechanics*, 2nd edn, Houghton Mifflin Co., Boston (1980)

SABERSKY, R.H., ACOSTA, A.J. and HAUPTMANN, E. G. *Fluid Flow. A First Course in Fluid Mechanics*, 2nd edn, Macmillan, New York (1971)

SHAPIRO, A.H. *Shape and Flow. The Fluid Dynamics of Drag*, Anchor, New York (1961)

WEBBER, N. *Fluid Mechanics for Civil Engineers*, E. & F.N. Spon, London (1965)

Exercises

3.1 Calculate the head loss per 100 m of pipe for a fluid of specific density 0.85 and kinematic viscosity 5×10^{-4} m^2 s^{-1}. Assume that the pipe has a diameter of 10 cm and the rate of flow is 0.01 m^3 s^{-1}.

3.2 Consider a pipe 15 cm diameter with a water flow rate of 0.04 m^3 s^{-1} ($v = 1 \times 10^{-6}$ m^2 s^{-1}). Calculate the head loss per kilometre if the pipe is made from galvanised iron and also if it is made from concrete. (One can use Figure 3.7 to calculate the rugosity.)

3.3 Determine the pressure drop (in N m^{-2}) for glycerin at 20°C for 100 m ($v = 2.2 \times 10^{-4}$ m^2 s^{-1}). Assume laminar flow, a pipe of diameter 20 mm and a flow rate of 10^{-6} m^3 s^{-1} ($\rho = 1818$ kg m^{-3}).

3.4 The same glycerin as in Exercise 3.3 flows in a 5 cm diameter cast iron tube at a velocity of 20 cm s^{-1}. Determine the shear stress at the wall and find whether the flow is laminar or turbulent. Assume that the pipe is vertical and the flow is upward.

3.5 Determine the friction factor for the manometer shown in Figure 3.9, assuming that $h_m = 1$ m and the liquid is water with a mean velocity of 2 m s^{-1} ($v = 10^{-6}$ m^2 s^{-1}).

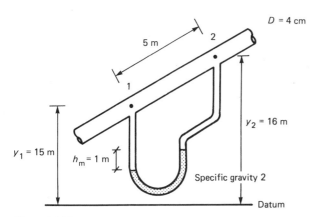

Figure 3.9 Manometer

3.6 Determine the head loss and the power required to pump water at 10°C at a rate of 0.1 m^3 s^{-1} through 1 km of 0.5 m diameter concrete pipe.

3.7 Assume that water at 20°C is to be pumped through a 2 m diameter galvanised iron pipe of 10 km length from a reservoir to an irrigation canal at a rate of 10 m^3 s^{-1}. The reservoir is assumed to be 100 m above the canal. Determine the pump power needed if the pump efficiency is 80%. Neglect inlet and outlet losses.

3.8   Consider oil flow in a 5 cm diameter vertical pipe. The pressure at
elevation 10 m is 100 kN m^{-2} and at elevation 0 m is 150 kN m^{-2}.
Determine the direction of the flow and the mean velocity of the fluid,
assuming the flow is laminar. (Specific gravity of oil=0.90, viscosity of
oil=4×10^{-1} N s m^{-2}.)

3.9   What force is required to support a vertical pipe of 10 cm diameter and
10 m long discharging oil on a reservoir at mean velocity of 1 m s^{-1}
(Figure 3.10)? The pipe itself weighs 500 N. Check if the flow is laminar.
(Specific gravity=0.85, μ=0. 12 N s m^{-2}.)

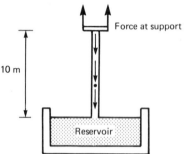

Figure 3.10

CHAPTER 4

Pipe networks

4.1 Introduction

This chapter deals with the analysis of pipe networks, with special emphasis on water distribution systems, which are the more common type of pipe network.

Urban water networks tend to have a large number of branches, with pipes interconnected approximately every 500 m. The network must be designed for water to flow in all pipes, avoiding water becoming stagnant in any one pipe. Also, it must be possible for the water to reach any distribution point by more than one path, so that distribution is not interrupted in the event of repairs or failure in any pipe.

The design of a water distribution system is based on the following two main factors:

(a)   demand for the fluid;
(b)   pressures which the system has to withstand.

Fluid demand depends on the size and type of distribution system being considered. For instance, in the case of residential water distribution networks, the demand is computed based on a consumption of 200 litres per person per day. Pressures are important, on the other hand, because the flow of water through the pipes is determined by pressure gradients. Low pressures will cause problems in distribution, while energy losses will be high for large pressures. In standard water networks, pressures are of the order of 20 to 60 N cm^{-2}. Pipes tend to be of at least 7.5 cm diameter. Energy losses, mainly due to friction, are of the order of 0.2 to 1.5 m for a 500 m pipe. They could become larger, however, for pipes of smaller diameters.

The analysis of pipe networks is normally done using computer programs. The system can be visualised as a series of elements, the pipes, connected at a specified number of nodes, as is indicated in Figure 4.1. The pipe sizes, the geometric dimensions of the network, and the consumptions at the nodes constitute the data. The system has to be solved for the energy heads at each of the nodes, and the discharges at each of the pipes, which are the unknowns.

The analysis of a pipe network is best done on a computer, using a systems approach. For this, the first step is the study of each element individually, to

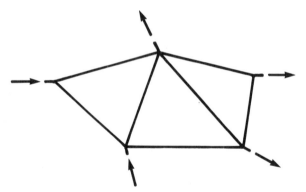

Figure 4.1 Schematic water network

determine a relationship linking the difference in energy head between the two element nodes, called head loss, and the element discharge. The next step is to establish equilibrium at each of the system nodes; this requires that discharges arriving at the node should equal discharges leaving it, including consumptions. This requirement leads to a system of simultaneous equations, governing the behaviour of the complete network. Solution of this system of equations gives the values of the energy heads at each of the network nodes. Finally, returning to the element level, head losses for each element are computed from the energy heads at its end nodes, and the element discharges are computed from the head losses, thus completing the network solution.

The critical step in an analysis such as the one described above is the determination of individual element behaviour. Two different alternatives for this are discussed in the present chapter. The first one is based on Poiseuille's formula which leads to a linear relationship between head loss and discharge for the element. The resulting formulation is simple to deal with but, unfortunately, is not very precise. The second alternative is based on the Hazen–Williams formula, commonly used in practice, and giving more precise results. The relationship between element discharge and head, however, leads to a more complex formulation.

4.2 Energy losses

According to Bernouilli, the total head at any point along a pipe is the sum of elevation, pressure, and kinematic heads. The energy head represents the addition of all these heads (Figure 4.2) where the slope of the energy line is mainly due to the frictional losses. The line called hydraulic level is the sum of the elevation and pressure heads and, consequently, is below the total energy line. Its slope is called 'hydraulic gradient'. If the kinematic energy is small, the two lines practically coincide. The importance of the hydraulic gradient is that it gives the pressure acting on the pipes and allows one to design them and their joints adequately.

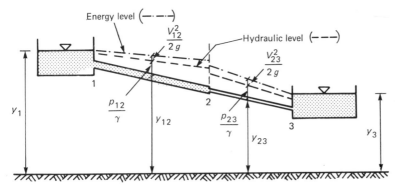

Figure 4.2 Energy and hydraulic levels

4.3 Element analysis

Once all elements and nodes of the network have been identified, a head loss versus discharge relationship must be defined for each element.

A generic element i is shown in Figure 4.3. This element connects nodes j and k. The values of the head at nodes j and k will be called H_j and H_k respectively.

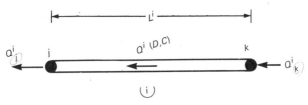

Figure 4.3 Pipe element: D, pipe diameter; C, roughness coefficient; L, length of pipe

The total head loss ΔH^i for the element is given by

$$\Delta H^i = H_k - H_j \tag{4.1}$$

The flow velocity for the element will be denoted by V^i. The element discharge Q^i will be given by

$$Q^i = \Omega^i V^i \tag{4.2}$$

where Ω^i is the pipe cross-sectional area.

The first step of the network analysis is to relate the head loss between the two element nodes to the element discharge. This can be done using any of the formulae considered in Chapter 3. Poiseuille's formula, for instance, can be written as

$$\Delta H = \frac{32\mu L}{\rho g D^2} V \tag{4.3}$$

where ΔH is the head loss between two points a distance L apart, μ is the fluid viscosity, ρ is the fluid density, g is the gravitational acceleration, D is the pipe diameter, and V is the fluid velocity.

Equation (4.3) can be inverted to obtain

$$V = \frac{\rho g D^2}{32 \mu L} \Delta H \tag{4.4}$$

Hence, the discharge is $Q = \Omega V = \frac{\pi \rho g D^4}{128 L \mu} \Delta H$ $\qquad$ (4.5)

Applying this equation for element i gives $Q^i = k^i \Delta H^i$ $\qquad$ (4.6)

where $k^i = \frac{\pi \rho g D_i^4}{128 L \mu}$ $\qquad$ (4.7)

with D_i and L_i being the element pipe diameter and length, respectively.

It is important to note that since k^i is a constant which depends only on the properties of the fluid and of element i, the relationship between the discharge and the head loss for the element is linear. This makes the overall analysis simpler, although due to the limitations of the Poiseuille formula, the results obtained using this approach are not very precise. However, a program will be implemented using this formulation, not for applications, but to introduce the basic steps and concepts of a matrix analysis program, and to provide the framework of more refined problems.

More precise results can be obtained using the Hazen–Williams formula. This formula (see equation (3.42)) gives

$$V = 0.3545 c D^{0.63} \frac{h_j^{0.54}}{L^{0.54}} \tag{4.8}$$

Hence, the discharge Q, in terms of the head load $h_j = \Delta H$, will be given by

$$Q = \Omega V = \left(0.2784 \frac{c D^{2.63}}{L^{0.54}} \right) \Delta H^{0.54} \tag{4.9}$$

or

$$Q = k \Delta H^{0.54} \tag{4.10}$$

where

$$k = 0.2784 \frac{c D^{2.63}}{L^{0.54}} \tag{4.11}$$

Applying the Hazen–Williams equation to element i gives

$$Q^i = \bar{k}^i (\Delta H^i)^{0.54} \tag{4.12}$$

where the constant $\bar{k}^i$ is to be computed according to expression (4.11). It is important to notice that the relation between the element discharge and head loss is, in this case, non-linear.

Equation (4.12) can also be written as

$$Q^i = \frac{\bar{k}^i}{(\Delta H^i)^{0.46}} \Delta H^i \tag{4.13}$$

or

$$Q^i = k^i \Delta H^i \tag{4.14}$$

which is similar to expression (4.6). Notice that this k^i is different from the constant obtained using the Poiseuille formula. In fact, k^i is no longer a constant since it depends on the value of the head loss ΔH^i. The same symbol is used, however, to avoid proliferation of notation.

4.4 Element matrix equation

Formula (4.14) allows one to compute the discharge for element i in terms of the head loss between its two nodes. That discharge will be positive when going from node k to node j, which will correspond to a larger head in node k than in node j. A discharge at each of the element end nodes can also be defined. It will be assumed that a nodal discharge will be positive when going into the node, and negative otherwise, as indicated in Figure 4.3 where Q_k^i is the discharge at node k and Q_j^i is the discharge at node j. Therefore,

$$Q_k^i = k^i \, \Delta H^i = k^i(H_k - H_j)$$
$$Q_j^i = -k^i \, \Delta H^i = -k^i(H_k - H_j)$$

(4.15)

These two equations can also be written, using matrix notation, as

$$\begin{Bmatrix} Q_k^i \\ Q_j^i \end{Bmatrix} = k^i \begin{bmatrix} 1 & -1 \\ -1 & 1 \end{bmatrix} \begin{Bmatrix} H_k^i \\ H_j^i \end{Bmatrix}$$

(4.16)

or

$$\mathbf{Q}^i = \mathbf{k}^i \mathbf{H}^i$$

(4.17)

where

$$\mathbf{Q}^i = \begin{Bmatrix} Q_k^i \\ Q_j^i \end{Bmatrix}$$

is the element nodal discharge vector,

$$\mathbf{k}^i = k^i \begin{bmatrix} 1 & -1 \\ -1 & 1 \end{bmatrix}$$

(4.18)

is the element characteristic matrix, and

$$\mathbf{H}^i = \begin{Bmatrix} H_k \\ H_j \end{Bmatrix}$$

(4.19)

is the element nodal head vector.

4.5 Total system of equations

So far the elements in the network have been considered individually, and expressions giving the discharges in terms of the nodal heads have been developed. To study the complete network, however, the interaction between the different elements will have to be taken into account. This implies that there must exist equilibrium at any given node of the network between the discharges of the elements connected to the node, including any eventual fluid input or consumption.

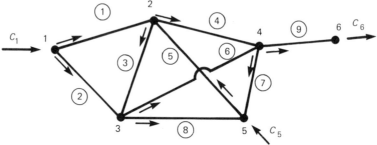

Figure 4.4 Pipe network

Figure 4.4 shows a simplified model of a pipe network. Nodes and elements are numbered for identification purposes. The quantities c_j are the consumptions at each node. In general, any C_j will be positive when fluid is input and negative when actual consumption occurs.

Equilibrium at any node means that the sum of the discharges of the elements connected to the node equals the consumption, each with their proper sign. Thus, for any node j,

$$\sum_i Q_j^i = C_j \tag{4.20}$$

where the summation runs over all elements connected to node j. For instance, specialisation of equation (4.20) for joint 5 of the network of Figure 4.4 gives

$$Q_5^5 + Q_5^7 + Q_5^8 = C_5 \tag{4.21}$$

as detailed in Figure 4.5. The element discharges can be obtained from equation (4.16) in terms of the nodal heads. For instance, for the three elements meeting at node 5, the matrix characteristic equations are

Element (5)

$$\begin{Bmatrix} Q_5^5 \\ Q_2^5 \end{Bmatrix} = k^5 \begin{bmatrix} 1 & -1 \\ -1 & 1 \end{bmatrix} \begin{Bmatrix} H_5 \\ H_2 \end{Bmatrix} \tag{4.22}$$

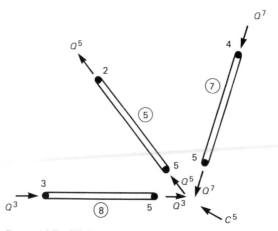

Figure 4.5 Equilibrium at node 5

Element (7)

$$\left\{\begin{matrix} Q_5^7 \\ Q_4^7 \end{matrix}\right\} = k^7 \begin{bmatrix} 1 & -1 \\ -1 & 1 \end{bmatrix} \left\{\begin{matrix} H_4 \\ H_5 \end{matrix}\right\} \tag{4.23}$$

Element (8)

$$\left\{\begin{matrix} Q_5^8 \\ Q_3^8 \end{matrix}\right\} = k^8 \begin{bmatrix} 1 & -1 \\ -1 & 1 \end{bmatrix} \left\{\begin{matrix} H_3 \\ H_5 \end{matrix}\right\} \tag{4.24}$$

Thus,

$$\begin{aligned} Q_5^5 &= -k^5(H_5 - H_2) \\ Q_5^7 &= -k^7(H_4 - H_5) \\ Q_5^8 &= -k^8(H_3 - H_5) \end{aligned} \tag{4.25}$$

Substituting these equations in expression (4.21) gives,

$$-k^5 H_2 - k^8 H_3 - k^7 H_4 + k^5 H_5 + k^7 H_5 + k^8 H_5 = C_5 \tag{4.26}$$

or

$$-k^5 H_2 - k^8 H_3 - k^7 H_4 + (k^5 + k^7 + k^8)H_5 = C_5 \tag{4.27}$$

This equation is already one of the rows of the total system of equations, which will be obtained by establishing equilibrium for each of the nodes in the network, in the same way as illustrated above for node 5. For the network of Figure 4.4, the total system of equations will be as follows:

$$\begin{bmatrix} k^1 + k^2 & -k^1 & -k^1 & 0 & 0 & 0 \\ -k^1 & k^1 + k^3 + k^4 + k^5 & -k^3 & -k^4 & -k^5 & 0 \\ -k^2 & -k^3 & k^2 + k^3 + k^6 + g & -k^6 & -k^8 & 0 \\ 0 & -k^4 & -k^6 & k^4 + k^6 + k^7 + k^8 & -k^7 & -k^9 \\ 0 & -k^5 & -k^8 & -k^7 & k^5 + k^7 + k^8 & 0 \\ 0 & 0 & 0 & -k^9 & 0 & -k^9 \end{bmatrix}$$

$$\times \left\{\begin{matrix} H_1 \\ H_2 \\ H_3 \\ H_4 \\ H_5 \\ H_6 \end{matrix}\right\} = \left\{\begin{matrix} C_1 \\ C_2 \\ C_3 \\ C_4 \\ C_5 \\ C_6 \end{matrix}\right\} \tag{4.28}$$

In compact notation,

$$\mathbf{KH} = \mathbf{C} \tag{4.29}$$

where $\mathbf{K}$ is the network characteristic matrix, $\mathbf{H}$ is the network head vector, and $\mathbf{C}$ is the network consumption vector.

The characteristic matrix $\mathbf{K}$ includes four contributions from each element. Element 5, for instance, gives the contributions shown in the following scheme:

	Node 1	Node 2	Node 3	Node 4	Node 5	Node 6
Node 1	•	•	•	•	•	•
Node 2	•	$+k^5$	•	•	$-k^5$	•
Node 3	•	•	•	•	•	•
Node 4	•	•	•	•	•	•
Node 5	•	$-k^5$	•	•	$+k^5$	•
Node 6	•	•	•	•	•	•

Notice that those contributions are added to positions (2,2), (2,5), (5,2), and (5,5), which are the intersections of the rows and columns corresponding to nodes 2 and 5, connected by element 5. Thus, each element adds contributions at the intersections of the rows corresponding to the nodes it connects, positive for diagonal positions and negative for off-diagonal positions.

Taking advantage of such a pattern, a systematic scheme for the assembling of the total system of equations can be implemented. The first step of such a scheme requires the creation of a connectivity table, showing the end nodes corresponding to each element. For instance, the connectivity table for the network of Figure 4.4 is given in Table 4.1. In specifying such a table, it is required to indicate which are the initial and final nodes for each element. It is really immaterial which of the element nodes will be selected as initial or final node, but such selection defines the positive sense for the element discharges. A positive discharge will go from the initial to the final node. These positive directions are shown in Figure 4.4 for the connectivity given in Table 4.1.

Once the connectivity table is available, and coefficients k^i are computed for every element, the assembling of the element characteristic matrix is straightforward. Starting with a null matrix, i.e. a matrix with all coefficients equal to zero, the following operations are performed for eaoh element:

(1)   add coefficient k^i to positions (k, k) and (j, j),
(2)   add coefficient $-k^i$ to positions (k, j) and (j, k),

TABLE 4.1. Connectivity table

Element	Initial node, k	Final node, j
1	1	2
2	1	3
3	2	3
4	2	4
5	5	2
6	3	4
7	4	5
8	3	5
9	4	6

according to the connectivity table. Once all elements are considered, the **K** matrix is assembled. To complete the total system of equations, it is necessary to form the nodal consumption vector **C**. This is done by adding the consumption for each node in the row corresponding to that node in vector **C**.

Several interesting features of the matrix **K** are evident from the assembling scheme. In particular, attention should be given to the following facts:

(a) If two generic nodes, say m and n, are not connected to each other, no contributions will be added to positions (m, n) and (n, m) which will thus remain equal to zero. Matrix **K** will be fully populated only when each node is connected to all other nodes in the network, which is rarely the case. In fact, for most large networks, the total percentage of non-null coefficients in matrix **K** will be small, and that matrix is said to be a sparse matrix.

(b) Whenever a coefficient is added to a position (m, n), it is also added to its symmetric position (n, m). Thus matrix **K** is a symmetric matrix, such that

$$k_{mn} = k_{nm} \qquad (4.30)$$

for any m and n, or

$$\mathbf{K} = \mathbf{K}^{\mathrm{T}} \qquad (4.31)$$

where $\mathbf{K}^{\mathrm{T}}$ is the transpose of matrix **K**. This property may be very useful to save storage space in the computer because if either k_{mn} or k_{nm} is available, the other is automatically known. Thus, for a symmetric matrix it is only necessary to store the coefficients on the main diagonal, plus the coefficients either above or below that main diagonal. Therefore, for an $N \times N$ system, it will be enough to store $(N^2 - N)/2 + N$ coefficients rather than the totality of the N^2 coefficients, which reduces the storage requirements almost by half. For instance, for $N = 100$, only 5500 coefficients, rather than 10 000, need to be stored.

(c) Using the symbol ' ●' for a non-null coefficient, and the symbol ' o' for a null coefficient, the **K** matrix shows the pattern indicated in Figure 4.6. The non-null coefficients are found to be within a band whose centre is the main diagonal. All coefficients outside the band are null. The coefficients within the band will be non-null for the most part, but the

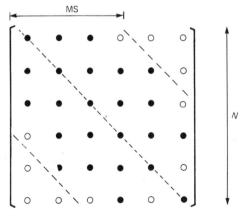

Figure 4.6 Pattern of matrix κ

band may also include some null coefficients. All coefficients on the main diagonal will be non-null unless there are isolated nodes, not connected to any elements, which is a physical impossibility.

Matrices such as the **K** matrix are called banded matrices. **K**, in particular, is a banded symmetric matrix. This bandedness can also be taken advantage of to reduce storage requirements. Two quantities are required to indicate the order of a banded matrix. These are the number of unknowns N and the half-bandwidth (MS), indicated in Figure 4.6. Notice that for $N = 100$ and $MS = 20$, it is only necessary to store 2000 coefficients rather than 10 000, due to symmetry and bandedness. Large systems tend to have small half-bandwidths, making possible large storage savings.

The band of a system depends on the way in which the nodes are ordered. To compute the half-bandwidth, it is necessary to find the maximum difference in the numbers of any two nodes connected to each other. The half-bandwidth is equal to that maximum difference plus one (because the diagonal is included). Thus, for instance, looking at Table 4.1, it is possible to see that the maximum difference for the network of Figure 4.4 is equal to 3 for element 5, connecting nodes 5 and 2. Therefore, the half-bandwidth for that system will be equal to 4.

4.6 Boundary conditions

Before the total system of equations can be solved, it is necessary to introduce the proper boundary conditions for at least some of the network nodes.

The two types of nodal quantities defined for a network are heads and consumptions. Thus, the two possible types of boundary conditions involve specifying either the head or the consumption, for any given node.

As heads are the nodal unknowns, prescribing a head has the effect of reducing the order of the total system of equations. For instance, if in the following hypothetical system of order 3,

$$k_{11}H_1 + k_{12}H_2 + k_{13}H_3 = C_1$$
$$k_{21}H_1 + k_{22}H_2 + k_{23}H_3 = C_2 \qquad (4.32)$$
$$k_{31}H_1 + k_{32}H_2 + k_{33}H_3 = C_3$$

the second unknown is prescribed such that

$$H_2 = \bar{H}_2 \qquad (4.33)$$

where $\bar{H}_2$ is a known value, the terms involving H_2, which is no longer an unknown, can be taken to the right-hand side of each equation, as follows:

$$k_{11}H_1 + k_{13}H_3 = C_1 - k_{12}\bar{H}_2$$
$$k_{21}H_1 + k_{23}H_3 = C_2 - k_{22}\bar{H}_2 \qquad (4.34)$$
$$k_{31}H_1 + k_{33}H_3 = C_3 - k_{32}\bar{H}_2$$

where there is one more equation than unknowns. Neglecting the second equation leads to the following system, of order 2:

$$k_{11}H_1 + k_{13}H_3 = C_1 - k_{12}\bar{H}_2$$
$$k_{31}H_1 + k_{33}H_3 = C_3 - k_{32}\bar{H}_2 \qquad (4.35)$$

which can be solved for H_1 and H_2. Thus, in order to introduce a prescribed unknown $\bar{H}_j$ condition, it will suffice to add the term $-k_{ij}\bar{H}_j$ to the ith position of the vector of nodal consumptions, with i ranging from 1 to N, but $i \neq j$, and then to eliminate the jth equation.

Although the scheme described above is very adequate for hand computations, it may be inefficient for computer implementation. The basic problem is that elimination of an equation from the system already assembled would require reordering the remaining equations, and this can be a time-consuming process in a computer. Therefore, in order to avoid such reordering, rather than eliminating completely the jth row, it is replaced by the condition equation (4.33) to render the following system:

$$k_{11}H_1 + 0 + k_{13}H_3 = C_1 - k_{12}\bar{H}_2$$

$$H_2 = \bar{H}_2 \tag{4.36}$$

$$k_{31}H_1 + 0 + k_{33}H_3 = C_3 - k_{32}\bar{H}_2$$

which is equivalent to system (4.35) plus equation (4.33) and does not require reordering. Writing system (4.36) in the following manner:

$$\begin{bmatrix} k_{11} & 0 & k_{13} \\ 0 & 1 & 0 \\ k_{31} & 0 & k_{33} \end{bmatrix} \begin{Bmatrix} H_1 \\ H_2 \\ H_3 \end{Bmatrix} = \begin{Bmatrix} C_1 - k_{12}\bar{H}_2 \\ \bar{H}_2 \\ C_3 - k_{32}\bar{H}_2 \end{Bmatrix} \tag{4.37}$$

it is evident that the introduction of the boundary conditions for prescribed heads, without reordering, can be implemented by performing the following steps:

(a) Add the contribution of the prescribed unknown $\bar{H}_j$ to the vector of nodal consumptions.
(b) Zero the jth column and jth row of matrix **K**.
(c) Make the (j, j) coefficient of matrix **K** equal to 1.
(d) Make the jth coefficient of the vector of nodal consumptions equal to $\bar{H}_j$.

A boundary condition of the second type, where the consumption rather than the head is prescribed, is handled by simply placing the value of the prescribed consumption in the proper position of the vector of nodal consumptions.

In general, either the head or the consumption will have to be known for every node in the network, but not both simultaneously. When neither of them is given, it is assumed that the nodal consumption is equal to zero, and the head is unknown. Finally, in order to solve the system, at least one head will have to be prescribed. As the discharges depend on the head differences and not on the heads themselves, prescribing one head arbitrarily, if required, will not affect the discharge results.

4.7 Solution of the system of equations and evaluation of results

The solution procedure to be applied will be different for the linear and for the non-linear formulations. In the first case, the coefficients of matrix **K** are constants, so that the total system of equations needs to be assembled and solved only once. This case will be examined first. For the non-linear formulation, the coefficients of matrix **K** are not constants as they depend on the heads. Solution procedures for the non-linear system of equations will be discussed later on.

Any standard computer program can be used for the solution of the linear system of simultaneous algebraic equations. In most cases, however, the computer programs used are based on the Gauss elimination technique or on some of its variations. The solution of the system of equations will provide the values of the previously unknown nodal heads. With these, discharges can be computed for every element. Establishing the equilibrium of the discharges of the elements connected to a node will give the nodal consumption at that node. If the consumption was part of the data, comparison with the computed value will give an idea of the accuracy of the solution.

Example 4.1
Considering the parallel pipe system shown in Figure 4.7, its analysis will be performed assuming that the flow is laminar, and for the following data:

Head at node 1	$H_1 = 10$ m
Consumption at node 2	$C_2 = -2$ m³ s^{-1}
Length of branch 1	$L_1 = 1000$ m
Length of branch 2	$L_2 = 2000$ m
Diameter of branch 1	$D_1 = 0.1$ m
Diameter of branch 2	$D_2 = 0.2$ m
Viscosity of water at 20°C	$v = 10^{-6}$ m² s^{-1}

The constants k^i for branches 1 and 2, respectively, are

$$k^1 = \frac{\pi \rho g D_1^4}{128 \mu L_1} = \frac{\pi g D_1^4}{128 v L_1}$$

$$= \frac{\pi \cdot 9.81}{128 \cdot 10^6 \cdot 1000} 10^{-4} = 0.024 \text{ m}^2 \text{ s}^{-1}$$

$$k^2 = \frac{\pi \cdot 9.81 \cdot 16}{128 \cdot 10^{-6} \cdot 1000} 10^{-4} = 0.385 \text{ m}^2 \text{ s}^{-1}$$

Thus the element equations for branches 1 and 2 will be

$$\begin{Bmatrix} Q_1^1 \\ Q_2^1 \end{Bmatrix} = \begin{bmatrix} 0.024 & -0.024 \\ -0.024 & 0.024 \end{bmatrix} \begin{Bmatrix} H_1 \\ H_2 \end{Bmatrix}$$

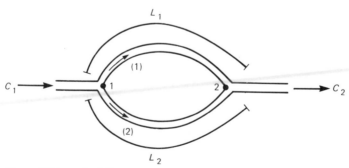

Figure 4.7 Network of Example 4.1

$$\begin{Bmatrix} Q_1^2 \\ Q_2^2 \end{Bmatrix} = \begin{bmatrix} 0.385 & -0.385 \\ -0.385 & 0.385 \end{bmatrix} \begin{Bmatrix} H_1 \\ H_2 \end{Bmatrix}$$

Assembling the total system leads to

$$\begin{bmatrix} 0.024+0.385 & -0.024-0.385 \\ -0.024-0.385 & 0.024+0.385 \end{bmatrix} \begin{Bmatrix} H_1 \\ H_2 \end{Bmatrix} = \begin{Bmatrix} C_1 \\ C_2 \end{Bmatrix}$$

or

$$\begin{bmatrix} 0.409 & -0.409 \\ -0.409 & 0.409 \end{bmatrix} \begin{Bmatrix} H_1 \\ H_2 \end{Bmatrix} = \begin{Bmatrix} C_1 \\ C_2 \end{Bmatrix}$$

Since $H_1 = 10$ m and $C_2 = -2$ m^2 s^{-1} we can write the second equation as

$$-0.409H_1 + 0.409H_2 = -2$$

or

$$0.409H_2 = -2 + 4.09 = 2.09$$

so that

$$H_2 = \frac{2.09}{0.409} = 5.11 \text{ m}$$

Hence:

$$Q^1 = k^1(H_1 - H_2) = 0.024(10 - 5.11) = 0.11735 \text{ m}^3 \text{ s}^{-1}$$
$$Q^2 = k^2(H_1 - H_2) = 0.385(10 - 5.11) = 1.88265 \text{ m}^3 \text{ s}^{-1}$$

so that

$$Q^1 + Q^2 = 0.11736 + 1.88265 = 2 \text{ m}^3 \text{ s}^{-1}$$

Example 4.2
This second example concerns the analysis of the network shown in Figure 4.8, which includes all relevant data. The element data, considering $v = 10^{-6}$ m^2 s^{-1}, are summarised in the following table:

Element	Length (m)	Diameter (m)	k^i (m^2 s^{-1})
1	1000	0.400	6.164
2	1000	0.200	0.385
3	2000	0.283	0.772
4	2000	0.283	0.772
5	2000	0.573	12.977

The system matrix can then be written

$$K = \begin{bmatrix} 6.164+0.385 & -6.164 & -0.385 & 0 \\ -6.164 & 6.164+0.772+0.772 & -0.772 & -0.772 \\ -0.385 & -0.772 & 0.385+0.772+12.977 & -12.977 \\ 0 & -0.772 & -12.977 & 0.772+12.977 \end{bmatrix}$$

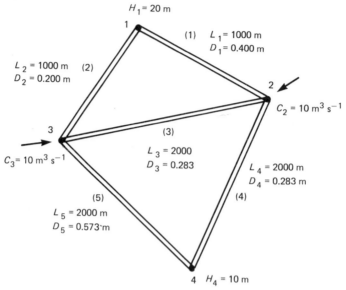

$H_1 = 20$ m

(1) $L_1 = 1000$ m
       $D_1 = 0.400$ m

$L_2 = 1000$ m   (2)
$D_2 = 0.200$ m

2

$C_2 = 10$ m^3 s^{-1}

3   (3)

$C_3 = 10$ m^3 s^{-1}

$L_3 = 2000$
$D_3 = 0.283$

$L_4 = 2000$ m
$D_4 = 0.283$ m

(5)   (4)

$L_5 = 2000$ m
$D_5 = 0.573$ m

4   $H_4 = 10$ m

Figure 4.8 Network for Example 4.2

Therefore, the total system is

$$\begin{bmatrix} 6.549 & -6.164 & -0.385 & 0.000 \\ -6.164 & 7.708 & -0.772 & -0.772 \\ -0.385 & -0.772 & 14.134 & -12.977 \\ 0.000 & -0.772 & -12.977 & 13.749 \end{bmatrix} \begin{Bmatrix} 20 \\ H_2 \\ H_3 \\ 10 \end{Bmatrix} = \begin{Bmatrix} C_1 \\ 10 \\ 10 \\ C_4 \end{Bmatrix}$$

The second and third equations give

$$7.708H_2 - 0.772H_3 = 10 + 6.164 \times 20 + 0.772 \times 10$$
$$-0.772H_2 + 14.134H_3 = 10 + 0.385 \times 20 + 12.977 \times 10$$

or

$$7.708H_2 - 0.772H_3 = 141.00$$
$$-0.772H_2 + 14.134H_3 = 147.47$$

The solution of this system is

$$H_2 = 19.443 \text{ m} \qquad H_3 = 11.495 \text{ m}$$

The consumptions at nodes 1 and 4 can be evaluated from the first and fourth rows of the total system of equations giving

$$C_1 = 6.549 \times 20 - 6.164 \times 19.443 - 0.385 \times 11.495 = 6.7$$
$$C_4 = -0.772 \times 19.443 - 12.977 \times 11.495 + 13.749 \times 10 = -26.7$$

Notice that

$$\sum_{i=1}^{5} C_i = 6.7 + 10 + 10 - 26.7 = 0$$

Also:

$$Q^1 = 6.164(20 - 19.443) = 3.43$$
$$Q^2 = 0.385(20 - 11.495) = 3.27$$
$$Q^3 = 0.772(19.443 - 11.495) = 6.14$$
$$Q^4 = 0.772(19.443 - 10) = 7.29$$
$$Q^5 = 12.977(11.495 - 10) = 19.40$$

4.8 Computer program for linear analysis of pipe networks

This section presents a complete computer program for linear analysis of pipe networks as a means of illustrating the details of a computer analysis method previously described.

When advisable flow charts will be presented, using the following symbols:

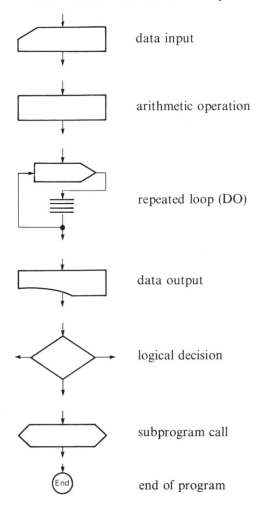

data input

arithmetic operation

repeated loop (DO)

data output

logical decision

subprogram call

end of program

Several versions of the FORTRAN language exist, some more powerful than the others. The programs presented in the book, however, were written using mostly basic FORTRAN statements, so that they can be used in most machines.

When implementing any non-trivial computer program, it is necessary to achieve a balance between efficiency and compactness on the one side, and clarity and generality on the other. In this case, the emphasis is on the last two aspects, both to provide a better understanding of the problem and to have a program which can be easily modified to solve other applications. To accomplish this, the program will be subdivided in a set of modular subprograms, separating specific operations for pipe network analysis from operations for the general matrix analysis process.

Although in this case there is only one unknown per node, and linear elements with two end nodes are used, other problems may have more than one unknown per node, or may use elements with more than two nodes, as will be described later on. It is not desired, though, to limit the general subprogram to handle only one unknown per node and two nodes per element. The mechanism used for this is to set two variables, NDF and NNE, equal to the actual number of degrees of freedom or unknowns per node and to the number of nodes per element, respectively, in the main program, and have all subprograms operate on the base of those variables. These subprograms will not need alteration when used for other problems.

Although the emphasis is on modularity and generality of applications, efficiency considerations are not disregarded. An effort is made to reduce storage requirements so that the program can also be used on minicomputers.

The key question, regarding making efficient use of the storage capacity available, is the structure to be given to the array containing the system matrix. Clearly, the use of a square array storing the full system matrix will be highly inefficient. Such an array will contain a large number of zero coefficients and duplicated information. Thus, it is important that proper advantage should be taken of the fact that the system matrix is symmetric and banded. To this end, only the coefficients on the main diagonal, and above the main diagonal but within the band, will be stored. Storage will be done in a rectangular array, by rows, as indicated in Figure 4.9. The half-bandwidth is called MS. Since the storage is done by rows starting with the coefficients on the main diagonal, then the main diagonal will become a column in the new array. Rows remain rows, but coefficients in a column of the full array will be placed in an inclined line in the new array, as shown in Figure 4.9.

The new storage organisation can be handled easily, provided a proper correspondence is established to determine the position of the coefficients in the full matrix organisation. The important point here is that a coefficient originally located in position (I, J) will occupy the position $(I, J - I + 1)$ in the new organisation. A diagonal coefficient in location (I, I), for instance, will have position $(I, 1)$ in the new organisation.

The system matrix will thus be stored in a two-dimensional rectangular array, according to the symmetric banded storage scheme. The geometry, connectivity, properties, and boundary conditions will all be stored in one-dimensional arrays. All the absolute dimensioning of the arrays will be done in the main program, while in the subprograms variable dimensioning will be used. Whenever the array dimensions need to be changed only the main

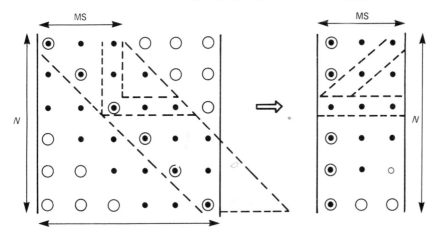

Figure 4.9 Symmetric banded storage

program is altered, while the subprograms remain unchanged.

The program is subdivided according to the analysis steps discussed in the previous section, with the operations organised as shown in the flowchart of Figure 4.10.

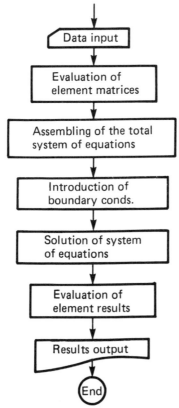

Figure 4.10 Flow diagram for program

The general integer variables used by the program, together with their meaning, are given below:

MNN = maximum possible number of nodes
MNE = maximum possible number of elements
MNB = maximum possible number of nodes with prescribed head
NN   = actual number of nodes
NE   = actual number of elements
NLN = number of nodes with specified consumption
NBN = actual number of nodes with prescribed head
NNE = number of nodes per element (which for this case is equal to 1)
NDF = number of degrees of freedom per node (which for this case is equal to 1)
NDFEL = number of degrees of freedom per element, given by NDF*NNE (which for this case is equal to 2)
NRMX = row dimension of the array TK, to store the total matrix
NCMX = column dimension of the array TK
N   = total number of unknowns for a problem, given by NDF*NN. It is also equal to the actual number of rows in the total matrix
MS   = actual half-bandwidth of the total stiffness matrix

The only real variable used, is

E   = value of the fluid density times the gravitational acceleration divided by the viscosity

The program uses several integer and real arrays to store both data and results. In most cases these are one-dimensional arrays so that, excluding the main program, all programs can be made independent of array dimension.

The integer arrays used in common are:

KON   One-dimensional array of element connectivities. KON(NNE*(L−1)+1) contains the first node and KON(NNE*(L−1)+2) the second node of element L

IB   One-dimensional array of boundary condition data. IB(2*J−1) contains the node number for the Jth support node. IB(2*J) is always zero in this program.

The real arrays used are:

X   One-dimensional array of x coordinates. X(J) contains the x coordinate of node J.

Y   One-dimensional array of y coordinates. Y(J) contains the y coordinate of node J.

PROP One-dimensional array of pipe diameters. PROP(L) contains the diameter corresponding to element L

AL   One-dimensional array of nodal consumptions. AL(J) contains the consumption for node J. It will have zero values for nodes with no consumption specified. After solution of the system equations AL is used to store the nodal heads. Thus after solution, AL(J) contains the head corresponding to node J.

TK   Two-dimensional array containing the total stiffness matrix, according to the symmetric banded storage scheme explained above. NRMX is its row dimension and NCMX is its column dimension.

ELST   Two-dimensional array storing the element matrix for the element being processed. Its row and column dimensions are equal to NDFEL.

V   One-dimensional auxiliary array used by the program performing the solution of the system of equations. Its dimension is equal to NCMX.

ELRE   One-dimensional array of element discharges. ELRE(L) contains the discharge corresponding to element *L*.

RENO   One-dimensional array originally containing prescribed nodal heads. RENO(J) contains the prescribed head for node *J*. It will contain zero values for nodes without prescribed heads.

   After solution is completed RENO contains the resultant discharges at the nodes, computed establishing equilibrium for the discharges of the elements connected to each node. Then, after solution, RENO(J) contains the nodal discharge resultant. For nodes with prescribed input or consumption, the resultant has to be equal to that input or consumption. Otherwise it contains zero.

Note that within some of the subprograms some auxiliary arrays may be used. Their meanings will be evident analysing the flow of operations of those subprograms. In most cases they are also described in the subprogram commentaries.

Finally, it should be mentioned that the programs presented in this book are part of an extensive set of programs for engineering applications, some of which are presented in other books by the same authors.

Program 1: Main program

The main program will initialise the basic program parameters, and then will call on a set of six different subprograms, each performing the operations relative to the analysis steps described previously. The sequence of operations is shown in Figure 4.11, corresponding to the following FORTRAN code:

```
C                    PROGRAM 1
C                 MAIN PROGRAM FOR
C          ANALYSIS OF LINEAR PIPE NETWORKS
C
          COMMON NN, NE, NLN, NBN, NDF, NNE, N, MS, IN, IO, E
          DIMENSION X(100), Y(100), KON(200), PROP(100), IB(60), TK(100, 20),
        * AL(100), ELRE(100), RENO(100), ELST(2, 2), V(20)
          EQUIVALENCE (TK(1, 1), ELRE(1))
C
C         INITIALIZATION OF PROGRAM PARAMETERS
C
C         MNN  = MAXIMUN NUMBER OF NODES ALLOWED
C         MNE  = MAXIMUN NUMBER OF ELEMENTS ALLOWED
C         MNB  = MAXIMUN NUMBER OF BOUNDARY NODES ALLOWED
C         NCMX = COLUMN DIMENSION FOR GLOBAL MATRIX OR
C                MAXIMUM HALF BAND WIDTH ALLOWED
C         NDF = NUMBER OF DEGREES OF FREEDOM PER NODE
C         NNE = NUMBER OF NODES PER ELEMENT
C         NDFEL = TOTAL NUMBER OF DEGREES OF FREEDOM
C                 PER ELEMENT
C
          MNN = 100
          MNE = 100
          MNB = 30
          NRMX =100
```

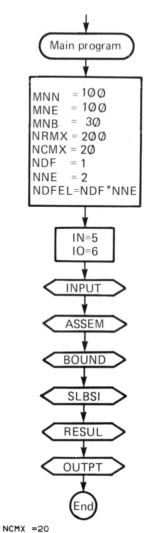

Figure 4.11 Main program flowchart

```
      NCMX =20
      NDF = 1
      NNE = 2
      NDFEL = NDF*NNE
C
C     ASSIGN DATA SET NUMBERS TO, IN, FOR INPUT AND
C     IO, FOR OUTPUT
C
      IN=5
      IO=6
C
C     APPLY THE ANALYSIS STEPS
C
      CALL INPUT(X, Y, KON, PROP, AL, IB, RENO)
C
C     CHECK FOR LIMITS
C
      IF(MNN-NN)1, 2, 2
    1 WRITE(IO, 101)
  101 FORMAT(/' **** TOO MANY NODES **** '/)
      GO TO 999
    2 IF(MNE-NE)3, 4, 4
    3 WRITE(IO, 103)
```

```
    103 FORMAT(/' **** TOO MANY ELEMENTS ****'/)
        GO TO 999
      4 IF(MNB-NBN)5, 7, 7
      5 WRITE(IO, 105)
    105 FORMAT(/' **** TOO MANY BOUNDARY NODES ****'/)
        GO TO 999
C
C       CHECK IF MAXIMUM HALF-BANDWIDTH WAS EXCEEDED
C
      7 IF(NCMX-MS)8, 6, 6
      8 WRITE(IO, 108)
    108 FORMAT(/' **** MAXIMUM HALF-BANDWIDTH EXCEEDED ****'/)
        GO TO 999
C
C       ASSEMBLING OF GLOBAL MATRIX
C
      6 CALL ASSEM(X, Y, KON, PROP, TK, ELST, AL, NRMX, NCMX, NDFEL)
        WRITE(IO, 3333) ((TK(IX, JX), JX=1, MS), IX=1, N)
   3333 FORMAT(3F20. 6)
        WRITE(IO, 4444) (AL(IX), IX=1, N)
   4444 FORMAT(F20. 6)
C
C       CHECK FOR ERROR CONDITIONS
C
        IF(MS)9, 9, 10
      9 WRITE(IO, 109)
    109 FORMAT(/' **** ERRORS DETECTED PREVENT ANALYSIS ****'/)
        GO TO 999
C
C       INTRODUCTION OF BOUNDARY CONDITIONS
C
     10 CALL DOUND(TK, AL, RENO, ID, NRMX, NCMX)
        WRITE(IO, 3333) ((TK(IX, JX), JX=1, MS), IX=1, N)
        WRITE(IO, 4444) (AL(IX), IX=1, N)
C
C       SOLUTION OF THE SYSTEM OF EQUATIONS
C
        CALL SLBSI(TK, AL, V, N, MS, NRMX, NCMX)
        WRITE(IO, 3333) ((TK(IX, JX), JX=1, MS), IX=1, N)
        WRITE(IO, 4444) (AL(IX), IX=1, N)
C
C       CHECK FOR ERROR CONDITIONS
C
        IF(MS)9, 11, 11
C
C       COMPUTATION OF MEMBER DISCHARGES
C
     11 CALL RESUL(KON, PROP, ELRE, RENO, X, Y, AL)
C
C       OUTPUT
C
        CALL OUTPT (AL, ELRE, RENO)
C
    999 CALL EXIT
C
        END
```

The dimensions declared in this main program allow a maximum of 100 nodes, 100 elements and 30 support nodes. Accordingly the integer variable NRMX, indicating the maximum number of rows in the total stiffness matrix, is set equal to 100 (total number of degrees of freedom, or unknowns, for 100 nodes). The maximum half-bandwidth, NCMX, is set equal to 20. All these values can be changed according to the memory capacity of the computer available.

The program also initialises the maximum number of nodes equal to 100 in MNN, the maximum number of elements equal to 100 in MNE, the maximum number of nodes with prescribed head equal to 30 in MNB, the nodal degrees of freedom equal to 1 in NDF, the number of nodes per element equal to 2 in

NNE, and the number of degrees of freedom per element equal to NDF*NNE, in NDFEL. The integer variables IN and IO, which are the data set number for the input and output devices, are set equal to 5 and 6, respectively. Note that these numbers should be set according to the conventions of the computer available.

A check is made in order to verify that the maximum total numbers of nodes, elements and nodes with prescribed head are not exceeded.

The analysis steps are applied calling the subprograms: INPUT, for data input; ASSEM, to compute the element matrices and to assemble the total system of equations; BOUND, to introduce the boundary conditions: SLBSI to solve the system of equations, RESUL, to compute the element discharges and the resultant nodal consumptions; and OUTPT, for result output. Note, in particular, that for efficiency reasons the subprogram ASSEM performs two of the analysis steps: the evaluation of the element matrices and the assembling of the total system of equations. This eliminates the eventual need to have an array to store all the element matrices, as required in the case in which both steps are carried out separately.

Checks for error conditions are made after the calls to subprograms ASSEM and SLBSI, such that computations are ended in the case of fatal errors. Notice that this is done checking the value of variable MS. This variable, which usually contains the half-bandwidth of the system matrix, is made equal to zero when fatal errors are detected, as a means of signalling the main program of such an occurrence.

It is important to mention that in order to change the capacity of this program it is necessary to change only the dimensions of the arrays and the initialisation of some variables in the main program, without having to change the other subprograms. Thus, to change the number of nodes, the variable MNN will have to be changed. The dimensions of arrays X, Y, AL and TK will have to be equal to that number. A change in the maximum number of elements allowed requires changing variable MNE. The dimensions of array PROP and ELRE will have to be equal to that number, while the dimension of array KON will have to be twice that number. To change the maximum number of nodes with prescribed head requires changing the value of variable MNB. The dimension of array IB will have to be equal to twice that number.

In some cases it may be necessary to alter the dimensions of the system matrix TK to allow for a greater or smaller half-bandwidth. The first dimension will have to be equal to the value assigned to variable NRMX, while the second dimension must coincide with the value assigned to variable NCMX. The dimension of auxiliary array V must also coincide with that number. Variable NRMX, in particular, must have the same value as variable MNN, for this case, because the number of nodal degrees of freedom is equal to 1. For other types of problems such variables may have different values.

Finally, it should be noticed that arrays TK and ELRE are made equivalent. This is done in order to save storage space and take advantage of the fact that array TK is only used up to the solution of the system of equations and array ELRE is only used after that step.

Program 2: Data input (INPUT)

All the input required by the program for linear analysis of pipe networks is read by the subprogram INPUT. The input of data consists of the following groups of cards:

(1) *Basic parameters card.* One card containing the number of nodes, number of elements, number of known consumption nodes, number of known head nodes, and fluid properties, with format 4I10, F10.0.
(2) *Nodal coordinate cards.* As many cards as there are nodes in the network. Each card will contain the node number, and its *x* and *y* coordinates, with format I10, 2F10.2.
(3) *Element connectivity and diameter cards.* As many cards as there are elements in the network. Each card will contain the element number, the numbers of its first and second nodes, and its diameter, with format 3I10, F10.5.
(4) *Nodal consumption or discharge cards.* As many cards as there are known nodal discharges. Each card contains the node number and the nodal discharge, with format I10, F12.4.

At the end of this chapter there is an example of the input data for a practical case.

The FORTRAN code for the subprogram INPUT is as follows:

```
C
C
C
      SUBROUTINE INPUT (X, Y, KON, PROP, AL, IB, RENO)
C
C             PROGRAM 2
C          PROGRAM FOR DATA INPUT
C
      COMMON NN, NE, NLN, NBN, NDF, NNE, N, MS, IN, IO, E
      DIMENSION X(1), Y(1), KON(1), PROP(1), AL(1), IB(1), RENO(1), IC(2)
C
C      IC = AUXILIARY STORAGE TO STORE THE CONCTIVITY OF
C           AN ELEMENT, AND THE BOUNDARY UNKNOWNS STATUS
C           INDICTORS
C
C      READ DASIC PARAMENTERS
C
C      NN = NUMBER OF NODES
C      NE = NUMBER OF ELEMENTS
C      NLN = NUMBER OF LOADED NODES
C      NBN = NUMBER OF BOUNDARY NODES
C      E = VALUE OF THE MASS DENSITY*GRAVITY ACCELERATION/VISCOSITY
C
      WRITE (IO, 20)
   20 FORMAT(' ', 130('*'))
      READ(IN, 1)NN, NE, NLN, NBN, E
      WRITE(IO, 21)NN, NE, NLN, NBN, E
   21 FORMAT(//' INTERNAL DATA'///' NUMBER OF NODES        : ', I5/
     *' NUMBER OF ELEMENTS     : ', I5/
     *' NUMBER OF NODES WITH KNOWN DISCHARGE: ', I5/
     *' NUMBER OF NODES WITH KNOWN HEAD:      ', I5/
     *' VALUE OF DENSITY*GRAVITY ACC./VISCOSITY: ', F15.2//
     * ' NODAL COORDINATES'/7X, 'NODE', 6X, 'X', 9X, 'Y')
    1 FORMAT(4I10, F10.0)
C
C      READ NODAL COORDINATES IN ARRAY X AND Y
C
      DO 1111 J=1, NN
      READ (IN, 2) I, X(I), Y(I)
 1111 WRITE(IO, 2) I, X(I), Y(I)
    2 FORMAT(I10, 2F10.2)
C
C      READ ELEMENT CONNECTIVITY IN ARRAY CON AND ELEMENT
C      DIAMETER IN ARRAY PROP
C
```

```
         WRITE(IO,22)
      22 FORMAT(/' ELEMENT CONNECTIVITY AND DIAMETER'/4X,'ELEMENT',3X,
         *'START NODE    END NODE      DIAMETER')
         DO 3 J =1,NE
         READ(IN,4) I,IC(1),IC(2),PROP(I)
         WRITE(IO,34) I,IC(1),IC(2),PROP(I)
         N1 = NNE*(I-1)
         KON(N1+1)=IC(1)
       3 KON(N1+2)=IC(2)
       4 FORMAT(3I10,F10.5)
      34 FORMAT(2I10,I12,F18.5)
C
C        COMPUTE N, ACTUAL NUMBER OF UNKNOWN, AND CLEAR RIGHT HAND
C        SIDE VECTOR
C
         N=NN*NDF
         DO 5 I=1,N
       5 AL(I)=0
C
C        COMPUTE HALF BANDWIDTH
C
         CALL BAND(NE,NDF,NNE,MS,IO,KON)
C
C        READ THE NODAL DISCHARGES AND STORE THEM IN ARRAY AL
C
         WRITE(IO,23)
      23 FORMAT(/' NODAL DISCHARGES '/8X,'NODE',5X,'VALUE')
         DO 6 I=1,NLN
         READ (IN,12) J,AL(J)
       6 WRITE (IO,12) J,AL(J)
      12 FORMAT(I10,F12.4)
C
C        READ BOUNDARY NODES DATA STORE PRESCRIBED HEAD VALUES IN RENO
C
         WRITE(IO,24)
      24 FORMAT(/' BOUNDARY CONDITION DATA'/8X,'NODE',5X,
         *'PRESCRIBED VALUES')
         DO 7 I=1,NBN
         READ (IN,8)J,RENO(J)
         WRITE(IO,9)J,RENO(J)
         IB(2*I-1)=J
       7 IB(2*I)=0
       8 FORMAT(I10,F10.4)
       9 FORMAT(I10,10X,F10.4)
         RETURN
         END
```

This subprogram can be easily understood simply by reading it. Therefore it does not require a detailed explanation. All data read are also printed, for checking purposes. The output formats are not identical to the input formats, but give a clearer and more detailed picture of the input data.

Before reading the nodal discharges the total number of system unknowns (N) is computed. Then the vector AL is cleared. This is done because in some computers unused memory positions cannot be assumed to be zero. Otherwise that DO can be eliminated. The nodal discharges are read and placed into the array AL. Thus after the reading of the nodal discharges is completed, the vector of independent coefficients of the total system of equations is already formed.

There is also a call to subroutine BAND, which computes the half-bandwidth for the network, based on the element connectivity.

The basic idea, here, was to keep the input simple, to facilitate the understanding of the analysis process. For practical applications, several enhancements, such as consideration of pumps, additional pipe boxes, etc. can be easily added later on (see Problems 4.5 and 4.6).

Program 3: Computation of the half-bandwidth (BAND)

In the case of network problems, where the elements connect only two nodes, the computation of the half-bandwidth is straightforward, and can be done checking all elements, and registering the maximum differences existing between the node numbers of the two nodes connected to each bar, then adding 1 to that number, and multiplying by the number of nodal degrees freedom. These operations can be organised according to the flowchart in Figure 4.12, where the half-bandwidth is stored in MS.

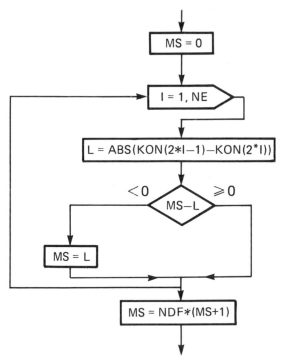

Figure 4.12 Determination of the bandwidth

If, however, we consider the possibility that an element can have more than two nodes, as will be the case for other applications, the computation of the half-bandwidth becomes a little more involved. In particular, rather than considering the difference between just two nodes for each element, each node will have to be compared with all remaining nodes to find the maximum nodal number difference, as shown by the flowchart in Figure 4.13. In order for the subprogram BAND to be as general as possible the second alternative is adopted, as it can be seen in the following FORTRAN code:

```
C
C
      SUBROUTINE BAND(NE, NDF, NNE, MS, IO, KON)
C
C              PROGRAM 3
C
C      COMPUTATION OF THE HALF-BANDWIDTH
C
      DIMENSION KON(1)
      N1=NNE-1
      MS=0
      DO 2 I=1, NE
      L1=NNE*(I-1)
      DO 2 J=1, N1
```

```
    L2=L1+J
    J1=J+1
    DO 2 K=J1,NNE
    L3=L1+K
    L=IABS(KON(L2)-KON(L3))
    IF(MS-L)1,2,2
  1 MS=L
  2 CONTINUE
    MS=NDF*(MS+1)
    WRITE(IO,3) MS
  3 FORMAT(//'---- HALF-BANDWIDTH IS EQUAL TO',I5' ----'/)
    RETURN
    END
```

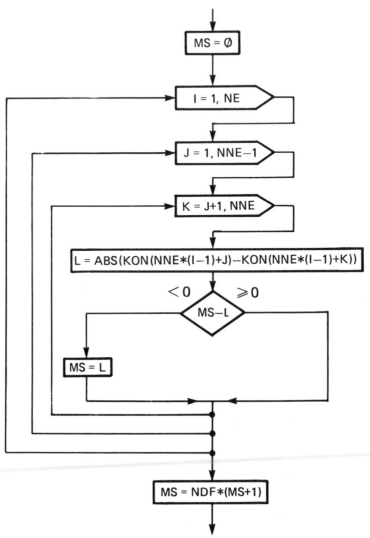

Figure 4.13 General bandwidth flowchart

Program 4: Assembling of the system matrix (ASSEM)

The subprogram ASSEM is the main program to assemble the total system matrix. It first clears the array TK and then, looping on the elements, calls the subprogram STIFF, to compute the element matrix, and ELASS, to add it to the array TK where the total system matrix must be stored.

The FORTRAN code for the subprogram ASSEM is as follows:

```
C
C
C
      SUBROUTINE ASSEM(X,Y,KON,PROP,TK,ELST,AL,NRMX,NCMX,NDFEL)
C
C              PROGRAM 4
C
C  ASSEMBLING OF THE TOTAL MATRIX FOR THE PROBLEM
C
      COMMON NN,NE,NLN,NBN,NDF,NNE,N,MS,IN,IO,E
      DIMENSION X(1),Y(1),KON(1),TK(NRMX,NCMX),ELST(NDFEL,NDFEL),
     *PROP(1),AL(1)
C
C      CLEAR SYSTEM MATRIX
C
      DO 10 I=1,N
      DO 10 J=1,MS
   10 TK(I,J)=0
C
C      ASSEMBLE SYSTEM OF EQUATIONS ELEMENT BY ELEMENT
C
C      STIFF WILL COMPUTE ELEMENT MATRIX FOR CURRENT
C              ELEMENT IN ARRAY ELST
C      ELASS WILL STORE ELEMENT MATRIX IN TOTAL SYSTEM
C              MATRIX TK
C
      DO 20 NEL=1,NE
      CALL STIFF(NEL,X,Y,PROP,KON,ELST,AL,NDFEL)
   20 CALL ELASS(NEL,KON,TK,ELST,NRMX,NCMX,NDFEL)
  999 RETURN
      END
```

Program 5: Computation of the element matrix (STIFF)

The element matrix, for each element in the network, is computed by subroutine STIFF. The FORTRAN code for this subprogram is as follows:

```
C
C
      SUBROUTINE STIFF(NEL,X,Y,PROP,KON,ELST,AL,NDFEL)
C              PROGRAM 5
C
C      COMPUTATION OF ELEMENT MATRIX
C
C
      COMMON NN,NE,NLN,NBN,NDF,NNE,N,MS,IN,IO,E
      DIMENSION X(1),Y(1),KON(1),PROP(1),ELST(NDFEL,NDFEL),AL(1)
C
C      NEL= CURRENT ELEMENT NEMBER
C      N1 = NUMBER OF START NODE
C      N2 = NUMBER OF END NODE
C
      L=NNE*(NEL-1)
      N1=KON(L+1)
      N2=KON(L+2)
C
C      COMPUTE LENGTH OF ELEMENT
C
      D=SQRT((X(N2)-X(N1))**2+(Y(N2)-Y(N1))**2)
```

```
C
C       CHECK FOR ERROR CONDITIONS
C
        IF(D)1,1,2
      1 WRITE(IO,101) NEL
    101 FORMAT(/' **** ZERO LENGTH FOR ELEMENT : ',I5,' ****'/)
        GO TO 4
      2 IF(PROP(NEL))3,3,5
      3 WRITE(IO,103) NEL
    103 FORMAT(/' **** ZERO DIAMETER FOR ELEMENT : ',I5,' ****'/)
      4 MS=0
        GO TO 999
C
C       COMPUTE ELEMENT MATRIX
C
      5 COEF=E*3.1416/128.*PROP(NEL)**4/D
        ELST(1,1)=COEF
        ELST(1,2)=-COEF
        ELST(1,2)=-COEF
        ELST(2,2)=COEF
    999 RETURN
        END
```

This subprogram computes the element matrix for the current element NEL, as given by

$$\mathbf{K}^i = \frac{\pi \rho g D_i^4}{128 L_i \mu} \begin{bmatrix} 1 & -1 \\ -1 & 1 \end{bmatrix} \tag{4.38}$$

according to the Poiseuille formula. Notice, in the subprogram, that the term $\rho g / \mu$ is contained in variable E, the length of the element is computed and stored in variable D, and the element diameter is in position NEL of array PROP.

The subprogram first set integer variables N1 and N2 equal to the start and end node numbers for element NEL. The length of the element is computed and stored in variable D. The matrix coefficient is computed and stored in variable COEF. Finally, the coefficients of the element matrix are placed in array ELST.

Notice that array AL, although not used, was included in the argument list for this subprogram, to facilitate future modifications, where an element vector is also required.

Program 6: Addition of an element matrix to the system matrix (ELASS)

The subprogram ELASS takes the element matrix for the current element NEL, stored in array ELMAT, and adds it to the total matrix in array TM. Both the arrays ELMAT and TM are passed through the argument list. These matrices may correspond to any other type of element and system matrices. In the present case, and according to the calling sequence for ELASS in subprogram ASSEM, the array ELMAT is equivalent to array ELST, and the array TM is equivalent to array TK.

To better explain the operations to be carried out by the subprogram ELASS let us first assume that the total matrix would be stored in a full square array, called TMF, not according to the symmetric banded storage scheme but as conventionally in matrix notation. We also assume that the element matrix is stored in full in array ELMF. In such case, the operations required for an element of NNE nodes, eventually greater than 2, are indicated in the flowchart of Figure 4.14, prepared according to the scheme presented in Section 4.5.

This operation requires the nodal submatrices of ELMF to be added into the corresponding hyper-rows and hypercolumns of TMF, as suggested by Figure 4.15 for an element of two nodes.

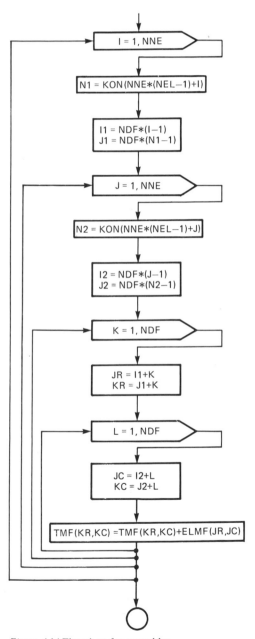

Figure 4.14 Flowchart for assembler

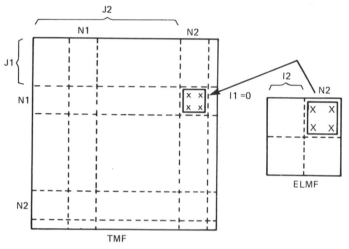

Figure 4.15 Assembling the element coefficients

The integer variable N1 assumes the number of different element nodes, the same applying for the integer variable N2. Each combination of N1 and N2 identifies a nodal submatrix in ELMF. The integer variables J1 and J2 are the number of rows and columns, respectively, before the first coefficient of the nodal submatrix corresponding to nodes N1 and N2, in the array TMF. The integer variables I1 and I2 are similar, but for the matrix ELMF. Then for each coefficient of ELMF, of row and column positions JR and JC it is possible to compute the corresponding row and column positions KR and KC in TMF, allowing adding up all coefficients of ELMF into the proper positions of TMF.

As explained before, however, it is more efficient to take advantage of the symmetry and banded characteristics of the total matrix. Using a symmetric banded storage scheme, only the upper triangular part of the total matrix, and up to the half-bandwidth, is stored in array TM. Consistently, only the upper triangular part of the element matrix is stored in array ELMAT. Based on these considerations the operations to be carried out by subprogram ELASS can be organised as shown by the flowchart given in Figure 4.16.

First, we notice that the DO loop on J starts in I, rather than in 1. This is to avoid considering both the off-diagonal submatrices representing the coupling between nodes N1 and N2, and between N2 and N1. We know that these submatrices are each the transpose of the other. On the other hand, since we are registering in TK only the upper triangular part of the total stiffness matrix, only one of those submatrices is needed. In particular, if $N1 < N2$ we need $K_{N1,N2}^{NEL}$ while if $N1 > N2$ we need $K_{N2,N1}^{NEL}$. Correspondingly, before adding a coefficient into TK, N1 and N2 are compared. If $N1 < N2$ the coefficients of $K_{N1,N2}^{NEL}$ are directly added to TK, properly computing the row and column subscripts for the symmetric banded storage scheme. When $N1 = N2$ we store in TK only the upper triangular part of $K_{N1,N1}^{NEL}$. Correspondingly the DO loop on L starts with $KI = K$, rather than with $KI = 1$. Finally, when $N1 > N2$ we interchange the corresponding row and column subscripts, to register in TK the transpose of $K_{N1,N2}^{NEL}$.

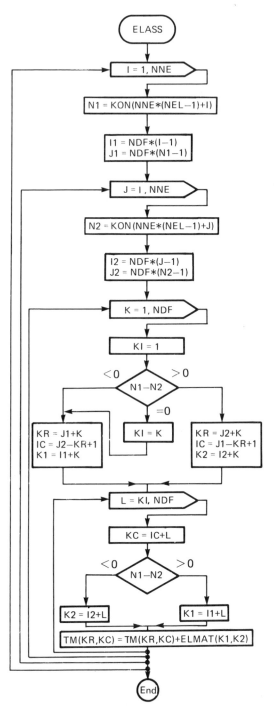

Figure 4.16 Flowchart for banded and symmetric assembler

Based on the flowchart in Figure 4.16 the FORTRAN code for the subprogram ELASS is the following:

```
C
C
      SUBROUTINE ELASS (NEL, KON, TM, ELMAT, NRMX, NCMX, NDFEL)
C
C             PROGRAM 6
C
C  THIS PROGRAM STORES THE ELEMENT MATRIX FOR ELEMENT NEL
C  IN THE TOTAL MATRIX FOR THE PROBLEM
C
      COMMON NN, NE, NLN, NBN, NDF, NNE, N, MS, IN, IO, E, G
      DIMENSION KON(1), TM(NRMX, NCMX), ELMAT(NDFEL, NDFEL)
C
C  NEL = CURRENT ELEMENT NUMBER
C  N1  = NUMBER OF START NODE
C  N2  = NUMBER OF END NODE
C
      L1=NNE*(NEL-1)
      DO 50 I=1, NNE
      L2=L1+I
      N1=KON(L2)
      I1=NDF*(I-1)
      J1=NDF*(N1-1)
      DO 50 J=I, NNE
      L2=L1+J
      N2=KON(L2)
      I2=NDF*(J-1)
      J2=NDF*(N2-1)
      DO 50 K=1, NDF
      K1=1
      IF(N1-N2) 20, 10, 30
C
C  STORE AN DIAGONAL SUBMATRIX
C
   10 KI=K
C
C  STORE AN OFF-DIAGONAL SUBMATRIX
C
   20 KR=J1+K
      IC=J2-KR+1
      K1=I1+K
      GO TO 40
C
C  STORE THE TRANSPOSE OF AN OFF-DIAGONAL SUBMATRIX
C
   30 KR=J2+K
      IC=J1-KR+1
      K2=I2+K
   40 DO 50 L=KI, NDF
      KC=IC+L
      IF(N1-N2) 45, 45, 46
   45 K2=I2+L
      GO TO 50
   46 K1=I1+L
   50 TM(KR, KC)=TM(KR, KC)+ELMAT(K1, K2)
      RETURN
      END
```

Program 7: Introduction of boundary conditions (BOUND)

The problem boundary conditions will be introduced according to the scheme discussed in the previous section. Let us first consider, for simplicity, the case in which the total system matrix is fully stored in a square array TMF. The corresponding operations can be organised in flowchart form as in Figure 4.17.

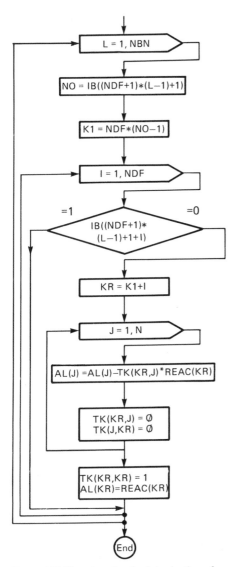

Figure 4.17 Flowchart for the introduction of
boundary conditions

The number of the support node being processed is stored in the integer N0. The integer K1 contains the number of rows in TK before the first row for node N0. When the indicator of the status of the Ith component of node N0 is equal to zero, in which case it is prescribed, the vector AL is modified to take into account the prescribed component, and the corresponding rows and columns of TK are zeroed. Then, the diagonal coefficient is made equal to 1, and the prescribed component is stored in AL(K1 + I).

In the case of storing the full matrix, all the coefficients of the corresponding row and column are made zero, as indicated in Figure 4.18 and the

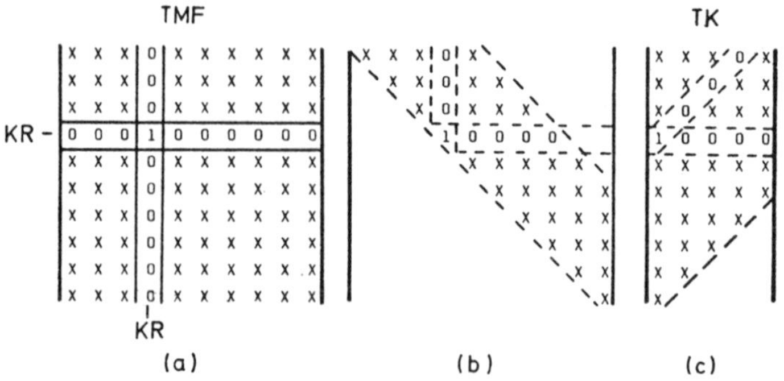

Figure 4.18 Boundary conditions

introduction of the boundary conditions is straightforward. If we store only the upper triangular part of the symmetric banded stiffness matrix, we have the case of Figure 4.18(b) where we have to zero the part of the column above the diagonal, and the part of the row to the right of the diagonal. When we use the symmetric banded storage the column coefficients are stored diagonally, as shown in Figure 4.18(c), and that is the case for the program being implemented. Then, when zeroing the row it must be checked that the column subscript does not exceed the total number of equations, as will happen when the row is one of the last rows of the matrix. Similarly, when zeroing the column it must be checked that the row subscript does not become zero, as will happen for one of the first columns of the matrix. Taking into account these considerations, the introduction of the boundary conditions can be carried out according to the flowchart in Figure 4.19.

The FORTRAN code for the subprogram BOUND, programmed according to the last flowchart, is the following:

```
C
C
        SUBROUTINE BOUND (TK, AL, RENO, IB, NRMX, NCMX)
C
C                PROGRAM 7
C
C   INTRODUCTION OF THE BOUNDARY CONDITIONS
C
        COMMON NN, NE, NLN, NDN, NDF, NNE, N, MS, IN, IO, E
        DIMENSION AL(1), IB(1), RENO(1), TK(NRMX, NCMX)
        DO 100 L=1, NDN
C
C   NO = NUMBER OF THE CURRENT BOUNDARY NODE
C
        L1=(NDF+1)*(L-1)+1
        NO=IB(L1)
        K1=NDF*(NO-1)
        DO 100 I=1, NDF
        L2=L1+I
        IF(IB(L2)) 100, 10, 100
C
C   PRESCRIBED UNKNOWN TO BE CONSIDERED
C
C   SET DIAGONAL COEFFICIENT OF TK EQUAL TO 1
C   PLACE PRESCRIBED UNKNOWN VALUE IN ARRAY AL
C
     10 KR=K1+I
        DO 50 J=2, MS
        KV=KR+J-1
        IF(N-KV) 30, 20, 20
```

```
C
C   MODIFY ROW OF TK AND CORRESPONDING ELEMENTS IN AL
C
    20 AL(KV)=AL(KV)-TK(KR,J)*RENO(KR)
       TK(KR,J)=0.
    30 KV=KR-J+1
       IF(KV) 50,50,40
C
C   MODIFY COLUMN IN TK AND CORRESPONDING ELEMENT IN AL
C
    40 AL(KV)=AL(KV)-TK(KV,J)*RENO(KR)
       TK(KV,J)=0.
    50 CONTINUE
       TK(KR,1)=1.
       AL(KR)=RENO(KR)
   100 CONTINUE
       RETURN
       END
```

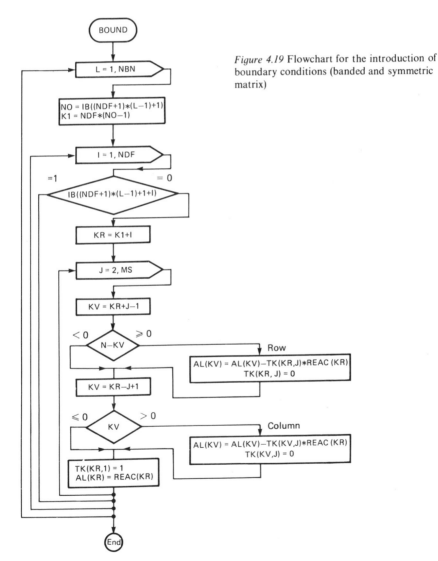

Figure 4.19 Flowchart for the introduction of boundary conditions (banded and symmetric matrix)

Program 8: Solution of the system of equations (SLBSI)

The solution of the system of equations is performed with a standard program
for symmetric banded systems, which uses the Gauss elimination method. The
variables included in the arguments are explained in the program comments.
The FORTRAN code for this program is the following:

```
C
C
      SUBROUTINE SLBSI(A, B, D, N, MS, NX, MX)
C
C            PROGRAM 8
C SOLUTION OF LINEAR SYSTEMS OF EQUATIONS
C BY THE GAUSS ELIMINATION METHOD, FOR
C SYMMETRIC BANDED SYSTEMS
C
C A = ARRAY CONTAINING THE UPPER TRIANGULAR
C      PART OF THE SYSTEM MATRIX, STORED
C      ACCORDING TO THE SYMMETRIC BANDED
C      SCHEME
C B = ORIGINALLY IT CONTAINS THE INDEPENDENT
C      COEFFICIENTS. AFTAR SOLUTION IT CONTAINS
C      THE VALUES OF THE SYSTEM UNKNOWNS
C
C N = ACTUAL NUMBER OF UNKNOWNS
C MS= ACTUAL HALF-BANDWIDTH
C NX= ROW DIMENSION OF A AND B
C MX=   COLUMN DIMENSION OF A
C
C D = AUXILIARY VECTOR
C
      DIMENSION A(NX, MX), B(NX), D(MX)
      N1=N-1
      DO 100 K=1, N1
      C=A(K, 1)
      K1=K+1
      IF (ABS(C)-0. 000001)1, 1, 3
    1 WRITE(6, 2)K
    2 FORMAT('***** SINGULARITY IN ROW ', I5)
      MS=0
      GO TO 300
C
C DIVIDE ROW BY DIAGONAL COEFFICIENT
C
    3 NI=K1+MS-2
      L=MIN(NI, N)
      DO 11 J=2, MS
   11 D(J)=A(K, J)
      DO 4 J=K1, L
      K2=J-K+1
    4 A(K, K2)=A(K, K2)/C
      B(K)=B(K)/C
C
C ELIMINATE UNKNOWN X(K) FROM ROW I
C
      DO 10 I=K1, L
      K2=I-K1+2
      C=D(K2)
      DO 5 J=I, L
      K2=J-I+1
      K3=J-K+1
    5 A(I, K2)=A(I, K2)-C*A(K, K3)
   10 B(I)=B(I)-C*B(K)
  100 CONTINUE
C
C COMPUTE LAST UNKNOWN
C
      IF(ABS(A(N, 1))-0. 000001)1, 1, 101
  101 B(N)=B(N)/A(N, 1)
```

```
C
C APPLY BACKSUBSTITUTION PROCESS TO COMPUTE REMAINING UNKNOWNS
C
      DO 200 I=1,N1
      K=N-I
      K1=K+1
      NI=K1+MS-2
      L=MIN(NI,N)
      DO 200 J=K1,L
      K2=J-K+1
  200 B(K)=B(K)-A(K,K2)*B(J)
  300 RETURN
      END
```

Program 9: Evaluation of results (RESUL)

After performing the solution of the system of equations, the nodal heads become known and are stored in array AL. Subprogram RESUL uses these heads to compute the element and nodal discharges. The FORTRAN code for this subprogram is the following:

```
C
C
      SUBROUTINE RESUL(KON,PROP,ELRE,RENO,X,Y,AL)
C
C             PROGRAM 9
C
C     COMPUTATION OF ELEMENT DISCHARGES
C
      COMMON NN,NE,NLN,NBN,NDF,NNE,N,MS,IN,IU,E
      DIMENSION X(1),Y(1),KON(1),PROP(1),AL(1),
     *ELRE(1),RENO(1)
C
C     CLEAR REAC ARRAY OF RESULTANT NODAL CONSUMPTIONS
C
      DO 1 I=1,N
    1 RENO(I)=0.
C
C     NEL= NUMBER OF CURRENT ELEMENT
C     N1 = NUMBER OF START NODE
C     N2 = NUMBER OF END NODE
C
      DO 100 NEL=1,NE
      L=NNE*(NEL-1)
      N1=KON(L+1)
      N2=KON(L+2)
C
C     COMPUTE LENGTH OF ELEMENT AND PROPERTY COEFFICIENT
C
      D=SQRT((X(N2)-X(N1))**2+(Y(N2)-Y(N1))**2)
      COEF=E*3.1416*PROP(NEL)**4/(D*128.)
C
C     COMPUTE MEMBER DISCHARGE AND STORE IN ARRAY ELRE
C
      ELRE(NEL)=COEF*(AL(N1)-AL(N2))
C
C     ADD MEMBER DISCHARGE TO THE ARRAY RENO
C
      RENO(N1)=RENO(N1)+ELRE(NEL)
  100 RENO(N2)=RENO(N2)-ELRE(NEL)
C
      RETURN
      END
```

The first operation done by this subprogram is to clear array RENO, in which nodal discharges will be accumulated. Then it loops on the elements and for each element it finds the numbers of its two end nodes, N1 and N2, and computes its length D. The element discharge is computed according to the Poiseuille formula and is stored in position NEL of array ELRE. Finally, the contributions of the current elements are added, with the proper sign, to the position in array RENO corresponding to the two element nodes, N1 and N2. Thus, after all elements have been processed, array RENO will contain the resultant nodal discharges for each of the nodes in the network.

Program 10: Result output (OUTPT)

The FORTRAN code for subprogram OUTPUT, which prints nodal heads, nodal discharges, and element discharges, is the following:

```
C
C
      SUBROUTINE OUTPT(AL,ELRE,RENO)
C
C                PROGRAM 10
C                OUTPUT PROGRAM
C
C
      COMMON NN,NE,NLN,NBN,NDF,NNE,N,MS,IN,IO,E
      DIMENSION AL(1),RENO(1),ELRE(1)
C
C     WRITE NODAL HEADS
C
      WRITE(IO,1)
    1 FORMAT(//1X,130('*')//' RESULTS'//' NODAL HEADS'/7X,'NODE',
     *9X,'HEAD')
      DO 10 I=1,NN
   10 WRITE(IO,2)I,AL(I)
    2 FORMAT(I10,F15.4)
C
C     WRITE NODAL DISCHARGES
      WRITE(IO,3)
    3 FORMAT(/' NODAL DISCHARGES'/7X,'NODE',5X,'DISCHARGE')
      DO 20 I=1,NN
   20 WRITE(IO,2) I,RENO(I)
C
C     WRITE MEMBER DISCHARGES
C
      WRITE (IO,4)
    4 FORMAT(/' MEMBER DISCHARGES'/4X,' MEMBER       DISCHARGE')
      DO 30 I=1,NE
   30 WRITE (IO,2) I,ELRE (I)
      WRITE (IO,5)
    5 FORMAT (//1X,130('*'))
      RETURN
      END
```

An example of the use of the program for linear analysis
As an illustration of the use of the program for linear analysis of pipe networks, the simple network shown in Figure 4.20 is analysed, where all relevant data are shown. The input for the program is

5		6		3		1	10000000.
1	0.	0.					
2	500.	500.					
3	1100.	500.					
4	500.	1200.					
5	1100.	1200.					
1		1	2	0.15			
2		2	4	0.1			
3		2	5	0.075			
4		2	3	0.1			
5		4	5	0.15			
6		3	5	0.15			
3	−0.2						
4	−0.5						
5	−0.25						
1	100.						

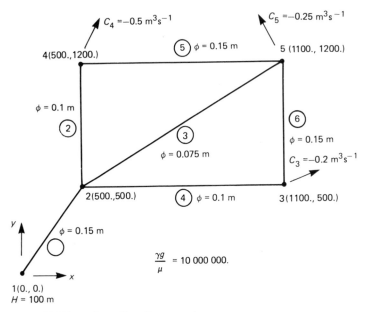

$C_4 = -0.5$ m^{3}s^{-1}

$C_5 = -0.25$ m^{3}s^{-1}

4(500.,1200.)

⑤ ϕ = 0.15 m

5 (1100., 1200.)

ϕ = 0.1 m

②

③

⑥

ϕ = 0.15 m

ϕ = 0.075 m

$C_3 = -0.2$ m^{3}s^{-1}

2(500.,500.)

④ ϕ = 0.1 m

3(1100., 500.)

ϕ = 0.15 m

$\dfrac{\gamma g}{\mu}$ = 10 000 000.

1(0., 0.)
H = 100 m

Figure 4.20 Network problem (linear case)

The output produced, showing both the input information and results, follow. Figure 4.21 also shows the results obtained.

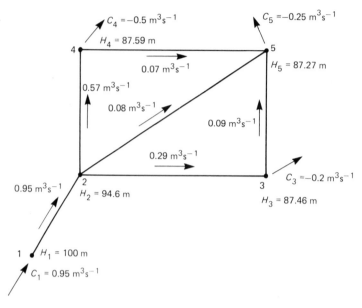

Figure 4.21   Network solution (linear case)

****

```
INTERNAL DATA

NUMBER OF NODES          :    5
NUMBER OF ELEMENTS       :    6
NUMBER OF NODES WITH KNOWN DISCHARGE:      3
NUMBER OF NODES WITH KNOWN HEAD:      1
VALUE OF DENSITY*GRAVITY ACC./VISCOSITY:      10000000.00

NODAL COORDINATES
     NODE        X              Y
      1         0.00          0.00
      2       500.00        500.00
      3      1100.00        500.00
      4       500.01        200.00
      5      1100.01        200.00

ELEMENT CONNECTIVITY AND DIAMETER
   ELEMENT    START NODE      END NODE         DIAMETER
      1           1              2             0.15000
      2           2              4             0.10000
      3           2              5             0.07500
      4           2              3             0.10000
      5           4              5             0.15000
      6           3              5             0.15000

--- HALF-BANDWIDTH IS EQUAL TO      4 ----


NODAL DISCHARGES
     NODE        VALUE
      3        -0.2000
```

```
    4       -0.5000
    5       -0.2500

BOUNDARY CONDITION DATA
    NODE        PRESCRIBED VALUES
    1               100.0000
```

****

```
RESULTS

NODAL HEADS
    NODE          HEAD
    1          100.0000
    2           94.5936
    3           87.4591
    4           87.5899
    5           87.2374

NODAL DISCHARGES
    NODE       DISCHARGE
    1           0.9500
    2          -0.0000
    3          -0.2000
    4          -0.5000
    5          -0.2500

MEMBER DISCHARGES
    MEMBER     DISCHARGE
    1           0.9500
    2           0.5730
    3           0.0852
    4           0.2918
    5           0.0730
    6           0.0918
```

****

4.9 Non-linear analysis of pipe networks

The total system of equations representing the behaviour of the pipe network, when the Hazen–Williams formula is used, has the form

$$K(H)H = C \qquad (4.39)$$

which, due to the fact that matrix **K** depends on the unknown nodal heads, is a non-linear system.

Several different approaches can be used to solve such non-linear systems. A simple solution scheme can be implemented following the steps outlined below:

(a) Assume initial values for the nodal heads.
(b) Compute coefficients of matrix **K**, based on current values of nodal heads, and form system of equations.
(c) Solve the system of equations to obtain a new set of nodal heads.
(d) Compare with the previous set of nodal heads. If different, repeat operations starting at step (b). Otherwise exit.

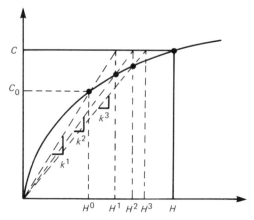

Figure 4.22 Iterative procedure

A simplified graphical description of this technique is shown in Figure 4.22, for a system with one head H, associated with a discharge C. After selecting an initial value for the head, H^0, the value of the coefficient linking head and discharge is computed, for that discharge level, and is shown in the figure as k^1. Having this coefficient, and knowing the value of C, a new value of the head, called H^1 in the figure, can be computed. This value will be, in general, different from the solution H, which is unknown. Then, the approximate value H^1 is used to compute a new coefficient k^2, and the process is repeated until the difference in the head for two successive steps is less than a given tolerance. A limit on the number of iterations may also be imposed eventually.

The computational implementation of this scheme will be as follows:

(a) Initialize step counter 'i' and head vector $\mathbf{H}$.
(b) Compute $\mathbf{K}^i$ using heads $\mathbf{H}$.
(c) Solve the system

$$\mathbf{K}^i \bar{\mathbf{H}} = \mathbf{C}$$

(d) Compare heads H and $\bar{H}$. If difference is larger than tolerance go to (e). Otherwise go to (f).
(e) Increment step counter i by 1 and check for maximum number of iterations. If exceeded print warning and go to (f). Otherwise make

$$\mathbf{H} = \bar{\mathbf{H}} \tag{4.40}$$

and go to (b).
(f) Compute element discharges and nodal discharges, print them out, and exit.

Convergence is supposed to be achieved, normally, when

$$\frac{[\sum_{i=1}^{n}(H_i - \bar{H}_i)^2]^{1/2}}{\sum_{i=1}^{n}|\bar{H}_i|} \leqslant \text{TOL} \tag{4.41}$$

where TOL is the accepted tolerance.

Although the scheme explained above is very easy to implement, its convergence may be a bit slow for practical applications. Thus, it may be convenient to use a method with better convergence behaviour, such as the Newton–Raphson method.

Newton–Raphson is a technique frequently used to find the roots of non-linear equations and solve other non-linear problems. Briefly, it can be described as follows. Suppose that we seek a value of x such that it makes a function of x, say $f(x), \equiv 0$. This value will be called x_0, hence

$$f(x_0) = 0 \qquad (4.42)$$

If we have an approximate value of x, say x_k, one can expand

$$f(x_0) \simeq f(x_k) + \frac{\partial f(x_k)}{\partial x} \delta x = 0 \qquad (4.43)$$

Hence

$$\delta x_k = -\frac{f(x_k)}{\partial f(x_k)/\partial x} \qquad (4.44)$$

and in this way, we find an increment of x such that the new value can be written,

$$x_{k+1} = x_k + \delta x_k \qquad (4.45)$$

as indicated in Figure 4.23. One can continue in this way until the solution is obtained with the degree of accuracy required.

The technique can be applied to a matrix system as follows. Let us assume that after assembling all the elements in a network, we have a system with $\mathbf{K}$ a function of $\mathbf{H}$, i.e.

$$\mathbf{K(H)H = C} \qquad (4.46)$$

For the next iteration, we can write a function $\mathbf{F}$ such that

$$\mathbf{F(H) = K(H_k)H - C = 0} \qquad (4.47)$$

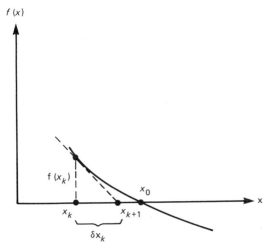

Figure 4.23 Approximation to a root of $f(x)=0$

The Newton–Raphson method gives the increments of **H**, i.e.

$$\delta \mathbf{H}_{k+1} \tag{4.48}$$

as a function of the derivative of the $\mathbf{K}(\mathbf{H}_k)$ matrix, i.e.

$$\mathbf{F}' = \frac{\partial}{\partial \mathbf{H}}[\mathbf{K}(\mathbf{H})\mathbf{H} - \mathbf{C}] = \frac{\partial}{\partial \mathbf{H}}[\mathbf{K}(\mathbf{H})\mathbf{H}] \tag{4.49}$$

We can find the **F**′ matrix by doing the derivatives with respect to $\mathbf{H}_i$ of all elements of the i column of **KH**. This gives a new incremental element matrix for which

$$\begin{Bmatrix} \delta Q_j \\ \delta Q_k \end{Bmatrix}_i = \left(\frac{0.54k^i}{\Delta H^{0.46}}\right)\begin{bmatrix} 1 & -1 \\ -1 & 1 \end{bmatrix}\begin{Bmatrix} \delta H_j \\ \delta H_k \end{Bmatrix} \tag{4.50}$$

where δ represents an increment in the function. We can now write

$$\begin{Bmatrix} \delta Q_j \\ \delta Q_k \end{Bmatrix}_i = \bar{k}_t\begin{bmatrix} 1 & -1 \\ -1 & 1 \end{bmatrix}\begin{Bmatrix} \delta H_j \\ \delta H_k \end{Bmatrix} \tag{4.51}$$

We can assemble these matrices as before, to obtain a new system:

$$\mathbf{K}_t \, \delta \mathbf{H} = \delta \mathbf{C} \tag{4.52}$$

Note that the $\delta \mathbf{C}$ right-hand side vector is obtained due to lack of equilibrium, i.e. by finding the difference between the external actions and those that can be equilibrated with our previous solution, i.e.

$$\delta \mathbf{C} = \mathbf{C} - \mathbf{K}(\mathbf{H}_k)\mathbf{H}_k \tag{4.53}$$

Generally, $\delta \mathbf{C} \neq \mathbf{0}$ but will become practically zero after a few iterations. Newton–Raphson generally assures fast convergence.

The basis of the Newton–Raphson technique is shown schematically in Figure 4.24. The first step is to select an initial solution H^1. A tangent coefficient, k_t^1, is computed using that solution. The discharge C^1 for that head

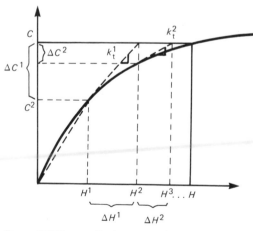

Figure 4.24 Newton–Raphson procedure

level will be, in general, different from the actual discharge C. The imbalance is given by

$$\Delta C^1 = C - C^1 \tag{4.54}$$

In order to correct this imbalance, the system

$$k_t^1 \, \Delta H^1 = \Delta C^1 \tag{4.55}$$

is solved, and the updated head is computed as

$$\mathbf{H}^2 = \mathbf{H}^1 + \Delta \mathbf{H}^1 \tag{4.56}$$

This new value for the head can again be used to compute a tangent coefficient $\mathbf{K}_t^2$, and the procedure can be repeated, until convergence is achieved.

The computational implementation of this method can be as follows:

(a) Compute initial solution $\mathbf{H}^1$, and set step counter i.
(b) Compute discharge imbalance $\Delta \mathbf{C}^i$.
(c) Compute tangent matrix $\mathbf{K}_t^i$.
(d) Solve the system of equations,

$$\mathbf{K}_t^i \, \Delta \mathbf{H}^i = \Delta \mathbf{C}^i \tag{4.57}$$

(e) Compute the actual total:

$$\mathbf{H}^{i+1} = \mathbf{H}^i + \Delta \mathbf{H}^i \tag{4.58}$$

(f) Check convergence. If achieved go to step (h). Otherwise go to step (g).
(g) Increment step counter by one, and check for iteration limit. If exceeded, print warning and go to step (h). Otherwise go to step (b).
(h) Compute element discharges and nodal discharges, print them out, and exit.

4.10 Program for non-linear analysis of pipe networks

The program for linear analysis of pipe networks, given at the beginning of the chapter, will be used as a base for the development of a program for non-linear analysis of pipe networks using the Newton–Raphson technique. This technique involves a sequence of linear analyses. The basic structure for this is already provided for by the original program. Then the fundamental modification is to introduce a scheme to iterate on the linear analysis. It will also be necessary to define the element behaviour according to the Hazen–Williams formula.

The main program is substantially modified, in order to implement the iterative Newton–Raphson procedure described in Section 4.9. Subprograms INPUT, STIFF and RESUL, suffer only slight changes, in order to read additional data, and to take into account the Hazen–Williams formula. Two new subprograms are introduced, being INCOE, to compute the element coefficients for the initial solution, and MULTI, to multiply a symmetric banded stored matrix times a vector; this operation is needed to compute the discharge imbalance ΔC^i. Subprograms ASSEM, BOUND, SLBSI, BAND and OUTPUT are the same as for the linear analysis.

The changes in the data structure are also few, as indicated below:

(a) *Integer variables.* Their meaning is unchanged. The new variables introduced are:

NMAX = Maximum number of iterations allowed before ending the iterative process, if convergence is not achieved.
KODE = Indicator for intermediate output. When different from zero results are printed for each iteration. Otherwise results are only printed after convergence is achieved.

(b) *Real variables.* The meaning of variable E is changed and a new variable, TOL, is introduced. Their actual meaning is as follows:

E   = Rugosity for the pipes
TOL = Tolerance used to test for convergence

(c) *Integer arrays.* Their meaning is unchanged.

(d) *Real arrays.* Arrays X, Y, PROP, AL, TK, ELST, V, and RENO are used without changes. Array ELRE stores the element discharges, but only after convergence is achieved. Before that it is used to store temporarily the consumption vector. The new arrays introduced are

H = Array used to store the actual nodal heads. The variations in the nodal heads are accumulated in array H after each iteration. H(J) contains the nodal head for joint J.
Q = Array used to store the right-hand side vector of the total system of equations, including the initial consumptions and the effect of the prescribed head values. Notice that these effects vary from one iteration to the next, as do the coefficients of matrix TK.

Program 11: Main program

The operations of the main program are summarised in the flowchart of Figure 4.25. As before, the main program initialises the basic parameters, calls INPUT to read the data and then checks that the limits relative to the maximum number of nodes, elements, and boundary nodes and band are not exceeded. The analysis process is divided in two parts, including the evaluation of an initial solution and the iteration to achieve convergence.

The nodal consumptions are read in array AL by subprogram INPUT. In the main program these data are also saved before starting the analysis, in arrays Q and ELRE.

The evaluation of the initial solution involves calling the subprograms: INCOE, to compute the element coefficients assuming that $\Delta H = 1$ for each element; ASSEM, to assemble the system of equations; BOUND, to introduce the boundary conditions; and SLBSI, solve the system of equations. The initial solution is thus computed, and the first approximations for the nodal heads are stored in array AL.

Before starting the iterative process the counter ISTEP is cleared. Then, within a loop, the program adds the previous solution to array H, evaluates the current consumption level C^i, and checks for convergence, exiting if achieved, or computing a new ΔH^i otherwise. The first time through the initial solution in AL is added to a null array H. Thus H starts the iterative process containing

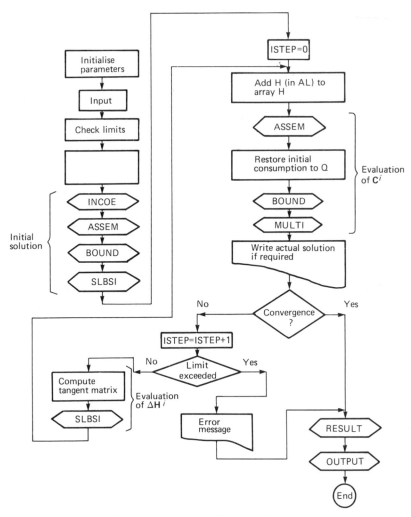

Figure 4.25 Flowchart for main program, non-linear analysis

the initial solution. To evaluate current consumption level C^i it is necessary first to form the actual system matrix, calling ASSEM, and to introduce the boundary conditions, calling BOUND. Before this the initial consumption data are restored in array Q and ELRE. After BOUND operates array Q will contain the system's vector, i.e. including the effect of prescribed heads. The multiplication of the system matrix TK times the nodal heads is performed calling the subprogram MULTI. The actual consumption level C^i is obtained in array AL.

The next step is to check convergence. If convergence was already achieved, then the elements of arrays Q and AL must be the same, and the iterative process is interrupted. In practice this is done not when those elements are the same, but when they are sufficiently closed, relative to a given tolerance TOL. The check is done using formula (4.41), applied to the nodal consumptions.

If convergence was not achieved a new nodal head increment ΔH^i must be computed, provided the iteration limit was not exceeded. For this the tangent matrix is computed, and the system of type (4.55) is solved, calling SLBSI. The coefficients of the tangent matrix are the same as those of matrix **K** multiplied by 0.54.

Rather than performing such multiplications, the equivalent and simpler process of dividing the elements of array AL by 0.54 is adopted. Notice that after convergence array AL contains the imbalance ΔC^i. Once ΔH^i is computed by SLBSI, and stored in array AL, a new iteration is started.

When convergence is achieved the element discharges are computed, calling subprogram RESUL, and the results are printed, calling subprogram OUTPUT.

```
C                     PROGRAM 11
C                   MAIN PROGRAM FOR
C      NON LINEAR ANALYSIS OF PIPE NETWORKS
C
       COMMON NN,NE,NLN,NBN,NDF,NNE,N,MS,IN,IO,E
       DIMENSION X(100),Y(100),KON(200),PROP(100),IB(60),TK(100,20),
      * AL(100),ELRE(100),RENO(100),ELST(2,2),Q(100),H(100),V(20)
C
C      INITIALIZATION OF PROGRAM PARAMETERS
C
C      MNN  = MAXIMUM NUMBER OF NODES ALLOWED
C      MNE  = MAXIMUM NUMBER OF ELEMENTS ALLOWED
C      MNB  = MAXIMUM NUMBER OF BOUNDARY NODES ALLOWED
C      NCMX = COLUMN DIMENSION FOR GLOBAL MATRIX OR
C             MAXIMUM HALF BAND WIDTH ALLOWED
C      NDF = NUMBER OF DEGREES OF FREEDOM PER NODE
C      NNE = NUMBER OF NODES PER ELEMENT
C      NDFEL = TOTAL NUMBER OF DEGREES OF FREEDOM
C              PER ELEMENT
C
       MNN = 100
       MNE = 100
       MNB = 30
       NRMX= 100
       NCMX= 20
       NDF = 1
       NNE = 2
       NDFEL = NDF*NNE
C
C      ASSIGN DATA SET NUMBERS TO,IN,FOR INPUT AND
C      IO,FOR OUTPUT
C
C      IN = 5
C      IO = 6



C
C      APPLY THE ANALYSIS STEPS
C
       CALL INPUT(X,Y,KON,PROP,AL,RENO,IB,NMAX,TOL)
C
C      CHECK FOR LIMITS
C
       IF(MNN-NN)1,2,2
     1 WRITE(IO,101)
   101 FORMAT(/' **** TOO MANY NODES ****'/)
       GO TO 999
     2 IF(MNE-NE)3,4,4
```

```
      3 WRITE(IO,103)
    103 FORMAT(/' **** TOO MANY ELEMENTS ****'/)
        GO TO 999
      4 IF(MNB-NBN)5,7,7
      5 WRITE(IO,105)
    105 FORMAT(' **** TOO MANY BOUNDARY NODES ****'/)
        GO TO 999
C
C       CHECK IF MAXIMUM HALF-BANDWIDTH WAS EXCEEDED
C
      7 IF(NCMX-MS)8,6,6
      8 WRITE(IO,108)
    108 FORMAT(/' **** MAXIMUM HALF-BANDWIDTH EXCEEDED ****'/)
        GO TO 999
C
C       SAVE INPUT CONSUMPTION VECTOR IN ARRAYS Q, ELRE
C       AND CLEAR NODAL HEAD ARRAY H
C
      6 DO 10 J=1,N
        Q(J)=AL(J)
        ELRE(J)=AL(J)
     10 H(J)=0
C
C       OBTAIN INITIAL SOLUTION
C
        CALL INCOE(X,Y,KON,PROP)
        IF(MS)12,11,11
C
C       CHECK FOR ERROR CONDITIONS
C
     11 CALL ASSEM(X,Y,KON,PROP,TK,ELST,H,NRMX,NCMX,NDFEL)
        CALL BOUND(TK,AL,RENO,IB,NRMX,NCMX)
        CALL SLBSI(TK,AL,V,N,MS,NRMX,NCMX)
C
C       READ KODE FOR INTERMEDIATE OUTPUT, INITIALIZE
C       STEP COUNTER, AND START ITERATIONS
C
        READ(IN,15) KODE
     15 FORMAT(I10)
C
C       CHECK FOR SINGULARITES
C
        IF(MS)12,12,13
     12 WRITE(IO,1012)
   1012 FORMAT(/' **** ERROR DETECTED DURING INITIAL SOLUTION ****'/
        GO TO 999
     13 ISTEP=0
        WRITE(IO,1097)
   1097 FORMAT(' ',70('*'))
C
C       ADD NODAL HEADS INCREMENT TO CURRENT TOTAL HEADS
C
     40 DO 50 J=1,N
     50 H(J)=H(J)+AL(J)
C
        IF(KODE)52,52,51
     51 WRITE(IO,1098) ISTEP
   1098 FORMAT(///' ********** ITERATION NUMBER',I5,' **********'//
       *' NODE         HEAD' ,/X,'TOTAL VECTOR COMPUTED VECTOR',
       */)
     52 CALL ASSEM(X,Y,KON,PROP,TK,ELST,H,NRMX,NCMX,NDFEL)
C
C       RESTORE INITIAL CONSUMPTION VECTOR IN ARRAY Q
C
        DO 30 J=1,N
```

```
   30 Q(J)=ELRE(J)
      CALL BOUND(TK,Q,RENO,IB,NRMX,NCMX)
      CALL MULTI(TK,H,AL,NRMX,NCMX)
      IF(KODE)1102,1102,1099
 1099 DO 1100 J=1,N
 1100 WRITE(IO,1101) J,H(J),Q(J),AL(J)
 1101 FORMAT(I5,3F15.6)
 1102 DEL = 0
      TOT = 0
      DO 60 J=1,N
      AL(J)=Q(J)-AL(J)
      DEL=DEL+(AL(J))**2
   60 TOT=TOT+ABS(Q(J))
C
C     CHECK CONVERGENCE AND ITERATION LIMIT
C
      ERROR=SQRT(DEL)/TOT
      IF (ERROR-TOL)70,70,80
   70 WRITE(IO,71)ISTEP
   71 FORMAT(/' CONVERGENCE ACHIEVED ON CYCLE',I5/)
      GO TO 100
   80 ISTEP=ISTEP+1
      IF(ISTEP-NMAX)90,90,81
   81 WRITE(IO,82)
   82 FORMAT(/' MAXIMUM NUMBER OF ITERATIONS REACHED WITHOUT
      CONVERGENCE *'//)
      GO TO 100
C
C     COMPUTE TANGENT SYSTEM MATRIX
C
   90 DO 89 J=1,N
   89 AL(J)=AL(J)/0.54
C
C     OBTAIN NEW NODAL HEADS INCREMENT
C
      CALL SLBSI(TK,AL,V,N,MS,NRMX,NCMX)
C
C     CHECK FOR SINGULARITIES
C
      IF(MS)92,92,40
   92 WRITE(IO,1092)
 1092 FORMAT(/' **** ERROR DETECTED DURING THE ITERATIONS ****'/)
      GO TO 999
      GO TO 40
  100 CALL RESUL(KON,PROP,ELRE,RENO,X,Y,H)
C
C     OUTPUT
C
      CALL OUTPT (H,ELRE,RENO)
C
  999 CALL EXIT
C
      END
C
C
      SUBROUTINE INPUT (X,Y,KON,PROP,AL,RENO,IB,NMAX,TOL)
```

Program 12: Data input (INPUT)

Subprogram INPUT is fundamentally the same as in the program for linear
network analysis. The only change is in reading the basic parameter cards.
Now, in addition to the number of nodes (NN), number of elements (NE),
number of nodal discharges given (NLN), number of nodal heads given
(NBN), and the variable E, also the maximum number of iterations (NMAX),

and the tolerance (TOL), are read. It should be noted that the meaning of E has changed, since it now stores the relative roughness.

```
C
C
      SUBROUTINE INPUT (X, Y, KON, PROP, AL, RENO, IB, NMAX, TOL)
C
C                     PROGRAM 12
C                PROGRAM FOR DATA INPUT
C
      COMMON NN, NE, NLN, NBN, NDF, NNE, N, MS, IN, IO, E
      DIMENSION X(1), Y(1), KON(1), PROP(1), AL(1), IB(1), RENO(1), IC(2)
C
C     READ BASIC PARAMETERS
C
C     NN = NUMBER OF NODES
C     NE = NUMBER OF ELEMENTS
C     NLN = NUMBER OF LOADED NODES
C     NBN = NUMBER OF BOUNDARY NODES
C     NMAX= MAXIMUM NUMBER OF ITERATIONS
C     TOL = TOLERANCE FOR CONVERGENCE
C     E = VALUE OF THE RELATIVE ROUGHNESS
C
      WRITE (IO, 20)
   20 FORMAT(' ', 70('*'))
      READ(IN, 1)NN, NE, NLN, NBN, NMAX, TOL, E
      WRITE(IO, 21)NN, NE, NLN, NBN, NMAX, TOL, E
   21 FORMAT(//' INTERNAL DATA'///' NUMBER OF NODES          : ', I5/
     *' NUMBER OF ELEMENTS     : ', I5/
     *' NUMBER OF NODES WITH KNOWN DISCHARGE: ', I5/
     *' NUMBER OF NODES WITH KNOWN HEAD:       ', I5/
     *' MAXIMUM NUMBER OF ITERATIONS:      ', I5/
     *' TOLERANCE: ', 16X, F10. 7/
     *' RELATIVE ROUGHNESS : 'F15. 7//
     * ' NODAL COORDINATES'/7X, 'NODE', 6X, 'X', 9X, 'Y')
    1 FORMAT(5I10, F10. 7, F15. 7)
C
C     READ NODAL COORDINATES IN ARRAY X AND Y
C
      READ (IN, 2) (I, X(I), Y(I), J=1, NN)
      WRITE (IO, 2) (I, X(I), Y(I), I=1, NN)
    2 FORMAT(I10, 2F10. 2)
C
C     READ ELEMENT CONNECTIVITY IN ARRAY KON AND ELEMENT
C     DIAMETER IN ARRAY PROP
C
      WRITE(IO, 22)
   22 FORMAT(// ' ELEMENT CONNECTIVITY AND DIAMETER'/4X, 'ELEMENT', 3X,
     *'START NODE     EMD NODE        DIAMETER')
      DO 3 J =1, NE
      READ(IN, 4) I, IC(1), IC(2), PROP(I)
      WRITE(IO, 34) I, IC(1), IC(2), PROP(I)
      N1 = NNE*(I-1)
      KON(N1+1)=IC(1)
    3 KON(N1+2)=IC(2)
    4 FORMAT(3I10, F10. 5)
   34 FORMAT(2I10, I12, F18. 5)
C
C     COMPUTE N, ACTUAL NUMBER OF UNKNOWNS, AND
C     CLEAR RIGHT HAND SIDE VECTOR
C
      N=NN*NDF
      DO 5 I=1, N
    5 AL(I)=0.
C
C     COMPUTE HALF BANDWIDTH AND STORE IN MS
C
      CALL BAND(NE, NDF, NNE, MS, IO, KON)
C
C     CALL THE NODAL DISCHARGES AND STORE THEM IN ARRAY AL
C
C     READ THE NODAL DISCHARGES '/8X, 'NODE', 5X, 'VALUE')
C
```

```
      WRITE(IO,23)
   23 FORMAT(//' NODAL DISCHARGES '/8X, 'NODE',5X, 'VALUE')
      DO 66 I=1,NLN
      READ (IN,10) J,W
      WRITE (IO,11) J,W
   10 FORMAT(I10,F12.4)
   11 FORMAT(I10,F12.4)
      AL(J)=W
   66 CONTINUE
C
C     READ BOUNDARY NODES DATA STORE PRESCRIBED HEAD VALUES IN RENO
C
      WRITE(IO,24)
   24 FORMAT(//' BOUNDARY CONDITION DATA'/8X, 'NODE',5X,
     *'PRESCRIBED VALUES')
      DO 77 I=1,NBN
      READ (IN,8)J,RENO(J)
      WRITE(IO,9) J,RENO(J)
      IB(2*I-1)=J
   77 IB(2*I)=0
    8 FORMAT(I10,F10.4)
    9 FORMAT(I10,10X,F10.4)
      RETURN
      END
```

Program 13: Evaluation of the initial element coefficient (INCOE)

This new subprogram is used to compute the constant part of the element coefficient k^i, according to formula (4.11). These are also used as the element coefficients in order to obtain the initial solution.

The operations are performed within a loop on the elements. For each element the values of the two end nodes are retrieved from the connectiviy array KON and are stored in N1 and N2, the element length is computed storing it in D, and the coefficient $\bar{k}^i$ is evaluated. This coefficient is stored in PROP(NEL), which, prior to that, contained the element diameter.

```
C
C
C
      SUBROUTINE INCOE(X,Y,KON,PROP)
C
C             PROGRAM 13
C
C     EVALUATION OF THE INITIAL 'K' COEFFICIENTS
C
      COMMON NN,NE,NLN,NBN,NDF,NNE,N,MS,IN,IO,E,G
      DIMENSION X(1),Y(1),KON(1),PROP(1)
C
      DO 10 NEL=1,NE
      L=NNE*(NEL-1)
      N1=KON(L+1)
      N2=KON(L+2)
      D=SQRT((X(N2)-X(N1))**2+(Y(N2)-Y(N1))**2)
C
C     CHECK FOR ZERO LENGTH OR DIAMETER
C
      IF(D)1,1,2
    1 WRITE(IO,101) NEL
  101 FORMAT(//' **** ZERO LENGTH FOR ELEMENT :',I5,' ****'/)
      GO TO 4
    2 IF(PROP(NEL))3,3,5
    3 WRITE(IO,103) NEL
  103 FORMAT(//' **** ZERO DIAMETER FOR ELEMENT :',I5,' ****'/)
    4 MS=0
      GO TO 10
    5 PROP(NEL)=0.2784*PROP(NEL)**2.63*E/(D**0.54)
   10 CONTINUE
      RETURN
      END
```

Program 14: Computation of the element matrix (STIFF)

The only difference from Program 5 is that coefficient COEF must now be computed according to the Hazen–Williams formula. This is different for the initial solution and for the iteration. The head loss ΔH^i, stored in DH, is checked. When zero it indicates that the initial solution is being evaluated. In that case COEF is made equal to PROP(NEL), which contains the coefficient $\bar{k}^i$, evaluated by subprogram INCOE. Otherwise, for the iterations, COEF is made equal to $\bar{k}^i$ divided by $\Delta H^{0.46}$, as indicated in formula (4.13). This subprogram does not contain the checks on zero length and diameter, now performed by the subprogram INCOE, which is outside the iterative loop.

```
C
C
        SUBROUTINE STIFF(NEL, X, Y, PROP, KON, ELST, H, NDFEL)
C
C                  PROGRAM 14
C
C       COMPUTATION OF ELEMENT MATRIX
C
C
        COMMON NN, NE, NLN, NBN, NDF, NNE, N, MS, IN, IO, E
        DIMENSION X(1), Y(1), KON(1), PROP(1), ELST(NDFEL, NDFEL), H(1)
C
C       NEL= CURRENT ELEMENT NUMBER
C       N1 = NUMBER OF START NODE
C       N2 = NUMBER OF END NODE
C
        L=NNE*(NEL-1)
        N1=KON(L+1)
        N2=KON(L+2)
C
C       COMPUTE LENGTH OF ELEMENT
C
        D=SQRT((X(N2)-X(N1))**2+(Y(N2)-Y(N1))**2)
C
C       COMPUTE ELEMENT MATRIX
C
        DH=H(N1)-H(N2)
        IF(ABS(DH)-0.0000001)10,10,21
     10 COEF=PROP(NEL)
        GO TO 3
     21 COEF=PROP(NEL)*(ABS(DH))**(-0.46)
      3 ELST(1,1)=COEF
        ELST(1,2)=-COEF
        ELST(2,1)=-COEF
        ELST(2,2)=COEF
        RETURN
        END
```

Program 15: Multiplication of a symmetric banded matrix by a vector (MULTI)

This program performs the multiplication of the system matrix, stored in array TK, by the nodal heads, stored in array H, to produce the actual consumptions, in array AL.

The only complication, in this case, derives from the fact that the system matrix is stored according to the symmetric banded scheme. Thus, the elements below the diagonal are not registered. The multiplication of a row of TK times the vector must proceed as suggested in Figure 4.26(a), for symmetric

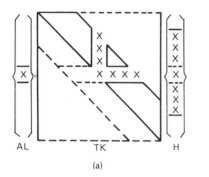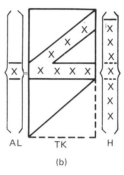

(a)   (b)

Figure 4.26 Multiplication with matrix arrays: (a) symmetric, non-banded;
(b) symmetric, banded

non-banded storage, or in Figure 4.26(b) for the case of symmetric banded
storage adopted in this program. The multiplication of row I starts by the
columns above diagonal element (DO 50), representing the non-existent part of
row I before the diagonal, and then follows with the part of row I after the
diagonal element (DO 100 on J). In each case checks have to be performed so
that the storage bounds are not exceeded.

```
C
C
C
      SUBROUTINE MULTI (TK,H,AL,NRMX,NCMX)
C
C                PROGRAM 15
C
C     MULTIPLICATION OF A BANDED MATRIX TK TIMES
C     TIMES A VECTOR H STORING RESULTS IN VECTOR AL
C
      COMMON NN,NE,NLN,NBN,NDF,NNE,N,MS,IN,IO,E
      DIMENSION TK(NRMX,NCMX),H(1),AL(1)
C
      DO 100 I=1,N
      AL(I)=0
      K1=I-MS+1
      IF(K1)10,10,11
   10 K1=1
   11 IF(I+MS-1-N)12,12,13
   12 K2=MS
      GO TO 14
   13 K2=N-I+1
   14 DO 50 J=K1,I
      K=I-J+1
      AL(I)=AL(I)+TK(J,K)*H(J)
   50 CONTINUE
      IF (I-N)15,101,101
   15 DO 100 J=2,K2
      AL(I)=AL(I)+TK(I,J)*H(I+J-1)
  100 CONTINUE
  101 RETURN
      END
```

Program 16: Evaluation of results (RESUL)

This subprogram is very similar to subprogram 9, for linear analysis.

The operations include clearing array RENO, in which the member
contributions to the nodal consumptions will be accumulated, and to loop on

the elements. For each element the values of the end nodes are retrieved, and the length and head loss are computed. The member discharge, for element NEL, is computed in ELRE(NEL), according to the Hazen–Williams formula.

```
C
C
      SUBROUTINE RESUL(KON, PROP, ELRE, RENO, X, Y, H)
C
C              PROGRAM 16
C      COMPUTATION OF ELEMENT DISCHARGES
C
      COMMON NN, NE, NLN, NBN, NDF, NNE, N, MS, IN, IO, E
      DIMENSION KON(1), PROP(1), ELRE(1), RENO(1), X(1), Y(1), H(1)
C
C      CLEAR ARRAY RENO
C
      DO 1 I=1, N
    1 RENO(I)=0.
C
C      NEL= NUMBER OF CURRENT ELEMENT
C
C      N1 = NUMBER OF START NODE
C      N2 = NUMBER OF END NODE
C
      DO 100 NEL=1, NE
      L=NNE*(NEL-1)
      N1=KON(L+1)
      N2=KON(L+2)
      K1=NDF*(N1-1)
      K2=NDF*(N2-1)
C
C      COMPUTE MEMBER DISCHARGE AND STORE IN ARRAY ELRE
C
      A=H(N1)-H(N2)
      ELRE(NEL)=SIGN(1., A)*PROP(NEL)*(ABS(A))**0.54
C
C      ADD MEMBER DISCHARGE TO ARRAY RENO
C
      RENO(N1)=RENO(N1)+ELRE(NEL)
      RENO(N2)=RENO(N2)-ELRE(NEL)
  100 CONTINUE
C
      RETURN
      END
```

An example of the use of the non-linear analysis program
In order to illustrate the use of the program for non-linear analysis of pipe networks, the example shown in Figure 4.27 will be analysed.
    The input data for this example are the following:

8		12		7		1		20	0.0001	110.
1	0.		0.							
2	0.		500.							
3	250.		0.							
4	250.		500.							
5	550.		0.							
6	750.		500.							
7	950.		-100.							
8	850.		200.							
1		1		2	0.1524					
2		1		3	0.1524					
3		2		3	0.1524					
4		2		4	0.127					
5		3		4	0.1016					
6		3		5	0.127					

7		4	5	0.1016	
8		4	6	0.1524	
	9		5	6	0.127
10		5	7	0.127	
11		7	8	0.1016	
12		6	8	0.1524	
1	−0.0311				
3	0.09				
3	−0.0113				
4	−0.011				
5	−0.0101				
6	0.02				
8	−0.015				
7	0.0				
1					

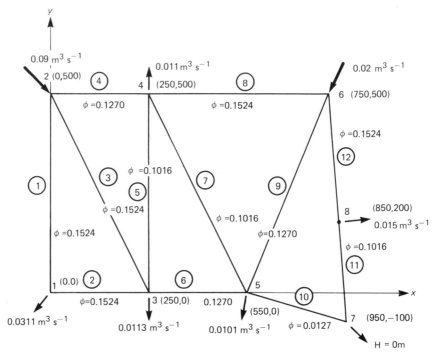

Figure 4.27 Network problem

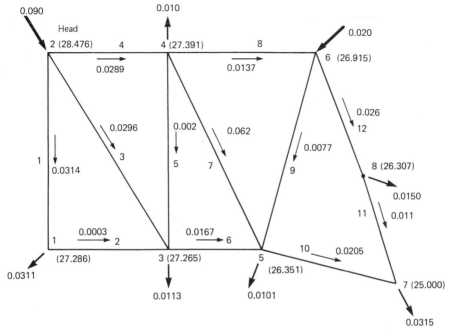

Figure 4.28 Network solution (linear case)

The output produced is the following:

****

INTERNAL DATA

NUMBER OF NODES   :   8
NUMBER OF ELEMENTS   :   12
NUMBER OF NODES WITH KNOWN DISCHARGE :   7
NUMBER OF NODES WITH KNOWN HEAD: 1
MAXIMUM NUMBER OF ITERATIONS: 20
TOLERANCE: 0.0001000
RELATIVE ROUGHNESS :   110.0000000

NODAL COORDINATES
      NODE   X   Y
        1   0.00   0.00
        2   0.00   500.00
        3   250.00   0.00
        4   250.00   500.00
        5   550.00   0.00
        6   750.00   500.00
        7   950.00   -100.00
        8   850.00   200.00

ELEMENT CONNECTIVITY AND DIAMETER
    ELEMENT   START NODE   END NODE   DIAMETER
        1   1   2   0.15240
        2   1   3   0.15240
        3   2   3   0.15240

4	2	4	0.12700
5	3	4	0.10160
6	3	5	0.12700
7	4	5	0.10160
8	4	6	0.15240
9	5	6	0.12700
10	5	7	0.12700
11	7	8	0.10160
12	6	8	0.15240

---- HALF-BANDWIDTH IS EQUAL TO   3 ----

NODAL DISCHARGES

NODE	VALUE
1	-0.0311
2	0.0900
3	-0.0113
4	-0.0110
5	-0.0101
6	0.0200
8	-0.0150

BOUNDARY CONDITION DATA

NODE	PRESCRIBED VALUES
7	0.0000

****

********** ITERATION NUMBER   0 **********

NODE	HEAD	TOTAL VECTOR	COMPUTED VECTOR
1	7.135602	-0.031100	-0.014892
2	11.269601	0.090000	0.046630
3	7.112920	-0.011300	-0.004993
4	7.025511	-0.011000	-0.001952
5	4.138389	-0.010100	-0.009599
6	5.540396	0.020000	0.012186
7	0.000000	0.000000	0.000000
8	2.972596	-0.015000	-0.010140

********** ITERATION NUMBER   1 **********

NODE	HEAD	TOTAL VECTOR	COMPUTED VECTOR
1	16.157736	-0.031100	-0.028829
2	27.407265	0.090000	0.080082
3	16.165642	-0.011300	-0.008156
4	15.769382	-0.011000	-0.008217
5	10.471498	-0.010100	-0.010660
6	13.000090	0.020000	0.018601
7	0.000000	0.000000	0.000000
8	7.534222	-0.015000	-0.014353

********** ITERATION NUMBER   2 **********

NODE	HEAD	TOTAL VECTOR	COMPUTED VECTOR
1	18.807871	-0.031100	-0.030227
2	32.597206	0.090000	0.089528
3	18.795029	-0.011300	-0.011910
4	18.226379	-0.011000	-0.010826
5	12.519736	-0.010100	-0.010153
6	15.223040	0.020000	0.019958

```
7      0.000000        0.000000        0.000000
8      9.040369       -0.015000       -0.014996
```

********** ITERATION NUMBER   3 **********

NODE	HEAD	TOTAL VECTOR	COMPUTED VECTOR
1	18.901880	-0.031100	-0.031929
2	32.832912	0.090000	0.089999
3	18.904886	-0.011300	-0.010470
4	18.320322	-0.011000	-0.010999
5	12.611050	-0.010100	-0.010100
6	15.314146	0.020000	0.020000
7	0.000000	0.000000	0.000000
8	9.109765	-0.015000	-0.015000

********** ITERATION NUMBER   4 **********

NODE	HEAD	TOTAL VECTOR	COMPUTED VECTOR
1	18.911158	-0.031100	-0.030713
2	32.836639	0.090000	0.090000
3	18.904610	-0.011300	-0.011686
4	18.321049	-0.011000	-0.011000
5	12.611249	-0.010100	-0.010100
6	15.314624	0.020000	0.020000
7	0.000000	0.000000	0.000000
8	9.110153	-0.015000	-0.015000

********** ITERATION NUMBER   5 **********

NODE	HEAD	TOTAL VECTOR	COMPUTED VECTOR
1	18.904755	-0.031100	-0.031336
2	32.834141	0.090000	0.090000
3	18.904552	-0.011300	-0.011065
4	18.320351	-0.011000	-0.011000
5	12.610976	-0.010100	-0.010100
6	15.314151	0.020000	0.020000
7	0.000000	0.000000	0.000000
8	9.109784	-0.015000	-0.015000

********** ITERATION NUMBER   6 **********

NODE	HEAD	TOTAL VECTOR	COMPUTED VECTOR
1	18.906290	-0.031100	-0.031184
2	32.835152	0.090000	0.090000
3	18.905300	-0.011300	-0.011215
4	18.321047	-0.011000	-0.011000
5	12.611502	-0.010100	-0.010100
6	15.314709	0.020000	0.020000
7	0.000000	0.000000	0.000000
8	9.110219	-0.015000	-0.015000

********** ITERATION NUMBER   7 **********

NODE	HEAD	TOTAL VECTOR	COMPUTED VECTOR
1	18.906328	-0.031100	-0.031109
2	32.834858	0.090000	0.090000

```
3      18.904755     -0.011300     -0.011291
4      18.320658     -0.011000     -0.011000
5      12.611160     -0.010100     -0.010100
6      15.314381      0.020000      0.020000
7       0.000000      0.000000      0.000000
8       9.109965     -0.015000     -0.015000

CONVERGENCE ACHIEVED ON CYCLE    7
```

****

RESULTS

```
NODAL HEADS
      NODE         HEAD
        1        18.9063
        2        32.8349
        3        18.9048
        4        18.3207
        5        12.6112
        6        15.3144
        7         0.0000
        8         9.1100

NODAL DISCHARGES
      NODE      DISCHARGE
        1        -0.0311
        2         0.0900
        3        -0.0113
        4        -0.0110
        5        -0.0101
        6         0.0200
        7        -0.0315
        8        -0.0150

MEMBER DISCHARGES
     MEMBER     DISCHARGE
        1        -0.0314
        2         0.0003
        3         0.0296
        4         0.0289
        5         0.0020
        6         0.0167
        7         0.0062
        8         0.0137
        9        -0.0077
       10         0.0205
       11        -0.0110
       12         0.0260
```
****

Bibliography

BOOTH, A.D. *Numerical Methods*, Butterworths, Sevenoaks (1966)

BREBBIA, C.A. and FERRANTE, A.J. *Computational Methods for the Solution of Engineering Problems*, Pentech Press, London (1979); 2nd edn (1980)

CONNOR, J.J. and BREBBIA, C.A. *Finite Element Techniques for Fluid Flow*, Newnes–Butterworths, Sevenoaks (1976); 2nd edn (1977)

FADDEEVA, V.N. *Computational Methods of Linear Algebra*, Dover Publications, New York (1959)

HILDEBRAND, F.B. *Methods of Applied Mathematics*, 2nd edn, Prentice Hall, New Jersey (1965)

Exercises

4.1 The pipe elements shown in the Figure 4.29, all have the same length and diameter. Take $L=1000$ m and $D=0.1$ m. Assume laminar flow and $C_2=C_3=1$ m^3 s^{-1}. Determine the discharge in each pipe for $H_1=10$ m.

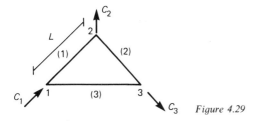

Figure 4.29

4.2 Solve Problem 4.1 using the Hazen–Williams formulation.

4.3 Solve the system shown in the Figure 4.30, for laminar flow. Take

$v=10^{-6}$ m^2 s^{-1} $H_1=10$ m

$C_2=C_3=-20$ m^3 s^{-1} $L_1=L_2=L_5=L_6=1000$ m

$C_4=40$ m^3 s^{-1} $L_3=L_4=1500$ m

$D_1=D_2=0.4$ m $D_3=D_4=D_5=D_6=0.2$ m

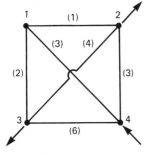

Figure 4.30

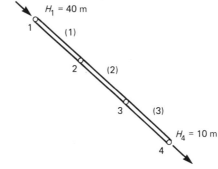

Figure 4.31

4.4 Find the flow rate for the pipe system shown in the Figure 4.30, assuming laminar flow. Take

$L_1=1000$ m $D_1=0.5$ m

$L_2=2000$ m $D_2=0.8$ m

$L_3=\ \ 500$ m $D_3=0.2$ m

4.5 Frequently it is necessary to modify the length of a pipe of a given network in order to account for additional losses, or to correct the pipe length as

computed from the coordinates of its extreme nodes. Show how you
would introduce this capability in the previous programs a) by reading a
length correction for each network pipe component, and b) by doing
away with the nodal coordinates input. In both cases indicate which
modifications will be required in the program subroutines. Which way is
better?

4.6   Indicate which changes will have to be introduced in the formulations
and in the programs to account for pumps in the network.

4.5   Solve the pipe network system shown in Figure 4.32. Take

$D_1 = D_4 = 0.1$ m $L_1 = L_4 = 100$ m

$D_2 = D_3 = D_4 = 0.2$ m $L_2 = L_3 = 120$ m

$L_5 = 160$ m

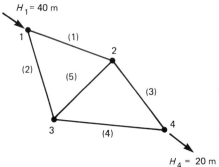

Figure 4.32

4.6   Consider the pipe network shown in Figure 4.33. Solve it for laminar flow
using matrix analysis. Assume that the heads at junctions 1 and 4 are

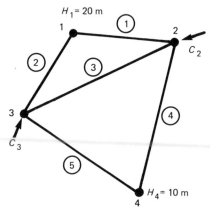

Element	Length (m)	Diameter (m)
1	1000	0.400
2	1000	0.200
3	2000	0.283
4	2000	0.283
5	2000	0.573

Figure 4.33

known ($H_1 = 20$ m and $H_4 = 10$ m) and take the following values for discharge:

$$C_2 = C_3 = -10 \text{ m}^3 \text{ s}^{-1}$$

Determine the heads at 2 and 3 and the values of discharges at 1 and 4 (C_1 and C_4). Compute the discharges in each of the pipes and check for equilibrium.

Suggested laboratory workshop

The purpose of this workshop is to demonstrate how pipe networks can be analysed using the linear analysis and non-linear analysis programs, and to compare the numerical solutions for each program and with experimental results. The suggested procedure is:

(1)   Assemble a sample network in the laboratory and measure heads and discharges for given nodal input and consumptions.
(2)   Design a numerical model for the network and run the program for linear analysis.
(3)   Run the program for non-linear analysis using the same numerical model as in (2).

The analysis of the results can include:

(1)   Has equilibrium been achieved?
(2)   Compare and discuss heads and discharges for linear and non-linear cases.
(3)   Discuss if the pressures are everywhere within the range of 20 to 60 N cm^{-2}.
(4)   Check the pipe velocities and Re numbers.

Chapter 5

Open channel flow

5.1 Introduction

Open channel flow problems have the common characteristic of having a free surface, but they range from channels used for navigation and irrigation to closed pipes which are partially full; i.e. the flow in them has a free surface such as in the case of sewage pipes. The important difference from the pipe flow studied in Chapter 4 is that the channels are not under pressure.

This chapter will deal only with steady flow, i.e. flow for which the velocities remain constant with time. This also implies that transverse sections and depths are constant with time. Unsteady flow on the other hand, is the one for which the velocities vary with time. In practice for high velocities ($>7 \text{ m s}^{-1}$) the flow cannot be considered steady as mixing with air tends to occur and this produces a pulsating effect.

If the flow is steady and the velocity remains constant from one section of the channel to another, the flow is called *uniform*, a useful approximation in long channels. Otherwise the flow is called *non-uniform*. Uniform flow will be studied first.

5.2 Basic principles of uniform flow

The uniform flow relationships are obtained by considering the equilibrium of the gravitational and viscous forces. First we will consider what happens if the fluid is perfectly laminar. Although this hypothesis is seldom satisfied in practice, it will be useful as a model to give an idea of the fluid behaviour.

If we neglect the effect of the channel sides, the flow can be considered two dimensional as represented in Figure 5.1.

If the angle α is small (as it is in practice), $\cos \alpha \simeq 1$, and one can consider that $h \simeq h \cos \alpha$. At a section x–x, we can equilibrate the viscous shear forces given by

$$\tau = \mu \, \mathrm{d}v/\mathrm{d}y \tag{5.1}$$

with the component of the gravitational forces parallel to the bottom of the

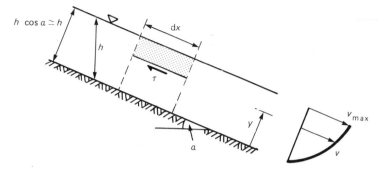

Figure 5.1 Laminar flow with free surface

channel and given by the volume of water over x–x, i.e.

$$\rho g(h-y)\sin\alpha \tag{5.2}$$

As an approximation, we can say $S \simeq \sin\alpha$, where S is the slope of the channel. Hence from equations (5.1) and (5.2)

$$\mu\frac{dv}{dy}=\rho g(h-y)S \tag{5.3}$$

Hence,

$$\frac{dv}{dy}=\frac{gS}{v}(h-y) \tag{5.4}$$

where y is the kinematic viscosity $v=\mu/\rho$. We can now integrate equation (5.4), taking into consideration that $v=0$ at $y=0$. This gives

$$v=\frac{gS}{v}y\left(h-\frac{y}{2}\right) \tag{5.5}$$

i.e. the distribution of velocities is *parabolic* with the maximum velocity at the free surface given by

$$v_{max}=\frac{gSh^2}{2v} \tag{5.6}$$

and the mean velocity given by

$$V=\frac{1}{h}\int_0^d v\,dy=\frac{gSh^2}{3v}=\frac{2}{3}v_{max} \tag{5.7}$$

The position of the mean velocity over the parabolic profile can be obtained by equations (5.5) and (5.7), which give

$$\tfrac{1}{2}y^2-yh+\tfrac{1}{3}h^2=0 \tag{5.8}$$

From equation (5.8) we find that $y=0.42h$, which is the depth at which the mean velocity occurs.

In practice, the distribution of velocities is very complex and depends on variables such as the shape of the channel, roughness of the surface, and the discharge.

The maximum velocity tends to occur a little below the free surface. This is sometimes due to the secondary movements induced by the lateral sides or walls. In a shallow channel this effect is negligible, and the maximum velocity occurs at the free surface.

It is customary to measure the mean velocity at a point $0.6h$ from the free surface (formula (5.8)) or at two points at depths $0.2h$ and $0.8h$, to adjust the parabola given by equation (5.5). In the transverse direction the distribution of velocities tends to be more irregular, with maximum velocities towards the centre.

Friction in the channel can be plotted in the same way as in pipes, i.e. using λ–Re curves, where λ is the friction coefficient and Re is the Reynolds number for pipes ($= VD/v$), but in channels the diameter D is replaced by the hydraulic radius R defined as the ratio between the cross-sectional area Ω and the wetted perimeter Γ:

$$R = \Omega/\Gamma \tag{5.9}$$

Notice that

$$R_{\text{pipe}} = \frac{\Omega}{\Gamma} = \frac{D}{4} \tag{5.10}$$

Hence, the relation between Reynolds numbers for pipes and channels is

$$(Re)_{\text{pipes}} = 4\,(Re)_{\text{channels}} \tag{5.11}$$

The friction loss equations of Chapter 3 can now be used:

(i) *Darcy–Weisbach equation.* Notice that with the Darcy–Weisbach equation, we have $\lambda = 2gDS/V^2$. Now we can substitute $D = 4R$ and we get

$$\lambda = \frac{8gRS}{V^2} \tag{5.12}$$

(ii) *Smooth channels.* Since $(Re)_{\text{pipes}} = 4(Re)_{\text{channels}}$ equation (3.30) now becomes

$$\frac{1}{\lambda^{1/2}} = 2 \ln \left(\frac{Re\,\lambda^{1/2}}{0.627} \right) \tag{5.13}$$

(iii) *Rough-surface channels.* Equation (3.31) for pipes now becomes, for channels,

$$\frac{1}{\lambda^{1/2}} = 2 \ln \left(\frac{14.8R}{k} \right) \tag{5.14}$$

(iv) *Transition law.* The transition law deduced by Colebrook and White (cf. equation (3.33))

$$\frac{1}{\lambda^{1/2}} = -2 \ln \left(\frac{k}{14.8R} + \frac{0.627}{Re\,\lambda^{1/2}} \right) \tag{5.15}$$

Having adjusted these variables, we can produce a λ–Re diagram as shown in Figure 5.2. Note that for laminar flow the λ–Re relation is represented by a straight line on a logarithmic scale. For a wide channel we can use the previous relationships, i.e. equations (5.7) and (5.12):

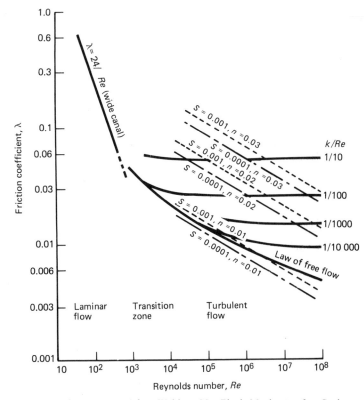

Figure 5.2 λ–*Re* curves (after Webber, N., *Fluid Mechanics for Civil Engineers*, E. & F. N. Spon, London (1965))

$$V = \frac{gSh^2}{3v}$$

$$S = \frac{3vV}{gR^2} = \frac{\lambda V^2}{8g\rho}$$

$$\text{(5.16)}$$

where $R \simeq h$. Hence

$$\lambda = 24/Re \qquad \qquad \text{(5.17)}$$

which is the slope of the line for laminar flow in Figure 5.2.

Note that for channels the transition regime is in the range $500 < (Re)_{\text{channel}} < 1000$. Sometimes the upper limit is taken as 2000 as it seems to be higher than for pipes, according to experimental results.

In practice, most channels operate in the turbulent region and are rougher than pipes.

5.3 Chezy and Manning formulae

Two formulae are commonly used to estimate head loss when designing channels; they are Chezy's and Manning's formulae.

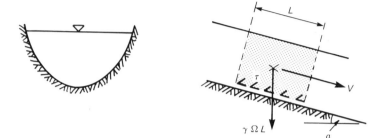

Figure 5.3 Sloping channel

5.3.1 Chezy's formula

The formula is deduced by considerations of equilibrium. Consider Figure 5.3, which shows a section of channel with a volume of water moving at a (mean) velocity V with cross-sectional area Ω and wet perimeter Γ.

At equilibrium the component of weight of water in the direction of the channel bottom has to equilibrate the shear stress on Γ, i.e.

$$\gamma \Omega L \sin \alpha = \tau \Gamma L \qquad (5.18)$$

The shear stresses are assumed to be proportional to the square of the mean velocity, i.e.

$$\tau = K V^2 \qquad (5.19)$$

when K is a constant coefficient.

Substituting equation (5.19) into equation (5.18) gives,

$$V^2 = \left(\frac{\gamma}{K}\right)\frac{\Omega}{\Gamma}\sin \alpha \qquad (5.20)$$

Note that Ω/Γ is the hydraulic radius R and $\sin \alpha = S$. Hence

$$V = C(RS)^{1/2} \qquad (5.21)$$

The constant $C = (\gamma/K)^{1/2}$ is called Chezy's coefficient.

In general, this coefficient depends on the roughness and the hydraulic radius (or form of the section). The influence of the Reynolds number is small.

Notice that if we use the Darcy–Weisbach equation (5.12), we can write

$$V = \left(\frac{8gRS}{\lambda}\right)^{1/2} \qquad (5.22)$$

and we can equate the velocity from equation (5.22) with (5.21) and obtain,

$$C = (8g/\lambda)^{1/2} \qquad (5.23)$$

Sometimes $\lambda^{1/2}$ is directly substituted by that obtained for rough channels, i.e. (e.g. equation (5.14)),

$$\frac{1}{\lambda^{1/2}} = 2 \ln\left(\frac{14.8R}{k}\right) \qquad (5.24)$$

Hence we can now see how the *C* coefficient varies as a function of hydraulic radius and roughness.

5.3.2 Manning's formula

Manning's formula is very popular and simple. It states that Chezy's coefficient for the SI system is

$$C = \frac{R^{1/6}}{n} \tag{5.25}$$

(In the obsolescent British f.p.s. system, the expression on the right-hand side must be multiplied by 1.48.) Hence, the mean velocity is now

$$V = \frac{1}{n} R^{2/3} S^{1/2} \tag{5.26}$$

where *n* is a roughness coefficient, values of which are given in Table 5.1. The formula is very appropriate for rough surfaces and turbulent flow, i.e. the conditions in which most channels operate.

TABLE 5.1. Values of *n* for channels of different characteristics and types (After Webber, N., *Fluid Mechanics for Civil Engineers*, E. & F.N. Spon, London (1965).)

Type	Surfaces or characteristics	n
Rivers and streams	Soil without weeds, with good alignment, and stones no larger than 3 inches	0.02–0.025
	Same as above, with poor alignment	0.03–0.05
	Same as above, with weeds and poor alignment	0.05–0.15
	Gravel without weeds, with good alignment and stones sized between 3 and 6 inches	0.03–0.04
	Same as above, with poor alignment	0.04–0.08
	Gravel with stones and pebbles larger than 6 inches, mountain streams	0.04–0.07
Lined channels and artificial channels	Soil with good alignment	0.018–0.025
	Soil with poor alignment, rocky river bed	0.025–0.04
	Rocks	0.025–0.045
Lined channels	Concrete	0.012–0.017
	Handcast bitumen	0.025–0.035
	Masonry, wrought and joint	0.013–0.02
	Smooth wood	0.011–0.013
	Rough wood	0.012–0.015
Tubes	Casting	0.010–0.014
	Concrete	0.011–0.015
	Glass ceramic	0.011–0.015
	Clay (drainage)	0.012–0.016
	Riveted steel	0.014–0.017
Models	Cement and sand mortar	0.011–0.013
	Hard polished board	0.009–0.011
	Perspex	0.009
	Crystal	0.009–0.010

5.4 Optimum hydraulic section for uniform flow

In order to obtain the maximum discharge for a channel section, we can examine the discharge given by Manning's formula, i.e.

$$Q = \frac{1}{n} \frac{\Omega^{5/3}}{\Gamma^{2/3}} S^{1/2} \tag{5.27}$$

when Ω is the cross-sectional area of the channel and Γ its perimeter. The condition for the section to be optimum is that Γ be a minimum. This means that optimum sections should be circular and these are not easy to construct Hence we study the two most common shapes for channels, i.e. rectangular and trapezoidal. We start by considering the trapezoidal shape and then reduce it to the rectangle (Figure 5.4).

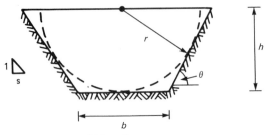

Figure 5.4 Trapezoidal section

Here,

$$\Omega = (b + sh)h \tag{5.28}$$

$$\Gamma = b + 2h(1 + s^2)^{1/2}$$

where s is the ratio between the horizontal and vertical projections of the sides. From equations (5.28) we can write

$$\Gamma = \frac{\Omega - sh^2}{h} + 2h(1 + s^2)^{1/2} \tag{5.29}$$

To minimise Γ, we equate the first derivative to zero:

$$\frac{d\Gamma}{dh} = -\frac{\Omega}{h^2} - s + 2(1 + s^2)^{1/2} = 0 \tag{5.30}$$

which gives

$$b + 2sh = 2h(1 + s^2)^{1/2} \tag{5.31}$$

Note that the left-hand side of (5.31) is the maximum width and the right-hand side is twice the length of the side wall. The section is such that we can draw a circumference with radius r (see Figure 5.4).

For a rectangular section, we have $s = 0$, hence

$$b = 2h \tag{5.32}$$

i.e. the width of the channel is equal to the diameter of the circumference drawn in Figure 5.5 for the optimum section.

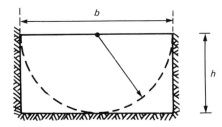

Figure 5.5 Optimum rectangular section

5.5 Program for computation of depth of flow

Although the problem of finding the depth of the channel flow, using Manning's formula, is not very difficult, it will be helpful to have a computer program to solve such a problem.

To devise a trial and error procedure for the solution of this problem we start with equation (5.26), which, multiplied by the area Ω, gives

$$Q = \frac{\Omega}{n} R^{2/3} S^{1/2} \tag{a}$$

Since the discharge Q and the channel slope S are data, the unknowns are the area Ω and the hydraulic radius R, both of which depend on the flow depth h. We can rewrite equation (a) as

$$\Omega R^{2/3} = \frac{nQ}{S^{1/2}} = C \tag{b}$$

Thus the solution of the problem consists in finding a depth h such that Ω and R satisfy equation (b). This will be done following the procedure shown in the flowchart of Figure 5.6.

The first step is to evaluate the quantity C of equation (b). Trial and error depths h_1 and h_2 are then set and the iterative process is started. For each iteration the area and the hydraulic radius for the channel are computed and the product $\Omega R^{2/3}$, called $C1$, is evaluated. If the value of that product is equal to C, within the limits of a given tolerance, the process is completed, and h_1 is the flow depth. Otherwise another value for h_1 is tried. If $C1$ is not less than the exact value C the new depth is h_2 plus half the difference between h_1 and h_2. If it is less than C the new depth is chosen between the last h_1 and the maximum channel depth h. In this last case a check is made to see if the required depth is greater than the maximum channel depth.

The FORTRAN program (Program 18) corresponding to this flowchart is implemented as a subroutine, to facilitate its use as a part of a more general program. The subroutine parameters are the following:

ROU   Roughness coefficient
Q   Required discharge
S   Slope of channel
ITMX Maximum number of iterations allowed
TOL   Tolerance to check for convergence
H   Maximum depth for channel

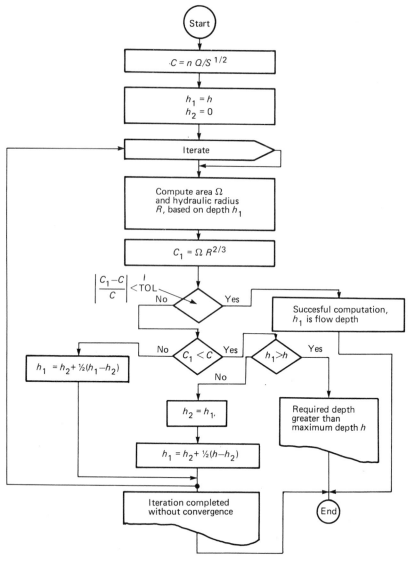

Figure 5.6 Flowchart of Program 18

B	Bottom width of channel section
A1	Angle of left slope of channel section
A2	Angle of right slope of channel section
H1	Computed depth of flow
AREA	Computed area
RAD	Computed hydraulic radius
IER	Equal to 1 if convergence achieved, to 2 if convergence is not achieved in ITMX iterations, and to 3 if required depth is larger than maximum channel depth.

Program 17 Main program for testing sub-routine (CHDEP)

The following main program may be used to test the CHDEP routine,

```
      IN=5
      IO=6
      READ(IN,2) ROU,S,H,B,T1,T2
   2 FORMAT(6F10.2)
      WRITE(IO,3) ROU,S,H,B,T1,T2
   3 FORMAT(///' *** CALCULATION OF DEPTH OF FLOW FOR A CHANNEL ***'//,
     *' ROUGHNESS COEFFICIENT            =',F10.5/,
     *' SLOPE OF CHANNEL                 =',F10.5/,
     *' MAXIMUM DEPTH FOR CHANNEL        =',F10.2/,
     *' BOTTOM WIDTH FOR SECTION         =',F10.2/,
     *' LEFT SLOPE FOR SECTION           =',F10.2/,
     *' RIGHT SLOPE FOR SECTION          =',F10.2)
   5 READ(IN,6) Q,TOL,ITMX
   6 FORMAT(2F10.2,I10)
      IF(Q.EQ.0.) GO TO 1000
      WRITE(IO,7) Q,TOL,ITMX
   7 FORMAT(//
     *' REQUIRED DISCHARGE               =',F10.2/,
     *' TOLERANCE FOR ITERATIVE PROCESS  =',F10.5/,
     *' MAXIMUM NUMBER OF ITERATIONS     =',I10)
C
      CALL CHDEP(ROU,Q,S,ITMX,TOL,H,B,T1,T2,H1,AREA,RAD,IER)
C
      GO TO(10,20,30),IER
  10 WRITE(IO,11) H1,AREA,RAD
  11 FORMAT(///' FOR THE DATA GIVEN THE RESULTS ARE :'//
     *' DEPTH OF FLOW                    =',F10.4/,
     *' AREA OF FLOW                     =',F10.4/,
     *' HYDRAULIC RADIUS                 =',F10.4)
      WRITE(IO,15)
  15 FORMAT(/' ',70('*'))
      GO TO 5
  20 WRITE(IO,21)
  21 FORMAT(/' **** ITERATIONS COMPLETED WITHOUT CONVERGENCE ****')
      GO TO 1000
  30 WRITE(IO,31)
  31 FORMAT(/' **** REQUIRED DEPTH GREATER THAN MAXIMUM DEPTH ****'/)
1000 CALL EXIT
      END
```

Program 18 Evaluation of depth of flow for channel

The listing of the Program 18 is the following:

```
      SUBROUTINE CHDEP(ROU,Q,S,ITMX,TOL,H,B,A1,A2,H1,AREA,RAD,IER)

C   CONVERT ANGLES IN DEGREES TO RADIANS
C
      T1=A1*0.01745329
      T2=A2*0.01745329
C
C   COMPUTE QUOTIENT AND INITIALIZE ITERATION VALUES
C
      C=ROU*Q/SQRT(S)
      H1=H
      H2=0.
C
C   START THE ITERATIONS
```

```
C
      DO 100 I=1,ITMX
C
C     COMPUTE AREA AND HYDRAULIC RADIUS
C
      AREA=H1*(B+H1*(COS(T1)/SIN(T1)+COS(T2)/SIN(T2))/2.)
      RAD=AREA/(B+H1*(1./SIN(T1)+1./SIN(T2)))
C
C     COMPUTE APPROXIMATE QUOTIENT
C
      C1=AREA*RAD**(2./3.)
C
C     CHECK CONVERGENCE
C
      IF(ABS((C1-C)/C).LE.TOL) GO TO 200
C
C     NOT YET
C
      IF(C1.LT.C) GO TO 40
      H1=H2+(H1-H2)/2.
      GO TO 100
   40 IF(H1.GT.H) GO TO 150
      H2=H1
      H1=H2+(H-H2)/2.
  100 CONTINUE
C
C     NO CONVERGENCE
C
      IER=2
      GO TO 999
  150 IER=3
      GO TO 999
C
C     CONVERGENCE WAS ACHIEVED
C
  200 IER=1
  999 RETURN
      END
```

As an example, using the following data:

```
0.016,0.002,5.,4.,45.,45.
10.,0.0001,100
20.,0.0001,100
50.,0.0001,100
100.,0.0001,100
200.,0.0001,100
230.4,0.001,100
300.,0.0001,100
0.
```

will lead to the results listed below:

```
*** CALCULATION OF DEPTH OF FLOW FOR A CHANNEL ***

ROUGHNESS COEFFICIENT           =    0.01600
SLOPE OF CHANNEL                =    0.00200
MAXIMUM DEPTH FOR CHANNEL       =       5.00
BOTTOM WIDTH FOR SECTION        =       4.00
LEFT SLOPE FOR SECTION          =      45.00
RIGHT SLOPE FOR SECTION         =      45.00


REQUIRED DISCHARGE              =      10.00
TOLERANCE FOR ITERATIVE PROCESS =    0.00010
MAXIMUM NUMBER OF ITERATIONS    =        100
```

```
FOR THE DATA GIVEN THE RESULTS ARE :

DEPTH OF FLOW            =      0.9289
AREA OF FLOW             =      4.5785
HYDRAULIC RADIUS         =      0.6908

****************************************************************

REQUIRED DISCHARGE                  =      20.00
TOLERANCE FOR ITERATIVE PROCESS     =      0.00010
MAXIMUM NUMBER OF ITERATIONS        =        100


FOR THE DATA GIVEN THE RESULTS ARE :

DEPTH OF FLOW            =      1.3838
AREA OF FLOW             =      7.4502
HYDRAULIC RADIUS         =      0.9414

****************************************************************

REQUIRED DISCHARGE                  =      50.00
TOLERANCE FOR ITERATIVE PROCESS     =      0.00010
MAXIMUM NUMBER OF ITERATIONS        =        100


FOR THE DATA GIVEN THE RESULTS ARE :

DEPTH OF FLOW            =      2.2955
AREA OF FLOW             =     14.4510
HYDRAULIC RADIUS         =      1.3773

****************************************************************

REQUIRED DISCHARGE                  =     100.00
TOLERANCE FOR ITERATIVE PROCESS     =      0.00010
MAXIMUM NUMBER OF ITERATIONS        =        100


FOR THE DATA GIVEN THE RESULTS ARE :

DEPTH OF FLOW            =      3.3021
AREA OF FLOW             =     24.1123
HYDRAULIC RADIUS         =      1.8076

****************************************************************

REQUIRED DISCHARGE                  =     200.00
TOLERANCE FOR ITERATIVE PROCESS     =      0.00010
MAXIMUM NUMBER OF ITERATIONS        =        100


FOR THE DATA GIVEN THE RESULTS ARE :

DEPTH OF FLOW            =      4.6677
AREA OF FLOW             =     40.4581
HYDRAULIC RADIUS         =      2.3519

****************************************************************

REQUIRED DISCHARGE                  =     230.40
TOLERANCE FOR ITERATIVE PROCESS     =      0.00100
MAXIMUM NUMBER OF ITERATIONS        =        100


FOR THE DATA GIVEN THE RESULTS ARE :

DEPTH OF FLOW            =      5.0000
```

```
AREA OF FLOW                     =    45.0000
HYDRAULIC RADIUS                 =     2.4804
```

****

```
REQUIRED DISCHARGE                    =     300.00
TOLERANCE FOR ITERATIVE PROCESS       =     0.00010
MAXIMUM NUMBER OF ITERATIONS          =        100
```

**** ITERATIONS COMPLETED WITHOUT CONVERGENCE ****

Notice that the last text case does not converge, because the flow depth for the required discharge would have been larger than the maximum depth.

5.6 Non-uniform flow

Non-uniform open channel flow is characterised by the free surface of the fluid being non-parallel to the bottom of the channel. The flow can vary slowly or rapidly over a length of the channel. The latter occurs when there are sudden changes in the channel characteristics, and losses of energy may occur due to turbulence. In spite of this, velocities are considered uniform over the section which simplifies the analysis of channel networks.

5.6.1 Critical depth

The *specific head* is defined as the energy head for a transverse section of the channel and is referred to the bottom of the channel. Note that the *total head* previously defined was referred to a reference plane. Hence the difference between the two is the distance y in Figure 5.7.

The specific energy ($\cos \theta \simeq 1$) is given by

$$E_s = h + \frac{V^2}{2g} = h + \frac{Q^2}{2g\Omega^2} \tag{5.33}$$

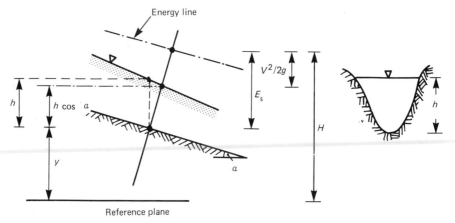

Figure 5.7 Non-uniform flow

Note that the total head is,

$$H = y + h + \frac{V^2}{2g} \tag{5.34}$$

The total energy line will slope downwards along the channel, but the specific energy can increase or diminish depending on the particular characteristic of channel and flow.

We can now draw a diagram showing how the specific energy varies with *water depth* for a constant discharge Q (Figure 5.8). Hence, for each depth we have a certain specific energy composed of two parts

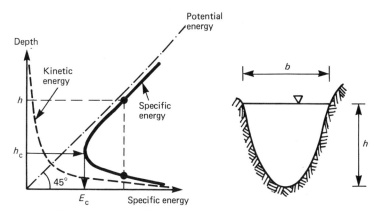

Figure 5.8 Specific energy–depth curve

(i)   The potential component due to the depth of channel, which can be drawn as a straight line at 45°.
(ii) The kinetic energy due to velocity terms, which is asymptotic with respect to the axis.

Note that the minimum specific energy E_c occurs at a point C for which we have a critical depth h_c and a critical velocity V_c. (*Critical* here does not mean velocity of transition from laminar to turbulent which is much smaller than V_c.) The *critical specific energy* E_c is the minimum for which the discharge Q can occur. Note that if E is different from E_s, we always have two values of h for which the flow can occur. The two depths (Figure 5.8) are called conjugates: one is an upper level and the other a lower level.

The critical depth defines the type of flow under study. If the depth $h > h_c$, the flow is called *subcritical* and if $h < h_c$, it is called *supercritical*. Subcritical flow is smooth and of the type occurring in rivers. Supercritical flows are rapid or torrential types.

The critical depth can be determined by differentiating (5.33), i.e. for $Q = $ constant,

$$\frac{dE_s}{dh} = 1 + \frac{Q^2}{2g} \frac{d}{dh}\left(\frac{1}{\Omega^2}\right)$$

$$= 1 - \frac{Q^2}{2g} \frac{2}{\Omega^3}\left(\frac{d\Omega}{dh}\right) = 0 \tag{5.35}$$

Note that $\Omega = \int_0^h b \, dh$ hence for rectangular channels, $d\Omega/dh = b$. The condition for critical depth becomes

$$\frac{Q^2 b}{g\Omega^3} = 1 \tag{5.36}$$

or,

$$\frac{Q^2 b_c}{g\Omega_c^3} = 1 \tag{5.37}$$

Hence, the critical velocity is

$$V_c = \frac{Q}{\Omega_c} = \left(\frac{g\Omega_c}{b_c}\right)^{1/2} \tag{5.38}$$

We can define the mean depth as

$$h_m = \Omega/b \tag{5.39}$$

and the mean depth for the critical section as

$$h_{mc} = \Omega_c/b_c \tag{5.40}$$

(Note that b will be a function of h in general and constant only for rectangular channels.) Equation (5.38) gives

$$V_c = (gh_{mc})^{1/2} \tag{5.41}$$

The expression can be interpreted as a velocity ratio (or Froude number), i.e.

$$F = \frac{V_c}{(gh_{mc})^{1/2}} = 1 \tag{5.42}$$

If V_c is replaced by V and $F > 1$, the flow is supercritical. If $F < 1$, the flow is subcritical. It is important to point out that $(gh)^{1/2}$ is the velocity of propagation or celerity of a gravitational wave in shallow water. Hence, if the flow is supercritical, gravitational waves produced by any perturbations will only propagate downstream. In subcritical flow, however, they can propagate upstream as well.

Example 5.1
Suppose that water flows in a 5 m wide rectangular channel, at a depth of 4 m and has a discharge of 25 m³ s⁻¹. We are requested to compute the Froude number, classify the flow, and determine the critical and conjugate depths.

To proceed with the solution we first compute the flow velocity:

$$V = \frac{Q}{\Omega} = \frac{25 \text{ m}^3 \text{ s}^{-1}}{(4 \text{ m}) \times (5 \text{ m})} = 1.25 \text{ m s}^{-1} \tag{a}$$

The Froude number is then

$$F = \frac{V}{(gh)^{1/2}} = \frac{1.25 \text{ m s}^{-1}}{[(9.81 \text{ m s}^{-2})(4 \text{ m})]^{1/2}} = 0.20 \tag{b}$$

Since $F < 1$, the flow is *subcritical*.

The specific energy is given by

$$E = h + \frac{V^2}{2g} = 4 \text{ m} + \frac{(1.25)^2 \text{ m}^2 \text{ s}^{-2}}{2 \times 9.81 \text{ m s}^{-2}} = 4.08 \text{ m} \tag{d}$$

but it can also be written as

$$E = h + \frac{q^2}{2gh^2}, \quad \text{where } q = Vh \text{ is the discharge per unit width} \tag{e}$$

In order to find the critical depth we equate the first derivative to zero:

$$\frac{dE}{dh} = 1 - \frac{q^2}{gh^3} = 0 \tag{f}$$

so that the critical depth is

$$h_c = \left(\frac{q^2}{g}\right)^{1/3} = \left(\frac{5^2}{9.81}\right)^{1/3} = 1.37 \text{ m} \tag{g}$$

Going back to expression (e) we can compute the conjugate depth to obtain $h = 0.605$ m.

Example 5.2
Consider water flowing at a rate of 16 m³ s⁻¹ in a 4 m wide rectangular channel. Determine the Froude number and the type of flow for depths of 0.5 m, 1.0 m and 1.5 m. Also find the critical depth.

The Froude number given by

$$F = \frac{V}{(gh)^{1/2}} = \frac{Q}{\Omega}\frac{1}{(gh)^{1/2}} = \frac{Q}{bh}\frac{1}{(gh)^{1/2}} = \frac{Q}{b(g)^{1/2}h^{3/2}} \tag{a}$$

Computing it for the three depths given one obtains

$F_{0.5} = 3.61$ supercritical flow

$F_{1.0} = 1.28$ supercritical flow

$F_{1.5} = 0.69$ subcritical flow

The critical depth will be given by

$$h_c = \left(\frac{q^2}{g}\right)^{1/3} = \left[\left(\frac{Q}{b}\right)^2\frac{1}{g}\right]^{1/3}$$
$$= 1.18 \text{ m}$$

5.6.2 Maximum discharge

Consider now that the specific energy is constant and the discharge is variable. We have

$$E_s = h + \frac{V^2}{2g} \tag{5.43}$$

whence

$$Q = \Omega[2g(E_s - h)]^{1/2} \tag{5.44}$$

The maximum discharge can be found by

$$\frac{dQ}{dh} = (2g)^{1/2}\left(-\Omega\frac{(E_s - h)^{-1/2}}{2} + (E_s - h)^{1/2}\frac{d\Omega}{dh}\right) = 0 \tag{5.45}$$

Remembering that $d\Omega/dh = b$ we can write,

$$E_s - h = \Omega/2b \tag{5.46}$$

or,

$$V^2/2g = \Omega/2b \tag{5.47}$$

$$\frac{Q^2 b}{g\Omega^3} = 1 \tag{5.48}$$

Notice that this is identical to condition (5.36) and means that for constant E_s, the maximum Q will be reached for the critical depth, i.e.

$$\frac{Q_{max}^2 b_c}{g\Omega_c^3} = 1 \tag{5.49}$$

This behaviour can be plotted as shown in Figure 5.9. For wide channels we can write (5.49) as

$$q^2/gh_c^3 = 1$$

An example of how flow can change for constant E_s is given by the sluice gate shown in Figure 5.10. We can identify three regimes:

(a)   When the gate is closed, $E_s = h_1$ upstream and $h_2 = 0$.

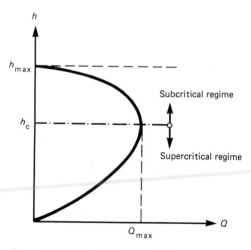

Figure 5.9 Relationship between discharge and depth for a constant specific energy

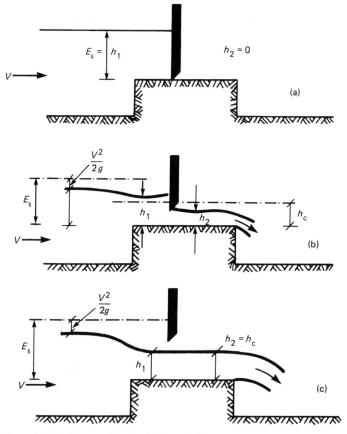

Figure 5.10 Sluice gate: (a) closed; (b) partially opened; (c) fully opened

(b) When the sluice is partially opened (opening less than h_c), we find that $h_1 > h_c$ and $h_2 < h_c$.

(c) If the gate is fully opened, we have $h_1 = h_2 = h_c$.

5.6.3 Critical slope

The slope required to produce a *uniform flow* in a channel with critical depth is called the critical slope S_c. To find it we can start from Manning's formula,

$$V = \frac{1}{n} R^{2/3} S^{1/2} \tag{5.50}$$

For the critical depth:

$$V = (gh_{mc})^{1/2} \qquad R = R_c \qquad S = S_c$$

Hence,

$$S_c = \frac{gh_{mc}n^2}{R^{4/3}} \tag{5.51}$$

Hence, if uniform flow in a channel is such that:

(i) $S < S_c$, the flow is subcritical;
(ii) $S > S_c$, the flow is supercritical.

These concepts are very important to define the behaviour of flow in open channels.

Transition from subcritical to supercritical may be simply due to change of the channel slope (Figure 5.11). For these cases, the flow may be such that $S < S_c$ until at a certain point $S = S_c$ and from then on the flow becomes supercritical without any sudden change.

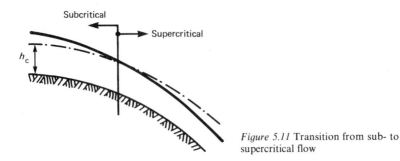

Figure 5.11 Transition from sub- to supercritical flow

This transition is not so smooth when the flow passes from supercritical to subcritical (Figure 5.12). For the case of a dam spillway, for instance, the transition presents a zone of loss of specific energy due to friction forces in a turbulent region. After that, the water tends to reach a normal level, and the flow becomes subcritical. The phenomenon in the transition region is called the *hydraulic* jump. This jump is a way of dissipating energy to reach the E_s needed for the downstream flow.

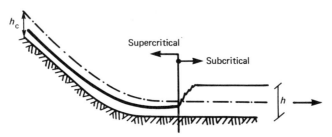

Figure 5.12 Transition from super- to subcritical flow

5.6.4 Analysis of the hydraulic jump

The loss of energy in the hydraulic jump is such that we cannot apply the Bernouilli or momentum equations. Instead we must use equilibrium of momentum.

Consider the case shown in Figure 5.13. The hydrostatic pressures p_1 and p_2 produce two resultants P_1 and P_2 such that

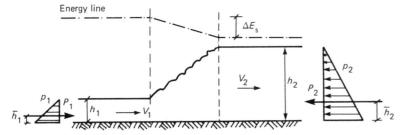

Figure 5.13 Loss of energy in a hydraulic jump

$$\Delta P = P_2 - P_1 = \gamma(\Omega_2 \bar{h}_2 - \Omega_1 \bar{h}_1) \qquad (5.52)$$

$\bar{h}_1$ and $\bar{h}_2$ are the distances from the top to centres of pressure of the Ω_1, Ω_2 areas, respectively.

The increase in momentum is given by

$$\Delta M = M_1 - M_2 = \frac{\gamma Q^2}{g\Omega_1 \Omega_2}(\Omega_2 - \Omega_1) \qquad (5.53)$$

For equilibrium we must have $\Delta P = \Delta M$ and so we can equate (5.52) and (5.53) to obtain

$$\Omega_2 \bar{h}_2 - \Omega_1 \bar{h}_1 = \frac{Q^2}{g\Omega_1 \Omega_2}(\Omega_2 - \Omega_1) \qquad (5.54)$$

The loss of specific energy in the hydraulic jump is given by

$$\Delta E_s = E_{s1} - E_{s2} = (h_1 - h_2) + \left(\frac{V_1^2 - V_2^2}{2g}\right)$$

$$= (h_1 - h_2) + \frac{Q^2}{2g\Omega_1^2 \Omega_2^2}(\Omega_2^2 - \Omega_1^2) \qquad (5.55)$$

If, as is common for hydraulic jumps, we use a rectangular section,

$$\Omega_1 = bh_1 \qquad \bar{h}_1 = \tfrac{1}{2}h_1$$
$$\Omega_2 = bh_2 \qquad \bar{h}_2 = \tfrac{1}{2}h_2$$

equation (5.54) becomes,

$$\frac{b}{2}(h_2^2 - h_1^2) = \frac{Q^2}{gbh_1 h_2}(h_2 - h_1) \qquad (5.56)$$

or

$$h_1^2 + h_1 h_2 - \frac{2q^2}{gh_2} = 0$$

where $q (= Q/b)$ is the discharge per unit width. Therefore

$$\left(\frac{h_1}{h_2}\right)^2 + \frac{h_1}{h_2} - 2F_2^2 = 0$$

Similarly we can write for h_1:

$$\left(\frac{h_2}{h_1}\right)^2 + \frac{h_2}{h_1} - 2F_1^2 = 0$$

From these equations one can find the following relationships:

$$h_2 = \tfrac{1}{2}h_1[(1+8F_1^2)^{1/2} - 1] \qquad h_1 = \tfrac{1}{2}h_2[(1+8F_2^2)^{1/2} - 1]$$

and   (5.57)

$$F_1 = \left\{\frac{1}{8}\left[\left(2\frac{h_2}{h_1}+1\right)^2 - 1\right]\right\}^{1/2} \qquad F_2 = \left\{\frac{1}{8}\left[\left(2\frac{h_1}{h_2}+1\right)^2 - 1\right]\right\}^{1/2}$$

The loss of energy in the jump is given by equation (5.55), which can be written as

$$\Delta E_s = (h_1 - h_2) + \frac{q^2}{2gh_1^2h_2^2}(h_2^2 - h_1^2)$$ (5.58)

Using equation (5.57) to eliminate q, we can write,

$$\Delta E_s = \frac{(h_2 - h_1)^3}{4h_1h_2}$$ (5.59)

Example 5.3
Water flows in a channel at a depth of 0.5 m and with a velocity of 20 m s^{-1}. If a downstream sill causes a hydraulic jump to be formed, what will be the depth and velocity downstream of the jump? What head loss is produced by the jump?

First we compute the Froude number upstream:

$$F_1 = \frac{V}{(gh_1)^{1/2}} = \frac{20 \text{ m s}^{-1}}{[(9.81 \text{ m s}^{-2})(0.5 \text{ m})]^{1/2}} = 9.03$$ (a)

Thus the flow is *supercritical*. Now, from equation (5.57) we have

$$h_2 = \tfrac{1}{2}h_1[(1+8F_1^2)^{1/2} - 1] = 6.14 \text{ m}$$ (b)

Then

$$V_2 = \frac{q}{h_2} = \frac{(20 \text{ m s}^{-1})(0.5 \text{ m})}{6.14 \text{ m}} = 1.63 \text{ m s}^{-1}$$ (c)

The head loss is calculated from expression (5.59), such that

$$h_L = \Delta E_s = \frac{(h_2 - h_1)^3}{4h_1h_2} = \frac{(6.14 - 0.5)^3}{4(0.5)(6.14)} = 14.61 \text{ m}$$ (d)

Example 5.4
Consider a horizontal channel with a sluice gate. Downstream of the gate the depth is 0.50 m for a flow rate of 2.00 m^3 s^{-1} per metre width. Find out if a hydraulic jump can be caused downstream and if so, the depth downstream of the jump.

The Froude number is given by

$$F_1 = \frac{q}{(gh^3)^{1/2}} = \frac{2.00}{[9.81(0.5)^3]^{1/2}} = 1.81 \tag{a}$$

Since the Froude number is greater than 1, the hydraulic jump will form. From equation (5.57) one can see that

$$h_2 = \tfrac{1}{2}h_1[(1+8F_1^2)^{1/2}-1] \tag{b}$$
$$= \tfrac{1}{2}(0.5)\{[1+8(1.81)^2]^{1/2}-1\} = 1.05 \text{ m} \tag{c}$$

5.7 The analysis of open channel flow

The analysis of an open channel, for gradually varied flow, can be done using a number of different methods. The basic problem is to determine the flow profile, and this requires the solution of the dynamic equation relevant to gradually varied flow. The techniques available include graphical integration, direct integration, and step methods.

The analysis of open channel systems, i.e. of channels with several branches, can be done on a computer, using matrix analysis procedures similar to those presented in Chapter 4 for pipe networks. In fact, the main steps in the analysis could be the same as in that case. The main differences will arise in the derivation of the element matrix, and in the evaluation of the hydraulic radius, which must be used instead of the pipe diameter. The main problem to be faced in the analysis formulation is the matching of the flow at the junction of two or more branches. This is still a subject for research.

5.7.1 Formulation for a channel segment

We consider a portion of length Δx of an open channel, such as shown in Figure 5.14. Calling S_0 the slope of the channel and S the slope of the energy gradient, we can write

$$\left(\frac{V_2^2}{2g}+h_2+Z_2\right) - \left(\frac{V_1^2}{2g}+h_1+Z_1\right) = -\Delta x\,S \tag{5.60}$$

In the limit as $\Delta x \to 0$, we have

$$\frac{\mathrm{d}}{\mathrm{d}x}\left(\frac{V^2}{2g}+h+Z\right) = -S \tag{5.61}$$

where S is usually defined using Manning's or Chezy's formula, i.e.

$$S = \frac{n^2 V^2}{R^{4/3}} \quad \text{or} \quad S = \frac{V^2}{c^2 R} \tag{5.62}$$

respectively. Note that,

$$S_0 = -\mathrm{d}Z/\mathrm{d}x \tag{5.63}$$

defines the bottom slope. Calling

$$E = h + \frac{V^2}{2g} \quad \text{and} \quad H = h + \frac{V^2}{2g} + Z$$

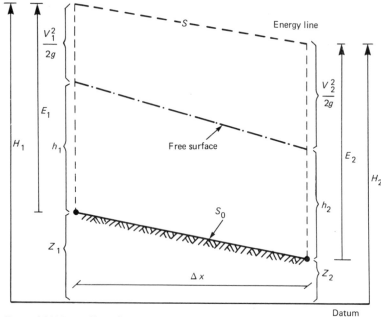

Figure 5.14 Non-uniform flow

we can write equation (5.61) as,

$$dE/dx = -S + S_0 \tag{5.64}$$

and

$$dH/dx = -S \tag{5.65}$$

Note that for uniform flow $S \equiv S_0$ and $h_1 = h_2$.
This equation can be written in terms of Q and h as follows:

$$\frac{dH}{dx} = \frac{d}{dx}\left(h + \frac{V^2}{2g} + Z\right) = -S \tag{5.66}$$

Hence,

$$\frac{dh}{dx} + \frac{1}{2g}\frac{d}{dx}\left(\frac{Q^2}{\Omega^2}\right) = -S + S_0 \tag{5.67}$$

Notice that, according to Manning's formula,

$$S = \frac{n^2 V^2}{a^2 R^{4/3}} \tag{5.68}$$

where a is a coefficient equal to 1 for the metric system and $a = 1.486$ for the obsolescent British f.p.s. system. Noticing that $Q = \Omega V$ we can write,

$$S = \frac{n^2}{a^2 R^{4/3}} \left(\frac{Q}{\Omega}\right)^2 \qquad (5.69)$$

We can further transform the convective term in equation (5.67), i.e.

$$\frac{1}{2g} \frac{d}{dx} \left(\frac{Q^2}{\Omega^2}\right) = -\frac{1}{g} \frac{Q^2}{\Omega^3} b \frac{dh}{dx} \qquad (5.70)$$

Hence equation (5.67) becomes,

$$\frac{dh}{dx} \left(1 - \frac{1}{g} \frac{Q^2}{\Omega^3} b\right) = \left[-\left(\frac{n^2}{a^2 R^{4/3} \Omega^2 S_0}\right)Q^2 + 1\right] S_0 \qquad (5.71)$$

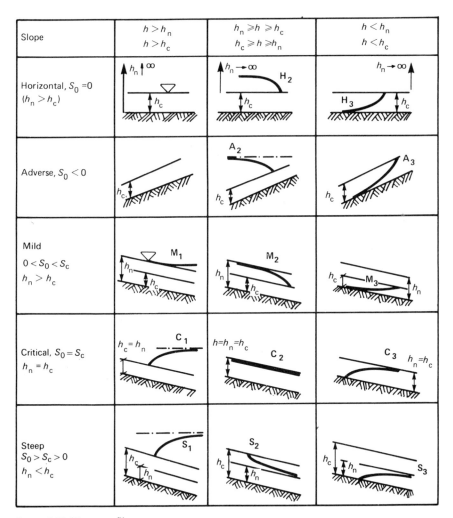

Slope	$h > h_n$ $h > h_c$	$h_n \geqslant h \geqslant h_c$ $h_c \geqslant h \geqslant h_n$	$h < h_n$ $h < h_c$
Horizontal, $S_0 = 0$ $(h_n > h_c)$		H_2	H_3
Adverse, $S_0 < 0$		A_2	A_3
Mild $0 < S_0 < S_c$ $h_n > h_c$	M_1	M_2	M_3
Critical, $S_0 = S_c$ $h_n = h_c$	C_1	C_2	C_3
Steep $S_0 > S_c > 0$ $h_n < h_c$	S_1	S_2	S_3

Figure 5.15 Water profile curves

Notice that $(a=1)$

$$\frac{Q^2 b}{g\Omega^3} = \frac{SR^{4/3}b}{n^2 g\Omega} = \frac{S}{S_c} \tag{5.72}$$

Hence equation (5.71) can be written as,

$$\frac{dh}{dx} = S_0 \frac{1 - S/S_0}{1 - S/S_c} \tag{5.73}$$

For the case of a rectangular channel this can be written as,

$$\frac{dh}{dx} = S_0 \frac{h_n^3 - h^3}{h_c^3 - h^3} \tag{5.74}$$

where h_n is normal flow depth, i.e. flow depth of *uniform* flow for the given Q and S_0 values, as given by $S = S_0$, i.e.

$$Q = \frac{1}{n} \Omega R^{2/3} S_0^{1/2} \tag{5.75}$$

5.7.2 Backwater curves

Notice that the free surface variation along a channel is given by equation (5.75) and depends on:

(1)   the sign of S_0;
(2)   the sign of numerator, i.e. difference between h and h_n (h is water depth);
(3)   the sign of denominator, i.e. difference between h_c and h.

We can investigate S_0 for the following three cases:

(i)   if the transitional water depth h is greater than h_n and h_c;
(ii)   if h is between h_n and h_c;
(iii)   if h is smaller than both h_n and h_c.

The appropriate water surface profiles are shown in Figure 5.15. They can be obtained by integrating numerically the equations of momentum and continuity.

Bibliography

WEBBER, N. *Fluid Mechanics for Civil Engineers*, E. & F.N. Spon, London (1965)
ABBOTT, M. *Computational Hydraulics*, Pitman, London (1979)
CHOW, V.T. *Open Channel Hydraulics*, McGraw-Hill, New York (1959)
ROBERSON, J.A. and CROWE, C.T. *Engineering Fluid Mechanics*, 2nd edn, Houghton Mifflin Co., Boston (1980)

Exercises

5.1   Water flows at critical depth with a velocity of $3 \, \text{m s}^{-1}$. What is the depth of flow?

5.2   A small wave is produced in a pond that is 20 cm deep. What is the speed of the wave in the pond?

5.3 A rectangular channel is 8 m wide and the discharge of water is 20 m³ s⁻¹. Plot the change of depth versus specific energy for these conditions. Let specific energy range from E min E = 9 m. What is the conjugate depth to 0.50 m depth?

5.4 What discharge of water will occur over a high, broad-crested weir (as shown in Figure 5.16), 18 m wide if the head on the weir is 0.80 m?

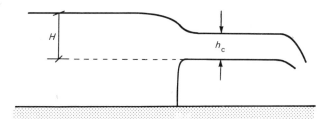

Figure 5.16

5.5 Suppose that water flows from a reservoir, such as the one shown in Figure 5.17, into a steep rectangular channel that is 6 m wide. The reservoir surface is 4 m above the channel bottom at its entrance. Compute the discharge in the channel.

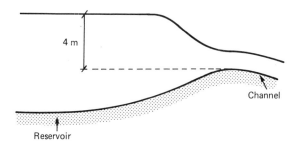

Figure 5.17

5.6 A hydraulic jump occurs in a wide rectangular channel. If the depths upstream and downstream are 40 cm and 1.6 m, respectively, what is the discharge per metre width of channel?

5.7 Using the Chezy equation, compute the normal discharge in a 16 m wide rectangular concrete channel of depth 4 m and with a slope of 0.0012. Apply Manning's formula for the C coefficient.

Chapter 6

Potential flow

6.1 Introduction

This chapter presents the theory relevant to two- and three-dimensional, non-viscous, incompressible flow, useful to provide the student with a knowledge of the way in which fluids behave in complex cases. Although the theory presented here refers to fluid flow cases, it can also be used by analogy to solve flow through porous media.

Ideal fluid flow provides, in many cases, a reasonable approximation to the behaviour of real fluids, and is important in many engineering applications. It allows us to draw flow nets indicating how the fluid moves inside complex domains.

An ideal flow must satisfy the following requirements:

(i) There should be no separation between fluid and solid boundaries, and the fluid should not penetrate the boundaries.

(ii) The continuity equation should be satisfied, i.e.

$$\frac{\partial u}{\partial x} + \frac{\partial v}{\partial y} + \frac{\partial w}{\partial z} = 0$$

for three-dimensional cases, or

$$\frac{\partial u}{\partial x} + \frac{\partial v}{\partial y} = 0$$

for two-dimensional cases.

(iii) Newton's second law of motion applies at each instant and at every point.

(iv) The flow is irrotational. It is impossible for an inviscid fluid to undergo rotation, because we cannot apply shear forces to an inviscid fluid particle to produce rotation.

Under these assumptions, the fluids can only withstand pressure forces and will react without changing volume.

The application of Newton's second law to a particle leads to Euler's equations, and these can then be integrated to yield Bernouilli's equation, as will be shown below.

148

The system of equations to be solved is given by:

(a) the continuity equation (one equation);
(b) the momentum equations, obtained from Newton's second law (two or three equations).

The necessary boundary conditions in velocities and pressures are obtained from condition (i) above.

In general, it is difficult to solve the governing equations in terms of velocities and pressures. Special functions, such as stream functions and velocity potentials, which will be discussed in this chapter, are sometimes used in order to find the solution.

The fluid particle will be referred to a special system of coordinates different from the system used for solids, for which the deformations are very small. This system is called an Eulerian reference system and is well suited for fluids. Consider a particle as shown in Figure 6.1 and take as independent variables

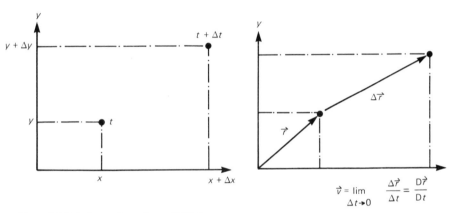

$$\vec{v} = \lim_{\Delta t \to 0} \frac{\Delta \vec{r}}{\Delta t} = \frac{D\vec{r}}{Dt}$$

Figure 6.1 Eulerian system of coordinates

the actual coordinates x, y and the time t. Any quantity such as pressure, velocity, etc., is a function of position and time. In general

$$f = f(x, y, t) \tag{6.1}$$

where f denotes the variable associated with the point (x, y) at time t. During a Δt increment, the material point moves from x to $x + \Delta x$ and from y to $y + \Delta y$, and the variable f changes to $f + \Delta f$.

Assuming f to be a continuous function, we can write

$$\Delta f = \frac{\partial f}{\partial x} \Delta x + \frac{\partial f}{\partial y} \Delta y + \frac{\partial f}{\partial t} \Delta t \tag{6.2}$$

In the limit as $\Delta t \to 0$, we have

$$\frac{Df}{Dt} = \lim_{\Delta t \to 0} \left(\frac{\Delta f}{\Delta t} \right) = \lim \left(\frac{\partial f}{\partial x} \frac{\Delta x}{\Delta t} + \frac{\partial f}{\partial y} \frac{\Delta y}{\Delta t} + \frac{\partial f}{\partial t} \right)$$

$$= \frac{\partial f}{\partial x} \lim_{\Delta t \to 0} \left(\frac{\Delta x}{\Delta t} \right) + \frac{\partial f}{\partial y} \lim_{\Delta t \to 0} \left(\frac{\Delta y}{\Delta t} \right) + \frac{\partial f}{\partial t} \tag{6.3}$$

The velocity components are,

$$u = \lim_{\Delta t \to 0} \left(\frac{\Delta x}{\Delta t} \right) \qquad v = \lim_{\Delta t \to 0} \left(\frac{\Delta y}{\Delta t} \right) \tag{6.4}$$

Hence equation (6.3) can be written,

$$\frac{Df}{Dt} = \frac{\partial f}{\partial t} + u \frac{\partial f}{\partial x} + v \frac{\partial f}{\partial y} \tag{6.5}$$

Since we are now actually following the material point or particle, the term 'material' derivative is used for $D(\ )/Dt$, which is also called the 'total' derivative. The first term in equation (6.5) is the 'local' time derivative and the last two are the convective terms.

6.2 Euler's equations of motion

These equations can now be derived for an inviscid and incompressible fluid using Newton's second law, i.e.

$$F = ma \tag{6.6}$$

Let us consider two body force components in the x and y directions, b_x and b_y, and assume at time t to have a differential of fluid as shown in Figure 6.2.

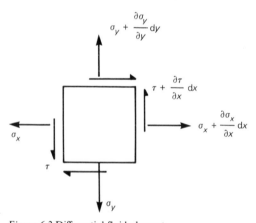

Figure 6.2 Differential fluid element

The state of equilibrium can be defined in terms of the stress rate component at any point and time. Here the equilibrium equations can be written as for a solid, i.e.

$$\frac{\partial \sigma_x}{\partial x} + \frac{\partial \tau}{\partial y} + \rho b_x = 0$$

$$\frac{\partial \sigma_y}{\partial y} + \frac{\partial \tau}{\partial x} + \rho b_y = 0 \tag{6.7}$$

where the b's are unit forces per unit volume and mass.

In order to include dynamic forces in this equation, we can use D'Alembert's principle, replacing ρb_x with

$$\rho b_x - \frac{D}{Dt}(\rho u) \tag{6.8a}$$

and ρb_y with

$$\rho b_y - \frac{D}{Dt}(\rho v) \tag{6.8b}$$

As the fluid is incompressible, its density ρ will remain constant, and we can write expressions (6.8a) and (6.8b) as

$$\rho b_x - \rho \frac{Du}{Dt} \tag{6.9}$$

$$\rho b_y - \rho \frac{Dv}{Dt}$$

This gives the following equilibrium equations:

$$\frac{\partial \sigma_x}{\partial x} + \frac{\partial \tau}{\partial y} + \rho b_x = \rho \frac{Du}{Dt}$$

$$\frac{\partial \sigma_y}{\partial y} + \frac{\partial \tau}{\partial x} + \rho b_y = \rho \frac{Dv}{Dt} \tag{6.10}$$

Note that if the fluid is inviscid, we cannot apply shear stress to a fluid particle, and hence the only two stresses are σ_x and σ_y. The fluid particle can only undergo *pressure*. Hence, we have in any direction,

$$\sigma_x = -p$$

$$\sigma_y = -p$$

and

$$\tau \equiv 0 \tag{6.11}$$

The state of stress is then defined by a single variable p, pressure, which is taken to be positive when compressive. Hence the equilibrium equations become,

$$-\frac{\partial p}{\partial x} + \rho b_x = \rho \frac{Du}{Dt}$$

$$-\frac{\partial p}{\partial y} + \rho b_y = \rho \frac{Dv}{Dt} \tag{6.12}$$

If the body forces are conservative, we can write

$$b_x = -\frac{\partial \Omega}{\partial x} \qquad b_y = -\frac{\partial \Omega}{\partial y} \tag{6.13}$$

In particular, if gravity is the only force acting, $\Omega = gh$ with h measured vertically upwards. Hence,

$$b_x = -g\frac{\partial h}{\partial x} \qquad b_y = -g\frac{\partial h}{\partial y} \tag{6.14}$$

Equation (6.12) can now be written,

$$-\frac{1}{\rho}\frac{\partial}{\partial x}(p+\gamma h)=\frac{\partial u}{\partial t}+u\frac{\partial u}{\partial x}+v\frac{\partial u}{\partial y}$$

$$-\frac{1}{\rho}\frac{\partial}{\partial y}(p+\gamma h)=\frac{\partial v}{\partial t}+u\frac{\partial v}{\partial x}+v\frac{\partial v}{\partial y} \tag{6.15}$$

The first terms on the right-hand side are the local accelerations or velocity changes with time, at a point. The other terms are the convective acceleration terms.

6.2.1 Natural coordinates

Let us now consider the x axis, renamed s, to be parallel to the velocity vector at a point (Figure 6.3), that is tangential to the streamline at that point. The y axis, now denoted n, is assumed to be perpendicular to s as shown in Figure 6.3.

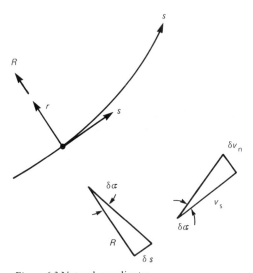

Figure 6.3 Natural coordinates

u is taken as v_s and v as v_n. Note that v_n is zero at the point under consideration, but $\partial v_s/\partial t$ is not necessarily zero. Equations (6.15) become

$$-\frac{1}{\rho}\frac{\partial}{\partial s}(p+\gamma h)=\frac{\partial v_s}{\partial t}+v_s\frac{\partial v_s}{\partial s}$$

$$-\frac{1}{\rho}\frac{\partial}{\partial n}(p+\gamma h)=\frac{\partial v_n}{\partial t}+v_s\frac{\partial v_n}{\partial s} \tag{6.16}$$

By looking at the changes of velocity from s to $s+\delta s$ (Figure 6.3), we can write

$$\frac{\delta s}{R}=\frac{\delta v_n}{v_s} \tag{6.17}$$

Hence in the limit

$$\frac{\partial v_n}{\partial s} = \frac{v_s}{R} \qquad (6.18)$$

Equations (6.16) can be written,

$$-\frac{1}{\rho}\frac{\partial}{\partial s}(p+\gamma h) = \frac{\partial v_s}{\partial t} + \frac{\partial}{\partial s}\left(\frac{v_s^2}{2}\right)$$

$$-\frac{1}{\rho}\frac{\partial}{\partial n}(p+\gamma h) = \frac{\partial v_n}{\partial t} + \frac{v_s^2}{R} \qquad (6.19)$$

For steady flow they become,

$$-\frac{1}{\rho}\frac{\partial}{\partial s}(p+\gamma h) = \frac{\partial}{\partial s}\left(\frac{v_s^2}{2}\right)$$

$$-\frac{1}{\rho}\frac{\partial}{\partial n}(p+\gamma h) = \frac{v_s^2}{R} \qquad (6.20)$$

If we integrate the first of these equations with respect to s, we find

$$\frac{1}{\rho}p + gh + \frac{v_s^2}{2} = \text{constant} \qquad (6.21)$$

which is Bernouilli's equation for a streamline. The constant of integration varies with n, from streamline to streamline. The second of equations (6.20) shows how the pressure head varies across streamlines and can be integrated when v_s and R are known functions of n.

6.3 Irrotational flow

Irrotational flow occurs when the fluid is inviscid. This important assumption will allow us to integrate Euler's equations for conservative body forces. It also leads to the existence of a velocity potential function.

A particle of inviscid fluid can only undergo pressure forces, acting at the mass centre of the particle. Torque cannot be exerted on the particle, and consequently no rotation can occur. Conversely, if an inviscid fluid particle has an initial rotation, there is no way of altering it.

The condition of no rotation is called the irrotationality condition, and it can be expressed mathematically. Consider the element of fluid shown in Figure 6.4. If a rotation of the element diagonal exists, it will be given by,

$$\omega = \frac{1}{2}\left(\frac{\partial v}{\partial x} - \frac{\partial u}{\partial y}\right) \qquad (6.22)$$

where ω is the average rotation or vorticity at time 't'.

For three-dimensional cases, there are three vorticity components, and we can find that the vorticity is proportional to the curl of the velocity vector, i.e.

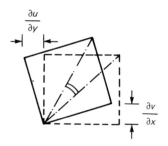

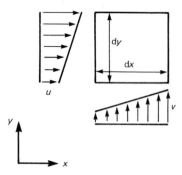

Figure 6.4 Element rotation

$$2\bar{\omega} = \vec{\Delta} \times \vec{v} = \begin{vmatrix} \vec{i} & \vec{j} & \vec{k} \\ \dfrac{\partial}{\partial x} & \dfrac{\partial}{\partial y} & \dfrac{\partial}{\partial z} \\ u & v & w \end{vmatrix} \tag{6.23}$$

$$= \left(\frac{\partial w}{\partial y} - \frac{\partial v}{\partial z} \right) \vec{i} + \left(\frac{\partial u}{\partial z} - \frac{\partial w}{\partial x} \right) \vec{j} + \left(\frac{\partial v}{\partial x} - \frac{\partial u}{\partial y} \right) \vec{k}$$

Let us how assume that the rotation is zero in a two-dimensional case; hence equation (6.22) gives

$$\frac{\partial v}{\partial x} = \frac{\partial u}{\partial y} \tag{6.24}$$

This restriction must hold at every point, except for singular points, and is the condition for an *exact* differential, that is

$$u\,dx + v\,dy \tag{6.25}$$

If the function being differentiated is φ, then

$$-d\varphi = u\,dx + v\,dy$$

$$= -\frac{\partial \varphi}{\partial x}\,dx - \frac{\partial \varphi}{\partial y}\,dy \tag{6.26}$$

The negative sign is conventionally used to indicate that the value of φ, *velocity potential*, decreases in the direction of the velocity. Notice that we have defined

$$u = -\frac{\partial \varphi}{\partial x} \qquad v = -\frac{\partial \varphi}{\partial y} \tag{6.27}$$

For three-dimensional flow we obtain,

$$u = -\frac{\partial \varphi}{\partial x} \qquad v = -\frac{\partial \varphi}{\partial y} \qquad w = -\frac{\partial \varphi}{\partial z} \tag{6.28}$$

It is evident that the assumption of a *velocity potential* is equivalent to the assumption of irrotational flow.

Substituting the relations (6.27) into the continuity equation gives

$$\frac{\partial u}{\partial x} + \frac{\partial v}{\partial y} = -\left(\frac{\partial^2 \varphi}{\partial x^2} + \frac{\partial^2 \varphi}{\partial y^2}\right) = 0 \tag{6.29}$$

or

$$\nabla^2 \varphi = 0 \tag{6.30}$$

that is φ satisfies Laplace's equation. The same result is obtained in three dimensions, that is

$$\frac{\partial u}{\partial x} + \frac{\partial v}{\partial y} + \frac{\partial w}{\partial z} = -\left(\frac{\partial^2 \varphi}{\partial x^2} + \frac{\partial^2 \varphi}{\partial y^2} + \frac{\partial^2 \varphi}{\partial z^2}\right) = 0$$

or $\tag{6.31}$

$$\nabla^2 \varphi = 0$$

In order to solve equations (6.30) or (6.31), the boundary conditions must also be known as we will see later (section 6.8).

6.4 Integration of Euler's equations

Let us now reconsider the two-dimensional Euler's equations defined in equation (6.15), as

$$-\frac{1}{\rho}\frac{\partial}{\partial x}(p + \gamma h) = \frac{\partial u}{\partial t} + u\frac{\partial u}{\partial x} + v\frac{\partial u}{\partial y}$$

$$-\frac{1}{\rho}\frac{\partial}{\partial y}(p + \gamma h) = \frac{\partial v}{\partial t} + u\frac{\partial v}{\partial x} + v\frac{\partial v}{\partial y} \tag{6.32}$$

Using the irrotationality condition, we can write,

$$\frac{\partial u}{\partial y} = \frac{\partial v}{\partial x} \tag{6.33}$$

and hence equation (6.32) becomes

$$-\frac{1}{\rho}\frac{\partial}{\partial x}(p + \gamma h) = \frac{\partial u}{\partial t} + \frac{1}{2}\frac{\partial}{\partial x}(u^2 + v^2)$$

$$-\frac{1}{\rho}\frac{\partial}{\partial y}(p + \gamma h) = \frac{\partial v}{\partial t} + \frac{1}{2}\frac{\partial}{\partial y}(u^2 + v^2) \tag{6.34}$$

Substituting u and v in terms of the potential function φ, we can write,

$$\frac{\partial}{\partial x}\left(\frac{p}{\rho}+gh+V^2-\frac{\partial\varphi}{\partial t}\right)=0$$

$$\frac{\partial}{\partial y}\left(\frac{p}{\rho}+gh+V^2-\frac{\partial\varphi}{\partial t}\right)=0 \qquad (6.35)$$

where $V^2=u^2+v^2$. The terms in parentheses are the same in both equations, and they are not functions of x or y since their derivatives are zero. Hence they define a function which depends only on t, that is

$$\frac{p}{\rho}+gh+V^2-\frac{\partial\varphi}{\partial t}=f(t) \qquad (6.36)$$

If the flow is steady then $\partial\varphi/\partial t=0$ and the function $f(t)$ becomes a constant, say E, as in the case of Bernouilli's equation seen in Chapter 1, that is

$$\frac{p}{\rho}+gh+V^2=E \qquad (6.37)$$

6.5 Stream function formulation

For non-turbulent perfect fluids of the type considered in this chapter, the particles follow a series of lines called streamlines as indicated in Figure 6.5. A streamline is a line drawn in the fluid so that its tangent at each point is in the direction of the fluid velocity. For steady flow, the streamlines do not change with time.

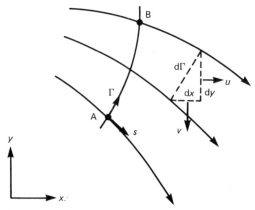

Figure 6.5 Streamlines

Consider two arbitrary points A and B shown in Figure 6.5, on two different streamlines at a fixed time t. The flow rate from A to B is a function of ψ, called the stream function, and which depends on x, y and t.

The fluid rate between two streamlines separated by an elemental distance is given by

$$d\psi = u\,dy - v\,dx \tag{6.38}$$

where $d\psi$ is an exact differential, and can also be written as

$$d\psi = \frac{\partial \psi}{\partial x}\,dx + \frac{\partial \psi}{\partial y}\,dy \tag{6.39}$$

Thus,

$$u = \frac{\partial \psi}{\partial y} \qquad v = -\frac{\partial \psi}{\partial x} \tag{6.40}$$

These equations are valid for rotational as well as irrotational flow. The ψ function is such that the incompressibility condition is identically satisfied, such that

$$\frac{\partial u}{\partial x} + \frac{\partial v}{\partial y} = \frac{\partial}{\partial x}\left(\frac{\partial \psi}{\partial y}\right) - \frac{\partial}{\partial v}\left(\frac{\partial \psi}{\partial x}\right) \doteq 0 \tag{6.41}$$

The flow rate between points A and B can now be written as,

$$Q = \int_A^B v_n\,d\Gamma = \int_A^B (un_x + vn_y)\,d\Gamma \tag{6.42}$$

where n_x and n_y are the direction cosines of the normal to line AB with respect to the x and y axes:

$$n_x = \frac{dy}{d\Gamma} \qquad n_y = -\frac{dx}{d\Gamma} \tag{6.43}$$

Hence equation (6.42) becomes

$$Q = \int_A^B (u\,dy - v\,dx) \tag{6.44}$$

Substituting the velocities in terms of the stream function, we obtain

$$Q = \int_A^B \left(\frac{\partial \psi}{\partial y}\,dy + \frac{\partial \psi}{\partial x}\,dx\right) = \int_A^B d\psi \tag{6.45}$$

Hence

$$Q = \psi(B) - \psi(A) \tag{6.46}$$

which shows that the rate of flow between A and B is equal to the difference between the stream functions at A and B.

Notice that the stream function formulation is such that irrotationality is not identically satisfied, as it was in the case of the velocity potential formulation. Here we need to satisfy the condition

$$2\omega = \frac{\partial v}{\partial x} - \frac{\partial u}{\partial y} = -\left(\frac{\partial^2 \psi}{\partial x^2} + \frac{\partial^2 \psi}{\partial y^2}\right) = 0 \tag{6.47}$$

or

$$2\omega = \nabla^2 \psi = 0 \tag{6.48}$$

which is also Laplace's equation.

6.6 Flow nets

We will now study the relationship between the velocity portential function φ and the stream function ψ. Lines of constant φ are called equipotentials, and the streamlines are lines on which $\psi = $ constant.

By definition, the ψ and φ lines are orthogonal. This can be shown by considering an increment of the two functions, that is

$$d\psi = \frac{\partial \psi}{\partial x} dx + \frac{\partial \psi}{\partial y} dy$$

$$d\varphi = \frac{\partial \varphi}{\partial x} dx + \frac{\partial \varphi}{\partial y} dy$$
(6.49)

We can now define two vectors tangential to the streamlines and equipotentials as shown in Figure 6.6, and which have the following expressions:

$$\vec{e}_\psi = \left(\frac{\partial \psi}{\partial x}, \frac{\partial \psi}{\partial y} \right) \qquad \vec{e}_\phi = \left(\frac{\partial \varphi}{\partial x}, \frac{\partial \varphi}{\partial y} \right)$$
(6.50)

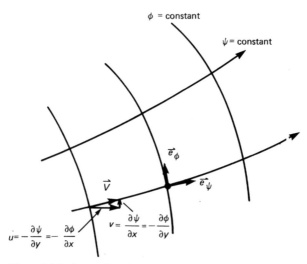

Figure 6.6 Orthogonality of equipotentials and streamlines

Performing a dot product multiplication gives

$$\vec{e}_\psi \cdot \vec{e}_\phi = \left(\frac{\partial \psi}{\partial x}, \frac{\partial \psi}{\partial y} \right) \cdot \left(\frac{\partial \varphi}{\partial x}, \frac{\partial \varphi}{\partial y} \right)$$

$$= (-v, u) \cdot (-u, -v) \equiv 0$$
(6.51)

Hence streamlines and equipotentials are orthogonal. The orthogonal net formed by ψ and φ is called a *flow net*. In steady flow, we can draw a flow net by considering orthogonality conditions at all points. This can be done

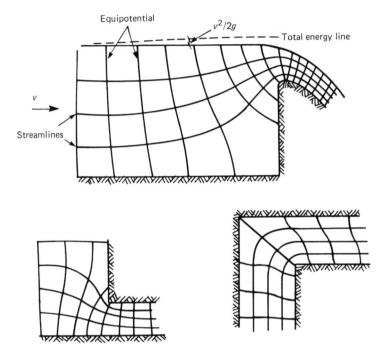

Figure 6.7 Flow nets

graphically, using an electrical analogy, or with some digital computer technique. The latter usually implies writing Laplace's equation in a finite difference form or using finite elements. An example of a flow net is given in Figure 6.7.

6.7 Some flow nets for two-dimensional flow

We now consider some simple flow patterns and then discuss how they can be combined to obtain more complex solutions.

6.7.1 Rectilinear flow

For a uniform flow having velocity V and going in a direction forming an angle α with the x axis as indicated in Figure 6.8 we have

$$u = V\cos \alpha \qquad v = V\sin \alpha$$

The stream functions are given by

$$\psi = \int \left(\frac{\partial \psi}{\partial x}\, dx + \frac{\partial \psi}{\partial y}\, dy \right) = \int (-v\, dx + u\, dy) \tag{6.52}$$

Since u and v are constants it follows that,

$$\psi = -vx + uy + c \tag{6.53}$$

where the value of c is arbitrary.

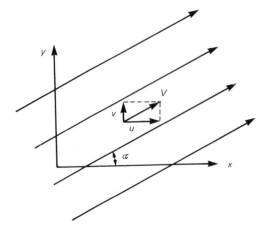

Figure 6.8 Uniform flow

If the flow is irrotational, we can take

$$\varphi = \int \left(\frac{\partial \varphi}{\partial x} \, dx + \frac{\partial \varphi}{\partial y} \, dy \right) = \int (-u \, dx - v \, dy)$$

$$= -ux - vy + c \tag{6.54}$$

Note that if $\alpha = 0$ and we set $c = 0$ in both cases

$$\psi = uy = Vy \tag{6.55}$$

$$\varphi = -ux = -Vx$$

which defines a series of lines parallel to the axes.

6.7.2 Flow round a corner

A potential function such as

$$\varphi = c(x^2 - y^2) \tag{6.56}$$

has the following stream function:

$$\psi = -2cxy \tag{6.57}$$

Working in polar coordinates,

$$x = r \cos \theta \qquad y = r \sin \theta \tag{6.58}$$

gives

$$\psi = -cr^2 \sin (2\theta) \qquad \varphi = cr^2 \cos (2\theta) \tag{6.59}$$

We can now plot the values of the functions φ and ψ obtaining hyperbolas which for the function φ have asymptotes at $y = \pm x$ (see Figure 6.9). The streamlines are rectangular hyperboles with their asymptotes given by the axes. Note that for $\theta = 0$ and $\pi/2$, we obtain $\psi = 0$.

The origin is a *stagnation* point, and the example represents flow round a corner at 90°. We can generalise it to give flow around a corner with an angle α

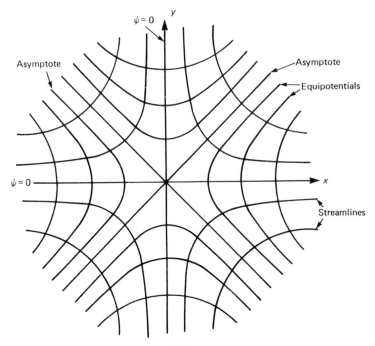

Figure 6.9 Flow around a corner at 90°

by taking

$$\varphi = Cr^{\pi/\alpha} \cos (\pi\theta/\alpha)$$

$$\psi = - Cr^{\pi/\alpha} \sin (\pi\theta/\alpha)$$ (6.60)

and the streamlines $\psi = 0$ are given by the line at $\theta = 0$ and $\theta = \alpha$ as shown in Figure 6.10.

6.7.3 Flow from a line source

A source is a line perpendicular to the (x, y) plane from which fluid flows in all directions at right angles to it. The *strength* of the source is the flow per unit time and per unit length and will be denoted $q = 2\pi\mu$. The velocity at a distance r is proportional to $2\pi\mu/2\pi r$ and

$$v_r = - \frac{\partial \varphi}{\partial r} = \frac{\mu}{r} \qquad v_t = \frac{1}{r} \frac{\partial \varphi}{\partial \theta} = 0$$ (6.61)

Hence the velocity potential is,

$$\varphi = - \mu \ln r$$ (6.62)

Note that φ satisfies Laplace's equation in polar coordinates, i.e.

$$\frac{\partial^2 \varphi}{\partial r^2} + \frac{1}{r} \frac{\partial \varphi}{\partial r} = 0$$ (6.63)

everywhere except at the singular point $r = 0$, i.e. the source.

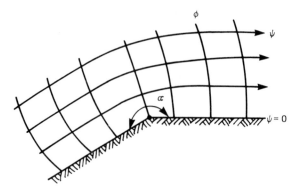

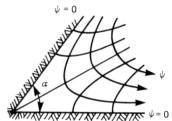

Figure 6.10 Flow around a corner of angle α

The streamlines are radial lines originating at the source. The tangential velocity is zero, that is

$$\frac{\partial \psi}{\partial r} = 0 \tag{6.64}$$

and the radial velocity is

$$v_r = -\frac{1}{r}\frac{\partial \psi}{\partial \theta} = \frac{\mu}{r} = -\frac{\partial \varphi}{\partial r} \tag{6.65}$$

Hence,

$$\psi = -\mu\theta \tag{6.66}$$

The ψ and φ lines are shown in Figure 6.11.

6.7.4 Vortex

We can also define the streamlines and equipotentials in the opposite way to Section 6.7.3, that is

$$\varphi = -\mu\theta \qquad \psi = -\mu \ln r \tag{6.67}$$

This implies that the equipotentials are radial lines, and the streamlines are circles. The point is now called a 'vortex'. As shown in Figure 6.12, the velocity is now in a *tangential* direction only because $\partial\varphi/\partial r = 0$, and its value is

$$v_t = -\frac{1}{r}\frac{\partial \varphi}{\partial \theta} = \frac{\mu}{r} \tag{6.68}$$

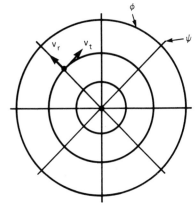

Figure 6.11 Flow net from source

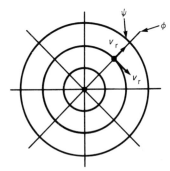

Figure 6.12 Flow net from a vortex

We can integrate around the vortex to obtain the circulation. For any circulation around a closed path and containing the vortex, as indicated in Figure 6.13, we obtain

$$\gamma = \int (V \cos \alpha) \, d\Gamma = \int_0^{2\pi} \frac{\mu}{r} r \, d\theta = 2\pi\mu \tag{6.69}$$

This value is the *strength* of the vortex.

Notice that at $r=0$, the velocity goes to infinity; hence, a vortex, as a source, is a singular point.

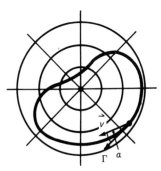

Figure 6.13 Circulation around the vortex

6.7.5 Doublet or dipole

A doublet is defined as the limiting case as a source and sink approach each other. Consider Figure 6.14 with a sink located at $(l, 0)$ and a source of equal strength at $(-l, 0)$. The streamline pattern corresponding to this configuration is shown in Figure 6.15. Assume that the source strength at 1 is m and that of the sink at 2 is $-m$. The stream function at a general observation point P is,

$$\psi = -\mu\theta_1 + \mu\theta_2 = \mu(\theta_2 - \theta_1) \qquad (6.70)$$

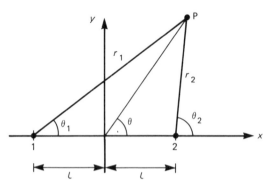

Figure 6.14 Doublet or dipole

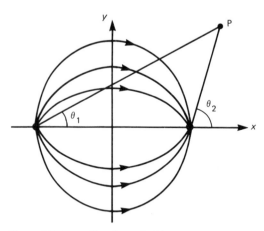

Figure 6.15 Streamlines for a doublet

We can also write,

$$\tan \theta_1 = \frac{y}{x+l}.$$

$$\tan \theta_2 = \frac{y}{x-l} \qquad (6.71)$$

Since

$$\tan(\theta_2 - \theta_1) = \frac{\tan\theta_2 - \tan\theta_1}{1 + \tan\theta_2 \tan\theta_1}$$

we can write

$$\tan(\theta_2 - \theta_1) = \frac{y/(x-l) - y/(x+l)}{1 + [y^2/(x-l)(x+l)]} = \frac{2ly}{x^2 - l^2 + y^2}$$

Thus one can obtain $(\theta_2 - \theta_1)$ and substitute it into equation (6.70), giving,

$$\psi = \mu \tan^{-1}\left(\frac{2ly}{x^2 - l^2 + y^2}\right) \tag{6.72}$$

When the source and sink are moved indefinitely close, maintaining the product $2\mu l$ constant, we obtain a *doublet* or *dipole*.

Hence as $2l$ tends to zero, ψ tends to the value

$$\mu\left(\frac{2ly}{x^2 - l^2 + y^2}\right) \longrightarrow \frac{cy}{x^2 + y^2} \tag{6.73}$$

where $c = 2\mu l = $ constant.

Working with polar coordinates,

$$\psi = \frac{cr \sin\theta}{r^2} = c\frac{\sin\theta}{r} \tag{6.74}$$

It is also possible to verify that,

$$\varphi = c\left(\frac{x}{x^2 + y^2}\right) = c\frac{\cos\theta}{r} \tag{6.75}$$

The lines of constant φ are circles through the origin with centres on the x axis and the lines of constant ψ are circles with centres on the y axis, as shown in Figure 6.16. At the origin the velocity goes to infinity giving rise to a singular point.

6.7.6 Uniform flow and source

We now consider the case of a source of strength $2\pi\mu$ located at the origin of coordinates as shown in Figure 6.17. Adding the stream function corresponding to the uniform flow and the source, we obtain:

$$\psi = Vy + (-\mu\theta)$$
$$= Vr \sin\theta - \mu\theta \tag{6.76}$$

Notice that the velocity decreases with increasing radius and that at some point to the left of the origin this velocity is equal and opposite to the one of the uniform stream (V). The velocity is zero at that point (point S), which is known as a *stagnation* point. At that point

$$V = \frac{\mu}{r} \qquad r = \frac{\mu}{V} \qquad v = -\frac{1}{r}\frac{\partial\psi}{\partial\theta} = -\frac{1}{r}(Vr \cos\theta - \mu) = 0 \tag{6.77}$$

Fluid from the source will be carried to the right. The streamline passing

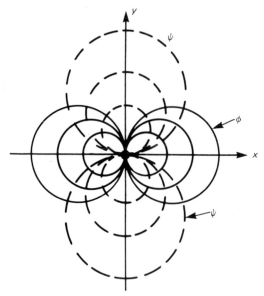

Figure 6.16 Equipotentials and streamlines for a
doublet (dipole)

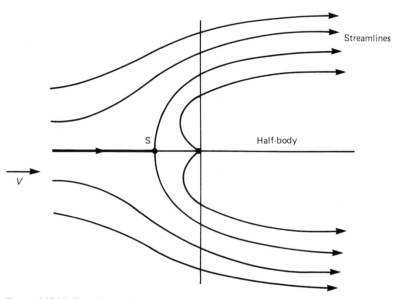

Figure 6.17 Uniform flow and source

through point S is the boundary dividing the flow from the source and the
uniform stream flow. Notice that because of this lack of interaction, the flow
pattern is identical to the one obtained if there was a solid body in a uniform
flow. Hence, the source can be used as a mathematical device to represent
obstructions in the flow.

The contour is defined by the equation evaluated at the stagnation value, that is for $y=0$ and $\theta=\pi$,

$$\psi = -\mu\pi \qquad \text{stagnation streamline} \qquad (6.78)$$

The velocity components at any point in the flow are given by

$$v_t = \frac{\partial\psi}{\partial r} = V\sin\theta \qquad (6.79)$$

$$v_r = -\frac{1}{r}\frac{\partial\psi}{\partial\theta} = V\cos\theta - \frac{\mu}{r} \qquad (6.80)$$

We can then obtain $v=(v_r^2+v_t^2)^{1/2}$ and from that the pressures, using Bernouilli's equation.

6.7.7 Source and sink of equal strength combined with uniform rectilinear flow

We can now define a closed body by using source and sink of equal strength and uniform flow (Figure 6.18), for which the stream function is given by

$$\psi = Vy + \mu(\theta_2 - \theta_1)$$

$$= Vy + \mu\tan^{-1}\left(\frac{2ly}{x^2 - l^2 + y^2}\right) \qquad (6.81)$$

Notice that the stagnation point can be supposed to be at a distance s from the origin. Hence, the velocity at that point is,

$$\left.\frac{\partial\psi}{\partial y}\right|_{\substack{y=0 \\ x=s}} \qquad V - \mu\frac{1}{s-l} + \mu\frac{1}{s+l} = 0 \qquad (6.82)$$

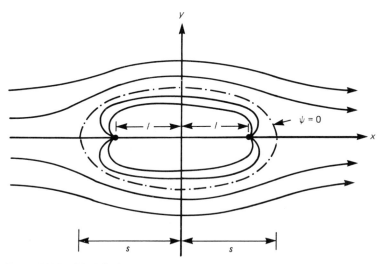

Figure 6.18 Rankine's body

Hence

$$s = \pm l \left(1 + \frac{2\mu}{Vl} \right)^{1/2} \tag{6.83}$$

Notice that at stagnation $\psi = 0$ and that this streamline describes Rankine's *oval* line. The shape of the solid boundary can be altered by varying the distance between source and sink as will be seen in Section 6.7.8.

6.7.8 Doublet and uniform rectilinear flow

In this case we make $l \to 0$ and obtain a doublet at the origin. As shown in Figure 6.19 this gives,

$$\psi = Vy + c \frac{\sin \theta}{r} = Vr \sin \theta + c \frac{\sin \theta}{r} \tag{6.84}$$

and Rankine's oval becomes a circle of radius R.

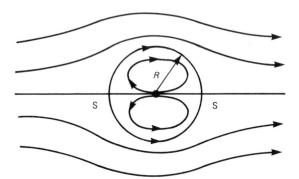

Figure 6.19 Doublet and uniform rectilinear flows; R is the radius of Rankine's oval

Notice that the streamline $\psi = 0$ can be found for $\theta = 0$, $\theta = \pi$ or $c = Vr^2$; that is ψ will be equal to zero along the axis and $r = (c/V)^{1/2} = \text{constant}$, so that

$$\frac{c}{V} = R^2 \tag{6.85}$$

The stream function becomes,

$$\psi = V \left(r - \frac{R^2}{r} \right) \sin \theta \tag{6.86}$$

This pattern corresponds to the fluid pattern obtained when there is a circular obstruction of radius R in a uniform flow.
    The velocities are,

$$v_r = -\frac{1}{r} \frac{\partial \psi}{\partial \theta} = -V \left(1 - \frac{R^2}{r^2} \right) \cos \theta$$

$$v_t = \frac{\partial \psi}{\partial r} = V \left(1 + \frac{R^2}{r^2} \right) \sin \theta \tag{6.87}$$

On the cylinder surface where $r = R$, we have

$$v_r = 0 \qquad v_t = 2V \sin \theta \qquad (6.88)$$

Stagnation points occur at $\theta = 0$ and π, and the velocity is maximum at $\theta = \pi/2$ and $3\pi/2$. The distribution of pressure around the cylinder can be determined from Bernouilli's equation:

$$p_0 + \tfrac{1}{2}\rho V^2 = p + \tfrac{1}{2}\rho v^2 \qquad (6.89)$$

where p_0 is the pressure upstream for the flow unperturbed by the cylinders. Hence,

$$p = p_0 + \tfrac{1}{2}\rho V^2 - 2\rho V^2 \sin^2 \theta \qquad (6.90)$$

The pressure can be plotted as shown in Figure 6.20. Notice that the net force is zero as we have not considered drag effects. This result is what is known as D'Alembert's paradox.

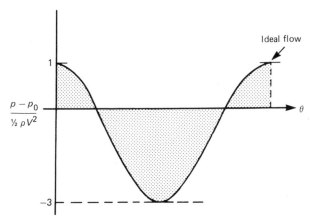

Figure 6.20 Pressure distribution

6.7.9 Flow around a circular cylinder with circulation (doublet, uniform rectilinear flow and vortex)

If we add a vortex to a doublet and a uniform flow stream function we obtain

$$\psi = V \left(r - \frac{R^2}{r} \right) \sin \theta + \frac{\gamma}{2\pi} \ln r \qquad (6.91)$$

The streamline $\psi = (\gamma/2\pi) \ln r$ is the circular cylinder $r = R$, and the others are shown in Figure 6.21. γ is the circulation as defined in equation (6.69).

The tangential velocity at the surface of the cylinder is

$$v_t = \frac{\partial \psi}{\partial r} \bigg|_{r=R} = 2V \sin \theta + \frac{\gamma}{2\pi R} \qquad (6.92)$$

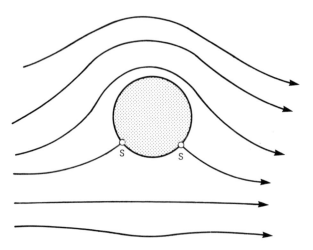

Figure 6.21 Streamlines for flow around a cylinder with circulation

Stagnation occurs when $v_t = 0$, that is

$$\sin \theta = -\frac{\gamma}{4\pi R V} \tag{6.93}$$

When $\gamma = 4\pi r V$ the two stagnation points will coincide.

The pressure on the cylinder with p_0 taken to be equal to zero at infinity, is

$$p = \frac{\rho V^2}{2}\left[1 - \left(2\sin\theta + \frac{\gamma}{2\pi R V}\right)^2\right] \tag{6.94}$$

We can now compute the *lift* force, which is

$$\begin{aligned}
\text{lift} &= -\int_0^{2\pi} pR \sin\theta \, d\theta \\
&= -\frac{\rho R V^2}{2}\int_0^{2\pi}\left[1 - \left(2\sin\theta + \frac{\gamma}{2\pi R V}\right)^2\right]\sin\theta \, d\theta \\
&= \rho V \gamma \tag{6.95}
\end{aligned}$$

Hence, the lift force is proportional to the fluid density ρ, velocity V and circulation γ. This force, which is at 90° with respect to V, is called the Magnus effect.

Example 6.1
A source of strength $\mu_1 = 2$ is located at $(1; 0)$ and another source of strength $\mu_2 = 4$ is at $(-1; 0)$, as shown in Figure 6.22. Calculate the velocities at points $(0; 0)$; $(0; 1)$, $(1; 1)$. For $y = 0$ determine the value of x for which the u velocity is zero.

Solution
Since

$$\varphi_1 = -\mu_1 \ln r_1$$
$$\varphi_2 = -\mu_2 \ln r_2 \tag{a}$$

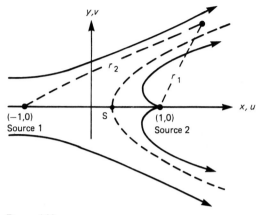

Figure 6.22

hence

$$\varphi = -(\mu_1 \ln r_1 + \mu_2 \ln r_2) \tag{b}$$

Thus

$$u = \frac{\partial \varphi}{\partial x} = \mu_1 \frac{\partial}{\partial x} (\ln r_1) + \mu_2 \frac{\partial}{\partial x} (\ln r_2)$$

$$v = \frac{\partial \varphi}{\partial y} = \mu_1 \frac{\partial}{\partial y} (\ln r_1) + \mu_2 \frac{\partial}{\partial y} (\ln r_2) \tag{c}$$

Considering that

$$r_1 = [(x-1)^2 + y^2]^{1/2} \tag{d}$$
$$r_2 = [(x+1)^2 + y^2]^{1/2}$$

then

$$u = \mu_1 \frac{x-1}{r_1^2} + \mu_2 \frac{x+1}{r_2^2}$$

$$v = \mu_1 \frac{y}{r_1^2} + \mu_2 \frac{y}{r_2^2} \tag{e}$$

Therefore:

(i) for $x = 0$, $y = 0$

$$u = -\mu_1 + \mu_2 = 2$$

$$v = 0 \tag{f}$$

(ii) for $x = 0$, $y = 1$

$$u = -\tfrac{1}{2}\mu_1 + \tfrac{1}{2}\mu_2 = 1$$

$$v = \tfrac{1}{2}\mu_1 + \tfrac{1}{2}\mu_2 = 3 \tag{g}$$

(iii) for $x = 1$, $y = 1$

$$u = 0 + \tfrac{1}{5}\mu_2 = \tfrac{4}{5}$$

$$v = \mu_1 + \tfrac{1}{5}\mu_2 = \tfrac{4}{5} \tag{h}$$

For $y=0$, to determine the value of x which makes the velocity u null, we write

$$u = \frac{\mu_1}{r_1^2}(x-1) + \frac{\mu_2}{r_2^2}(x+1) = 0 \tag{i}$$

Since

$$r_1^2 = (x-1)^2$$
$$r_2^2 = (x+1)^2$$

then

$$u = \mu_1 \frac{1}{x-1} + \mu_2 \frac{1}{x+1} = 0 \tag{k}$$

Hence

$$x = \tfrac{1}{3} \tag{l}$$

6.8 Finite element solution of potential flow problems

In many cases, a closed form solution of an engineering problem is very difficult or impossible to obtain. The engineer should then try to get an approximate solution, by means of some numerical technique, generally applied using a computer.

The finite element method is one of the more successful numerical techniques for the solution of problems governed by one or more differential equations. Basically, the finite element method involves the application of some error minimisation technique to a set of small regions into which the problem domain is subdivided. Modern weighted residual techniques are used for error minimisation, the most popular being the Galerkin method.

6.8.1 The Galerkin method

In order to illustrate the basic idea behind the Galerkin method let us consider again the potential equation

$$\frac{\partial^2 \varphi}{\partial x^2} + \frac{\partial^2 \varphi}{\partial y^2} = 0 \qquad \text{in } \Omega \tag{6.96}$$

which is normally subjected to an essential boundary condition of the type

$$\varphi = \bar{\varphi} \qquad \text{on } \Gamma_1 \tag{6.97}$$

and to a natural boundary condition of the type

$$q = \frac{\partial \varphi}{\partial n} = n_x \frac{\partial \varphi}{\partial x} + n_y \frac{\partial \varphi}{\partial y} = \bar{q} \qquad \text{on } \Gamma_2 \tag{6.98}$$

where n_x and n_y are the direction cosines of the normal to the surface. Figure 6.23 clarifies the nomenclature used. Ω is the two-dimensional problem

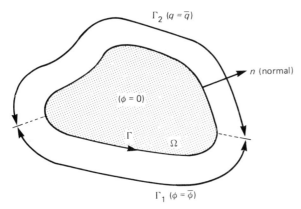

$\Gamma_2 \ (q = \bar{q})$

n (normal)

$(\phi = 0)$

Γ

Ω

$\Gamma_1 \ (\phi = \bar{\phi})$

Figure 6.23 Problem domain and boundary regions

domain. Γ_1 and Γ_2 are two parts of the problem boundary Γ. On part Γ_1 the boundary condition (6.97), in which the potential φ is equal to a known value $\bar{\varphi}$, is valid. On part Γ_2 the boundary condition (6.98), which indicates that the flux q is equal to the known value $\bar{q}$, is valid.

When φ is the exact solution, equations (6.96)–(6.98) are identically satisfied. However, if φ is an approximate solution errors are introduced, such that

$$\frac{\partial^2 \varphi}{\partial x^2} + \frac{\partial^2 \varphi}{\partial y^2} = \varepsilon_1 \neq 0 \qquad (6.99)$$

$$\bar{\varphi} - \varphi = \varepsilon_2 \neq 0 \qquad (6.100)$$

$$\bar{q} - n_x \frac{\partial \varphi}{\partial x} - n_y \frac{\partial \varphi}{\partial y} = \bar{q} - q = \varepsilon_2 \neq 0 \qquad (6.101)$$

To improve the approximate solution φ the errors must be minimised. Notice, however, that there is an error ε_1 for each point of the domain Ω. Similarly, there will be an error ε_2 and an error ε_3 for every point on the boundaries Γ_1 and Γ_2, respectively. Thus the minimisation of the errors has to be made in a global sense.

In weighted residual method the error minimisation equation is written as

$$\int_\Omega \varepsilon_1 w_{1,i} \, d\Omega + \int_{\Gamma_1} \varepsilon_2 w_{2,i} \, d\Gamma + \int_{\Gamma_2} \varepsilon_3 w_{3,i} \, d\Gamma = 0 \qquad (6.102$$

where $w_{1,i}$, $w_{2,i}$ and $w_{3,i}$, are different types of weighting or error distribution functions. Expression (6.102) thus represents a system of n equations, which should allow the approximate solution ϕ to be found.

In the Galerkin method, which is one of the several weighted residual techniques, the approximate solution selected is of the form

$$\varphi = \alpha_1 \Phi_1 + \alpha_2 \Phi_2 + \cdots + \alpha_n \Phi_n = \sum_{i=1}^{n} \alpha_i \Phi_i \qquad (6.103)$$

where the Φ_i's are linearly independent prescribed functions. Usually polynomials, trigonometric functions, or other well behaved functions are chosen. The α_i's are unknown adjustable parameters, the values of which will be determined by the solution of equations (6.102).

In the Galerkin method the approximation (6.103) is selected in such a way that the boundary condition (6.97) is identically satisfied, and the weighting functions w_i are taken equal to a combination of the prescribed functions Φ_i, i.e. $w = \sum_{i=1}^{n} \delta\alpha_i \Phi_i$, where $\delta\alpha_i$ are arbitrary coefficients.

Therefore

$$\int_{\Omega} \varepsilon_1 \Phi_i \, d\Omega + \int_{\Gamma} \varepsilon_3 \Phi_i \, d\Gamma = 0 \tag{6.104}$$

or

$$\int_{\Omega} \left(\frac{\partial^2 \varphi}{\partial x^2} + \frac{\partial^2 \varphi}{\partial y^2} \right) \Phi_i \, d\Omega + \int_{\Gamma_2} \frac{\partial \varphi}{\partial n} \Phi_i \, d\Gamma = 0 \qquad i = 1, 2, \ldots, n \tag{6.105}$$

Solution of this system of equations leads to the values of the adjustable parameters α_i, and thus the approximate solution (6.103) becomes known. There are an infinite number of approximate solutions of the form given by expression (6.103). The error minimisation procedure represented by expressions (6.104) or (6.105) provides the values of the α_i parameters defining the best solution of the form (6.103), in the Galerkin sense.

Example 6.2
Consider the Poisson equation

$$\frac{\partial^2 \varphi}{\partial x^2} + \frac{\partial^2 \varphi}{\partial y^2} = C \tag{a}$$

with the only boundary conditions being $\varphi = 0$ at $x = (0, a)$ and $y = (0, b)$ as indicated in Figure 6.24.

As a first approximation one can take

$$\varphi = \alpha x(x - a)y(y - b) \tag{b}$$

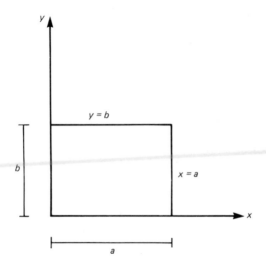

Figure 6.24 Two-dimensional domain for Poisson equation

where

$$n=1 \qquad \alpha_1 = \alpha \qquad \Phi_1 = x(x-a)y(y-b)$$

Notice that expression (a) satisfies the essential boundary condition for the problem.

Equations (6.102) then become

$$\int_\Omega \varepsilon_1 \Phi \, d\Omega = 0 \tag{c}$$

or

$$\int_0^a \int_0^b \left(\frac{\partial^2 \varphi}{\partial x^2} + \frac{\partial^2 \varphi}{\partial y^2} - C \right) x(x-a)y(y-b) \, dxdy = 0 \tag{d}$$

Since

$$\frac{\partial^2 \varphi}{\partial x^2} = 2\alpha(y^2 - yb) \tag{e}$$

then

$$\int_0^a \int_0^b [2\alpha(y^2 - yb) + 2\alpha(x^2 - xb) - C](x^2 - xa)(y^2 - yb) \, dxdy = 0 \tag{f}$$

Solution of this integral leads to the expression

$$-\frac{\alpha}{90}[a^3 b^3(a^2 + b^2)] - \frac{Ca^3 b^3}{36} = 0 \tag{g}$$

from which

$$\alpha = -\frac{5}{2}\left(\frac{C}{a^2 + b^2} \right) \tag{h}$$

and

$$\varphi = -\frac{5C}{2(a^2 + b^2)}(x^2 - xa)(y^2 - yb) \tag{i}$$

For the centre point, and considering $a = b$,

$$\varphi(x = \tfrac{1}{2}a, \ y = \tfrac{1}{2}b) = -\tfrac{5}{16}C(\tfrac{1}{2}a)^2 \tag{j}$$

Notice that this is a reasonable approximation to the exact solution

$$\varphi(x = \tfrac{1}{2}a, \ y = \tfrac{1}{2}a) = -\frac{36.64}{\pi_4} C(\tfrac{1}{2}a)^2 \tag{k}$$

The approximate solution can be improved by taking more terms in expression (b), like, for instance,

$$\varphi = \alpha_1(x^2 - xa)(y^2 - yb) + \alpha_2(x^3 - x^2 a)(y^3 - y^2 b) \text{ etc.} \tag{l}$$

but the solution becomes more complex now and one needs to use a calculator or computer. The generalisation of this error minimisation problem gives rise to finite elements.

6.8.2 The finite element formulation

In the Galerkin method the error minimisation is performed globally, for all the problem domain. In the finite element method the problem domain is ideally subdivided into a collection of small regions, of finite dimensions, called finite elements. The errors are computed over each element. Similarly, there will be an approximate solution selected for each element. Then, the error to be minimised will be the sum of the errors over each element. The great advantage of the finite element method is that its matrix formulation is very similar to the matrix formulation for the pipe system analysis, and for many other problems.

Let us consider that the problem domain for the Laplace equation is subdivided as shown in Figure 6.25, into a collection of m triangular elements, interconnected at n nodal points. The next step in the method is to select an approximate solution over each element. For instance, for the generic element e, shown in Figure 6.26, we can take the simplest possible approximation,

$$\varphi = \alpha_1 + \alpha_2 x + \alpha_3 y \tag{6.106}$$

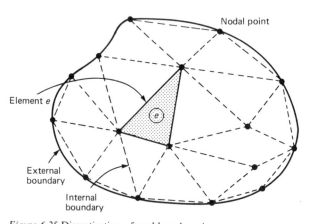

Figure 6.25 Discretisation of problem domain

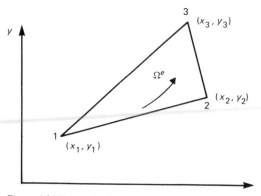

Figure 6.26 Triangular finite element

where

$$n=3 \qquad \Phi_1 = 1 \qquad \Phi_2 = x \qquad \Phi_3 = y \tag{6.107}$$

Equation (6.106) can now be specialised for the corner nodes giving,

$$\varphi_1 = \alpha_1 + \alpha_2 x_1 + \alpha_3 y_1$$
$$\varphi_2 = \alpha_1 + \alpha_2 x_2 + \alpha_3 y_2 \tag{6.108}$$
$$\varphi_3 = \alpha_1 + \alpha_2 x_3 + \alpha_3 y_3$$

or, in matrix form

$$\begin{pmatrix} \varphi_1 \\ \varphi_2 \\ \varphi_3 \end{pmatrix} = \begin{bmatrix} 1 & x_1 & y_1 \\ 1 & x_2 & y_2 \\ 1 & x_3 & y_3 \end{bmatrix} \begin{pmatrix} \alpha_1 \\ \alpha_2 \\ \alpha_3 \end{pmatrix} \tag{6.109}$$

Inverting this expression gives,

$$\begin{pmatrix} \alpha_1 \\ \alpha_2 \\ \alpha_3 \end{pmatrix} = \begin{bmatrix} C_{11} & C_{12} & C_{13} \\ C_{21} & C_{22} & C_{23} \\ C_{31} & C_{32} & C_{33} \end{bmatrix} \begin{pmatrix} \varphi_1 \\ \varphi_2 \\ \varphi_3 \end{pmatrix} \tag{6.110}$$

where

$$C_{11} = (x_2 y_3 - x_3 y_2)/\Omega^e \qquad\qquad C_{21} = (y_2 - y_3)/\Omega^e$$
$$C_{12} = (x_3 y_1 - x_1 y_3)/\Omega^e \qquad\qquad C_{22} = (y_3 - y_1)/\Omega^e$$
$$C_{13} = (x_1 y_2 - x_2 y_1)/\Omega^e \qquad\qquad C_{23} = (y_1 - y_2)/\Omega^e$$

$$C_{31} = (x_3 - x_2)/\Omega^e \tag{6.111}$$
$$C_{32} = (x_1 - x_3)/\Omega^e$$
$$C_{33} = (x_2 - x_1)/\Omega^e$$

where Ω^e is the area of the element we can write (6.110) as

$$\alpha_1 = C_{11}\varphi_1 + C_{12}\varphi_2 + C_{13}\varphi_3$$
$$\alpha_2 = C_{21}\varphi_1 + C_{22}\varphi_2 + C_{23}\varphi_3 \tag{6.112}$$
$$\alpha_3 = C_{31}\varphi_1 + C_{32}\varphi_2 + C_{33}\varphi_3$$

Then, equation (6.106) becomes

$$\varphi = \varphi_1 \psi_1 + \varphi_2 \psi_2 + \varphi_3 \psi_3 \tag{6.113}$$

where

$$\psi_1 = C_{11} + C_{21}x + C_{31}y$$
$$\psi_2 = C_{12} + C_{22}x + C_{32}y \tag{6.114}$$
$$\psi_3 = C_{13} + C_{23}x + C_{33}y$$

Notice that in expression (6.113) the adjustable parameters are now the unknown potentials at the nodal points. The prescribed functions ψ_i play essentially the same role as the original functions Φ_i. Thus the Galerkin equation for the element can be written as,

$$\int_{\Omega^e} \left(\frac{\partial^2 \varphi}{\partial x^2} + \frac{\partial^2 \varphi}{\partial y^2}\right)\psi_i \, d\Omega + \int_{\Gamma_2^e} \left(\bar{q} - n_x \frac{\partial \varphi}{\partial x} - n_y \frac{\partial \varphi}{\partial y}\right)\psi_i \, d\Gamma = 0 \qquad (6.115)$$

The second integral will only be needed if at least one of the element sides coincides with part of the external boundary Γ_2. Otherwise it should not be considered.

The order of differentiation in equation (6.115) can be reduced by one, using integration by parts. For instance,

$$\int_{\Omega^e} \left(\frac{\partial^2 \varphi}{\partial x^2} + \frac{\partial^2 \varphi}{\partial y^2}\right)\psi_i \, d\Omega = \int_{\Omega^e} \frac{\partial^2 \varphi}{\partial x^2} \psi_i \, d\Omega + \int_{\Omega^e} \frac{\partial^2 \varphi}{\partial y^2} \psi_i \, d\Omega$$

$$= \int_{\Omega^e} \frac{d}{dx}\left(\frac{\partial \varphi}{\partial x}\psi_i\right) d\Omega - \int_{\Omega^e} \frac{\partial \varphi}{\partial x}\frac{\partial \psi_i}{\partial x} \, d\Omega$$

$$+ \int_{\Omega^e} \frac{d}{dy}\left(\frac{\partial \varphi}{\partial y}\psi_i\right) d\Omega - \int_{\Omega^e} \frac{\partial \varphi}{\partial y}\frac{\partial \psi_i}{\partial y} \, d\Omega$$

$$= - \int_{\Omega^e} \left(\frac{\partial \varphi}{\partial x}\frac{\partial \psi_i}{\partial x} + \frac{\partial \varphi}{\partial y}\frac{\partial \psi_i}{\partial y}\right) d\Omega$$

$$+ \int_{\Gamma_2^e} \left(n_x \frac{\partial \varphi}{\partial x} + n_y \frac{\partial \varphi}{\partial y}\right)\psi_i \, d\Gamma \qquad (6.116)$$

Using this expression equation (6.115) can be written as

$$\int_{\Omega^e} \left(\frac{\partial \varphi}{\partial x}\frac{\partial \psi_i}{\partial x} + \frac{\partial \varphi}{\partial y}\frac{\partial \psi_i}{\partial y}\right) d\Omega - \int_{\Gamma_2^e} \bar{q}\psi_i \, d\Gamma = 0 \qquad (6.117)$$

Introducing approximations (6.113) leads to the following three equations

$$\int_{\Omega^e} [(\varphi_1 C_{21} + \varphi_2 C_{22} + \varphi_3 C_{23})C_{21} + (\varphi_1 C_{31} + \varphi_2 C_{32} + \varphi_3 C_{33})C_{31}] \, d\Omega$$

$$- \int_{\Gamma_2^e} \bar{q}(C_{11} + C_{21}x + C_{31}y) \, d\Gamma = 0$$

$$\int_{\Omega^e} [(\varphi_1 C_{21} + \varphi_2 C_{22} + \varphi_3 C_{23})C_{22} + (\varphi_1 C_{31} + \varphi_2 C_{32} + \varphi_3 C_{33})C_{32}] \, d\Omega$$

$$- \int_{\Gamma_2^e} \bar{q}(C_{12} + C_{22}x + C_{32}y) \, d\Gamma = 0 \quad (6.118)$$

$$\int_{\Omega^e} [(\varphi_1 C_{21} + \varphi_2 C_{22} + \varphi_3 C_{23})C_{23} + (\varphi_1 C_{31} + \varphi_2 C_{32} + \varphi_3 C_{33})C_{33}] \, d\Omega$$

$$- \int_{\Gamma_2^e} \bar{q}(C_{13} + C_{23}x + C_{33}y) \, d\Gamma = 0$$

These equations can be written in matrix form, as follows

$$\int_{\Omega^e} \begin{bmatrix} C_{21}^2 + C_{31}^2 & C_{22}C_{21} + C_{32}C_{31} & C_{23}C_{21} + C_{33}C_{31} \\ C_{21}C_{22} + C_{31}C_{32} & C_{22}^2 + C_{32}^2 & C_{23}C_{22} + C_{33}C_{32} \\ C_{21}C_{23} + C_{31}C_{33} & C_{22}C_{23} + C_{32}C_{33} & C_{23}^2 + C_{33}^2 \end{bmatrix} \begin{pmatrix} \varphi_1 \\ \varphi_2 \\ \varphi_3 \end{pmatrix} d\Omega$$

$$= \int_{\Gamma_2^e} \bar{q} \begin{pmatrix} C_{11} + C_{21}x + C_{31}y \\ C_{12} + C_{22}x + C_{32}y \\ C_{13} + C_{23}x + C_{33}y \end{pmatrix} d\Gamma = 0 \quad (6.119)$$

or, in a more compact form

$$\mathbf{K}^e \boldsymbol{\varphi}^e - \mathbf{P}^e = 0 \tag{6.120}$$

Since all coefficients are constant, the $\mathbf{K}^e$ matrix is

$$\mathbf{K}^e = \Omega^e \begin{bmatrix} C_{21}^2 + C_{31}^2 & C_{22}C_{21} + C_{32}C_{31} & C_{23}C_{21} + C_{33}C_{31} \\ C_{21}C_{22} + C_{31}C_{32} & C_{22}^2 + C_{32}^2 & C_{23}C_{22} + C_{33}C_{32} \\ C_{21}C_{23} + C_{31}C_{33} & C_{22}C_{23} + C_{32}C_{33} & C_{23}^2 + C_{33}^2 \end{bmatrix}$$

$$\tag{6.121}$$

with vector $\boldsymbol{\varphi}^e$ being

$$\boldsymbol{\varphi}^e = \begin{Bmatrix} \varphi_1 \\ \varphi_2 \\ \varphi_3 \end{Bmatrix} \tag{6.122}$$

The second integral of equation (6.119) only need to be considered for the boundary Γ_2 of the problem domain. For instance, if we have a constant value of $\bar{q}$ on side 2–3 of the triangle, this integral becomes

$$\int_{node\ 2}^{node\ 3} \bar{q} \psi_i d\Gamma = \bar{q} \frac{l_{23}}{2} \begin{Bmatrix} 0 \\ 1 \\ 1 \end{Bmatrix} \tag{6.123}$$

that is, the value of $\bar{q}$ can be averaged on nodes 2 and 3, where l_{23} is the distance from node 2 to 3. This is not always valid but can be done when $\bar{q}$ is constant and φ is linear. Similar results will be obtained for the other two sides of the triangle.

From the derivation presented above it follows that, for the generic element e, the Galerkin equations

$$\int_{\Omega^e} \varepsilon_1 \psi_i d\Omega + \int_{\Gamma_2^e} \varepsilon_3 \psi_i d\Gamma = 0 \qquad \text{for } i = 1, 2, 3 \tag{6.124}$$

become equal to

$$\mathbf{K}^e \boldsymbol{\varphi}^e - \mathbf{P}^e = 0 \tag{6.125}$$

which, for the triangular element takes the following general form:

$$\begin{bmatrix} k_{11}^e & k_{12}^e & k_{13}^e \\ k_{21}^e & k_{22}^e & k_{23}^e \\ k_{31}^e & k_{32}^e & k_{33}^e \end{bmatrix} \begin{Bmatrix} \varphi_1 \\ \varphi_2 \\ \varphi_3 \end{Bmatrix} - \begin{Bmatrix} p_1^e \\ p_2^e \\ p_3^e \end{Bmatrix} = \begin{Bmatrix} 0 \\ 0 \\ 0 \end{Bmatrix} \tag{6.126}$$

6.8.3 Assembling of the total system of equations

Expressions (6.124) or (6.125) are the product of the application of the Galerkin equation to one of the m finite elements into which the problem domain has been subdivided. Thus, in order to write the Galerkin equation for the complete domain, it is necessary to add up the contributions from all elements and all sides on Γ_2, leading to

$$\sum_{e=1}^{m} \int_{\Omega^e} \left(\frac{\partial \psi}{\partial x} \frac{\partial \psi_i}{\partial x} + \frac{\partial \psi}{\partial y} \frac{\partial \psi_i}{\partial y} \right) d\Omega - \sum_{e=1}^{s} \int_{\Gamma_2^e} q\psi_i d\Gamma = 0 \tag{6.127}$$

which can be represented by a matrix equation also having the form

$$\mathbf{K}\varphi - \mathbf{P} = 0 \tag{6.128}$$

or,

$$\begin{bmatrix} k_{11} & k_{12} & \cdots & k_{1n} \\ k_{21} & k_{22} & \cdots & k_{2n} \\ \vdots & \vdots & \cdots & \vdots \\ k_{n1} & k_{n2} & \cdots & k_{nn} \end{bmatrix} \begin{Bmatrix} \varphi_1 \\ \varphi_2 \\ \vdots \\ \varphi_n \end{Bmatrix} = \begin{Bmatrix} p_1 \\ p_2 \\ \vdots \\ p_n \end{Bmatrix} \tag{6.129}$$

where n is the number of nodal points of the finite element mesh.

Equations (6.128) will generally be written as

$$\mathbf{K}\varphi = \mathbf{P} \tag{6.130}$$

where the coefficients of matrices $\mathbf{K}$ and $\mathbf{P}$ are known. $\mathbf{K}$ will be a symmetric matrix, if the systematic K^e are also symmetric. The solution of that system of equations provides the values of the nodal unknowns φ_i. Then, if it is required to know the value of φ at an interior point of an element, it can be computed using equation (6.113). Also, from the values of the unknown φ, other results, such as derivatives of φ, can be computed.

To illustrate the assembling of the systems of equations (6.130) we consider the simple mesh indicated by Figure 6.27 having four triangular elements, and six nodal points. The element matrix equations will be of the form:

Element 1 (nodal points 1, 4, 2)

$$\begin{bmatrix} k_{11}^1 & k_{14}^1 & k_{12}^1 \\ k_{41}^1 & k_{44}^1 & k_{42}^1 \\ k_{21}^1 & k_{24}^1 & k_{22}^1 \end{bmatrix} \begin{Bmatrix} \varphi_1 \\ \varphi_4 \\ \varphi_2 \end{Bmatrix} = \begin{Bmatrix} p_1^1 \\ p_4^1 \\ p_2^1 \end{Bmatrix} \tag{6.131}$$

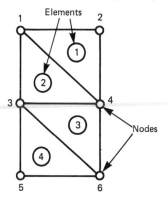

Figure 6.27 Finite element mesh

Element 2 (nodal points 3, 4, 1)

$$
\begin{bmatrix} k_{33}^2 & k_{34}^2 & k_{31}^2 \\ k_{43}^2 & k_{44}^2 & k_{41}^2 \\ k_{13}^2 & k_{14}^2 & k_{11}^2 \end{bmatrix} \begin{Bmatrix} \varphi_3 \\ \varphi_4 \\ \varphi_1 \end{Bmatrix} = \begin{Bmatrix} p_3^2 \\ p_4^2 \\ p_1^2 \end{Bmatrix}
\tag{6.132}
$$

Element 3 (nodal points 3, 6, 4)

$$
\begin{bmatrix} k_{33}^3 & k_{36}^3 & k_{34}^3 \\ k_{63}^3 & k_{66}^3 & k_{64}^3 \\ k_{43}^3 & k_{46}^3 & k_{44}^3 \end{bmatrix} \begin{Bmatrix} \varphi_3 \\ \varphi_6 \\ \varphi_4 \end{Bmatrix} = \begin{Bmatrix} p_3^3 \\ p_6^3 \\ p_4^3 \end{Bmatrix}
\tag{6.133}
$$

Element 4 (nodal points 5, 6, 3)

$$
\begin{bmatrix} k_{55}^4 & k_{56}^4 & k_{53}^4 \\ k_{65}^4 & k_{66}^4 & k_{63}^4 \\ k_{35}^4 & k_{36}^4 & k_{33}^4 \end{bmatrix} \begin{Bmatrix} \varphi_5 \\ \varphi_6 \\ \varphi_3 \end{Bmatrix} = \begin{Bmatrix} p_5^4 \\ p_6^4 \\ p_3^4 \end{Bmatrix}
\tag{6.134}
$$

Finally, adding up all the element contributions, by nodal points, we obtain

$$
\begin{bmatrix}
k_{11}^1+k_{11}^2 & k_{12}^1 & k_{13}^2 & k_{14}^1+k_{14}^2 & 0 & 0 \\
k_{21}^1 & k_{22}^1 & 0 & k_{24}^1 & 0 & 0 \\
k_{31}^2 & 0 & k_{33}^2+k_{33}^3+k_{34}^4 & k_{34}^2+k_{34}^3 & k_{35}^4 & k_{36}^3+k_{36}^4 \\
k_{41}^1+k_{41}^2 & k_{42}^1 & k_{43}^2+k_{43}^3 & k_{44}^1+k_{44}^2+k_{44}^3 & 0 & k_{46}^3 \\
0 & 0 & k_{53}^4 & 0 & k_{55}^4 & k_{56}^4 \\
0 & 0 & k_{63}^3+k_{63}^4 & k_{64}^3 & k_{65}^4 & k_{66}^3+k_{66}^4
\end{bmatrix}
$$

$$
\times \begin{Bmatrix} \varphi_1 \\ \varphi_2 \\ \varphi_3 \\ \varphi_4 \\ \varphi_5 \\ \varphi_6 \end{Bmatrix} = \begin{Bmatrix} p_1^1+p_1^2 \\ p_2^1 \\ p_3^2+p_3^3+p_3^4 \\ p_4^1+p_4^2+p_4^3 \\ p_5^4 \\ p_6^3+p_6^4 \end{Bmatrix}
\tag{6.135}
$$

We can now see that the system (6.135) can be systematically formed, by adding:

(1) in **K**: k_{rs}^i in row r and column s
(2) in **P**: p_r^i in row r

a procedure which can be very efficiently carried out by a computer. Note that this is the same scheme as that explained in Chapter 4 when assembling the governing equations for pipe systems.

6.8.4 Introduction of the boundary conditions

Once the system of equations has been assembled, we must proceed to introduce the essential boundary conditions, of the form $\varphi = \bar{\varphi}$. In the continuous model, these are conditions valid for the boundary surface, or line, called Γ_1, and their nature is also continuous. In the discrete model, however, we will have to apply them at the nodal points lying on the boundary Γ_1, and thus they become discrete boundary conditions.

The boundary conditions can be introduced in the system (6.129) by eliminating the rows corresponding to the prescribed unknowns, and putting in the right-hand side the contributions of those prescribed unknowns. For instance, let us assume that the boundary conditions for the problem of the previous section are

$$\varphi_1 = \bar{\varphi}_1 \qquad \varphi_2 = \bar{\varphi}_2 \tag{6.136}$$

Then the system of equations (6.135) becomes

$$\begin{bmatrix} k_{33} & k_{34} & k_{35} & k_{36} \\ k_{43} & k_{44} & k_{45} & k_{46} \\ k_{53} & k_{54} & k_{55} & k_{56} \\ k_{63} & k_{64} & k_{65} & k_{66} \end{bmatrix} \begin{Bmatrix} \varphi_3 \\ \varphi_4 \\ \varphi_5 \\ \varphi_6 \end{Bmatrix} = \begin{Bmatrix} p_3 - k_{31}\bar{\varphi}_1 - k_{32}\bar{\varphi}_2 \\ p_4 - k_{41}\bar{\varphi}_1 - k_{42}\bar{\varphi}_2 \\ p_5 - k_{51}\bar{\varphi}_1 - k_{52}\bar{\varphi}_2 \\ p_6 - k_{61}\bar{\varphi}_1 - k_{62}\bar{\varphi}_2 \end{Bmatrix} \tag{6.137}$$

In practice, the scheme described above may be inconvenient, since it requires a reorganisation of rows and columns, which would be particularly inefficient for large systems, or when working with more than one problem variable. Several other schemes are used, which can be more efficient, but are in general strongly dependent upon the program organisation, and data structure selected. For example, we can adopt the scheme discussed in Chapter 4 for the pipe network system.

6.8.5 Solution of the system of equations and computation of secondary results

The governing equation, having linear coefficients,

$$\mathbf{K}\varphi = \mathbf{P} \tag{6.138}$$

can be solved using any standard computer program for the solution of linear systems of simultaneous equations.

It is important to notice that in general the system matrices have special characteristics. Normally they are sparse banded matrices, with a few elements different from zero. In many cases they are also symmetric matrices. All these characteristics must be taken into account when implementing a finite element program, to minimise the amount of computer memory required, and to improve the efficiency of the solution.

The formulation of a finite element problem is made in terms of some problem variables, which are taken as the basic unknowns. However, knowledge of the values of other variables may be even more important than those of the basic unknowns. For instance, in the fluid flow problem the sooution can be formulated in terms of the potential or the stream functions, but we might be interested in knowing the flow velocities, or in a solid mechanics problem we can take the displacement as basic unknowns, but we will also be interested in knowing the stresses. Thus, the last step, once the system of equations is solved, requires a return to the element level, to compute from the basic unknowns all other results which may be of interest. The way to proceed, in this case, depends on the type of problem and on the type of results sought.

6.9 Finite element program for the solution of the Laplace equation

In what follows a computer program for the solution of the Laplace equation is presented. The case considered is that given by equation (6.96) to be solved using the simple triangular elements of Section 6.8.

The program for analysis of pipe systems, given in Chapter 4, will be taken as a basis introducing the proper modifications, as indicated below.

6.9.1 Data structure

The meaning of the integer variables is unchanged, with the exception of NLN which is not needed any more. Variable NBN represents the number of nodes for which the variable φ is prescribed.

In comparison with the program of Chapter 4 the meaning of the arrays is now as follows:

KON   Unchanged, but contains three connectivities rather than two.
IB   Unchanged.
X   Unchanged.
Y   Unchanged.
PROP It will now store the boundary flux vectors q for each side of each element. Thus PROP $(3*(L-1)+I)$ contains the value of q for the Ith side of element L. The order of the element sides is defined in accordance with the element connectivity. The first side goes from the first to the second node, the second side from the second to the third node, and the third side from the third to the first node.
AL   Same as before, containing the system vector of independent coefficients, one for each node.
TK   Unchanged.
ELST Unchanged.
V   Unchanged.
RENO It is first used, the same as before, to store the values of prescribed boundary unknowns, although in this case there will be just one value for each boundary node. Later it will contain the x and y derivatives of the basic unknown for each node. Thus, RENO $(2*J-1)$ and RENO $(2*J)$ will contain the x and y derivatives, respectively, of the unknown for node J.

Note that the array ELRE is not needed any more, and is therefore eliminated.

In what follows there is the description of all programs which have been modified, or are new. The programs ASSEM, ELAS, BOUND, SLBSI and BAND, are the same as before, and are therefore not included.

Program 19: Main program

The array dimensions are altered to allow for a maximum of 100 nodes, 100 elements, and 30 boundary nodes. The integer NLN, although not needed, remains in COMMON to minimise the changes to be introduced.

The basic parameters are initialised in accordance with the characteristics of this type of problem. The sequence of subroutines called to apply the analysis steps is the same as before, although the array ELRE is eliminated from the parameters list of programs FORCE and OUTPT.

The corresponding FORTRAN code is given below:

```
C*********************************************************************
C
C                   PROGRAM 19
C                 MAIN PROGRAM FOR
C        SOLUTION OF POTENTIAL PROBLEMS
C
        COMMON NN, NE, NLN, NBN, NDF, NNE, N, MS, IN, IO
        DIMENSION X(100), Y(100), KON(200), PROP(300), IB(60),
       *TK(100, 20), AL(100), RENO(200), ELST(3, 3), V(20)
C
C  INITIALIZATION OF PROGRAM PARAMETERS
C
C  MNN    = MAXIMUM NUMBER OF NODES ALLOWED
C  MNE    = MAXIMUM NUMBER OF ELEMENT ALLOWED
C  MNB    = MAXIMUM NUMBER OF BOUNDARY NODES ALLOWED
C  NRMX   = ROW DIMENSION FOR THE TOTAL MATRIX OF THE PROBLEM
C  NCMX   = COLUMN DIMENSION FOR THE TOTAL MATRIX
C           OR MAXIMUN BAND-WIDTH ALLOWED
C  NDF    = NUMBER OF DEGREES OF FREEDOM PER
C           NODE
C  NNE    NUMBER OF NODES PER ELEMENT
C  NDFEL = TOTAL NUMBER OF DEGREES OF FREEDOM
C          FOR ONE ELEMENT
C
        MNN=100
        MNE=100
        MNB=60
        NRMX=100
        NCMX=20
        NDF=1
        NNE=3
        NDFEL=NDF*NNE
C
C  ASSIGN DATA SET NUMBERS TO IN, FOR INPUT,
C  AND IO, FOR OUTPUT
C
        IN=5
        IO=6
C
C APPLY THE ANALYSIS STEPS
C
C  INPUT
C
        CALL INPUT(X, Y, KON, PROP, AL, IB, RENO)
C
C  CHECK FOR LIMITS
C
        IF(MNN-NN)1, 2, 2
      1 WRITE(IO, 101)
    101 FORMAT(/' **** TOO MANY NODES **** '/)
        GO TO 999
      2 IF(MNE-NE)3, 4, 4
      3 WRITE(IO, 103)
    103 FORMAT(/' **** TOO MANY ELEMENTS ****'/)
        GO TO 999
      4 IF(MNB-NBN)5, 6, 6
      5 WRITE(IO, 105)
    105 FORMAT(/' **** TOO MANY BOUNDARY NODES ****'/)
        GO TO 999
C
C  ASSEMBLING OF THE TOTAL MATRIX FOR THE PROBLEM
C
      6 CALL ASSEM(X, Y, KON, PROP, TK, ELST, AL, NRMX, NCMX, NDFEL)
C
C  CHECK FOR ERROR CONDITIONS
```

```
C
      IF(MS)7,7,8
    7 WRITE(IO,107)
  107 FORMAT(/' **** ERRORS DETECTED PREVENT ANALYSIS ****'/)
      GO TO 999
C
C  INTRODUCTION OF BOUNDARY CONDITIONS
C
    8 CALL BOUND(TK,AL,RENO,IB,NRMX,NCMX)
C
C  SOLUTION OF THE SYSTEM OF EQUATIONS
C
      CALL SLBSI(TK,AL,V,N,MS,NRMX,NCMX)
C
C  CHECK FOR ERROR CONDITIONS
C
      IF(MS)7,9,9
C
C  COMPUTATION OF SECONDARY RESULTS
C
    9 CALL RESUL(KON,PROP,RENO,X,Y,AL)
C
C  OUTPUT
C
      CALL OUTPT(AL,RENO)
C
  999 CALL EXIT
      END
C
C
```

Program 20: Input program (INPUT)

Considering the case of the program of Chapter 4, the input cards are now as follows:

(1) *Basic parameters card.* It includes the number of nodes NN, the number of elements NE, and the number of boundary nodes NBN, with format 3I10.
(2) *Nodal coordinates cards.* Unchanged.
(3) *Element connectivity and properties card.* There will be a card for each element containing the element number, the numbers of the three element nodes, and the values of the normal flux vector q for each of the three element sides, with format 4I10, 3F10.4.
(4) *Boundary data cards.* Same as before. There will be one card for each boundary node, containing the node number, and the value of the prescribed unknown.

The FORTRAN code for the subprogram INPUT is given below.

```
      SUBROUTINE INPUT(X,Y,KON,PROP,AL,IB,RENO)
C
C                PROGRAM 20
C          PROGRAM FOR DATA INPUT
C
      COMMON NN,NE,NLN,NBN,NDF,NNE,N,MS,IN,IO
      DIMENSION X(1),Y(1),KON(1),PROP(1),AL(1),IB(1),RENO(1),W(3),IC(3)
C
C  W =   AN AUXILIARY VECTOR TO TEMPORARELY STORE A SET OF
C        FLUXES ON ELEMENT SIDES
C  IC = AUXILIARY ARRAY TO STORE TEMPORARELY THE CONNECTIVITY
C        OF AN ELEMENT.
C
C  READ BASIC PARAMETERS
C
C  NN  = NUMBER OF NODES
```

```
C  NE  = NUMBER OF ELEMENTS
C  NBN = NUMBER OF BOUNDARY NODES
      WRITE(IO,20)
   20 FORMAT(' ',79('*'))
      READ(IN,1)  NN,NE,NBN
      WRITE(IO,21) NN,NE,NBN
   21 FORMAT(///' INTERNAL DATA'///' NUMBER OF NODES          : ',I5/
     *' NUMBER OF ELEMENTS        : ',I5/
     *' NUMBER OF BOUNDARY NODES: ',I5/
     *' NODAL COORDINATES'/7X,'NODE',6X,'X',9X,'Y')
    1 FORMAT(3I10)
C
C  READ NODAL COORDINATES IN ARRAY X AND Y
C
      READ(IN,2) (I,X(I),Y(I),J=1,NN)
      WRITE(IO,2) (I,X(I),Y(I),I=1,NN)
    2 FORMAT(I10,2F10.2)
C
C  READ ELEMENT CONNECTIVITY IN ARRAY KON
C  AND THE BOUNDARY FLUXES ON EACH OF THE ELEMENT SIDES
C
      WRITE(IO,22)
   22 FORMAT(/' ELEMENT CONNECTIVITY AND FLUXES'/4X,'ELEMENT',16X,
     *'NODES',13X,'QN1',7X,'QN2',7X,'QN3')
      DO 3 J=1,NE
      READ(IN,4) I,IC(1),IC(2),IC(3),W(1),W(2),W(3)
      WRITE(IO,34) I,IC(1),IC(2),IC(3),W(1),W(2),W(3)
      N1=NNE*(I-1)
      PROP(N1+1)=W(1)
      PROP(N1+2)=W(2)
      PROP(N1+3)=W(3)
      KON(N1+1)=IC(1)
      KON(N1+2)=IC(2)
    3 KON(N1+3)=IC(3)
    4 FORMAT(4I10,3F10.4)
   34 FORMAT(4I10,3F10.3)
C
C  COMPUTE N, ACTUAL NUMBER OF UNKNOWNS
C  AND CLEAR THE RIGHT HAND SIDE VECTOR
C
      N=NN*NDF
      DO 5 I=1,N
    5 AL(I)=0.
C
C  COMPUTE HALF BAND WIDTH
C
      CALL BAND(NE,NDF,NNE,MS,IO,KON)
C
C  READ BOUNDARY NODE DATA AND STORE THE
C  PRESCRIBED UNKNOWN VALUE IN ARRAY RENO
C
      WRITE(IO,24)
   24 FORMAT(/' BOUNDARY CONDITION DATA'/8X,'NODE',5X,
     *'PRESCRIBED VALUES')
      DO 7 I=1,NBN
      READ(IN,8) J,RENO(J)
      WRITE(IO,9) J,RENO(J)
      IB(2*I-1)=J
    7 IB(2*I)=0
    8 FORMAT(I10,F10.4)
    9 FORMAT(I10,10X,F10.4)
      RETURN
      END
```

Program 21: Computation of element matrices (STIFF)

The subprogram STIFF will now compute the element matrices $\mathbf{K}^e$, and $\mathbf{P}^e$, according to equations (6.121) and (6.123), respectively.

The integers N1, N2, and N3, are the numbers of the three nodes of element NEL. The real variables D1, D2, and D3, contain the lengths of the three element sides, while A contains the element area. The arrays C2 and C3 contain the second and third row of the matrix **C**, computed according to equation (6.111).

Based on the variables described above, the subprogram STIFF computes the matrix $\mathbf{K}^e$ storing the corresponding coefficients in array ELST. Then it computes the vector $\mathbf{P}^e$ adding it into array AL.

```
C
C
        SUBROUTINE STIFF(NEL,X,Y,PROP,KON,ELST,AL,NDFEL)
C
C                PROGRAM 21
C  COMPUTATION OF THE ELEMENT MATRIX EQUATION
C
        COMMON NN,NE,NLN,NBN,NDF,NNE,N,MS,IN,IO
        DIMENSION X(1),Y(1),KON(1),PROP(1),ELST(NDFEL,NDFEL),AL(1),
       *C2(3),C3(3)
C
C  NEL  = NUMBER OF CURRENT ELEMENT
C  N1,N2,N3 = NUMBERS OF FIRST, SECOND, AND THIRD ELEMENT NODE
C  D1,D2,D3 = LENGTH OF FIRST, SECOND, AND THIRD ELEMENT SIDES
C
        L=NNE*(NEL-1)+1
        N1=KON(L)
        N2=KON(L+1)
        N3=KON(L+2)
        D1=SQRT((X(N2)-X(N1))**2+(Y(N2)-Y(N1))**2)
        D2=SQRT((X(N3)-X(N2))**2+(Y(N3)-Y(N2))**2)
        D3=SQRT((X(N1)-X(N3))**2+(Y(N1)-Y(N3))**2)
C
C  COMPUTE SECOND ROW (C2), AND THIRD ROW (C3), OF MATRIX C
C
C  A   = AREA OF ELEMENT
C
        C2(1)=Y(N2)-Y(N3)
        C2(2)=Y(N3)-Y(N1)
        C2(3)=Y(N1)-Y(N2)
        C3(1)=X(N3)-X(N2)
        C3(2)=X(N1)-X(N3)
        C3(3)=X(N2)-X(N1)
        A=(C2(1)*C3(2)-C2(2)*C3(1))/2.
        DO 5 I=1,3
        C2(I)=C2(I)/2./A
      5 C3(I)=C3(I)/2./A
C
C  CHECK FOR ERROR CONDITIONS
C
        IF(A)1,1,2
      1 WRITE(IO,101) NEL
    101 FORMAT(/' **** ZERO OR NEGATIVE AREA FOR ELEMENT : ',I5,' ****'/)
        MS=0
        GO TO 999
C
C  COMPUTE ELEMENT MATRIX
C
      2 DO 10 I=1,3
        DO 10 J=1,3
     10 ELST(I,J)=A*(C2(I)*C2(J)+C3(I)*C3(J))
C
C  COMPUTE ELEMENT VECTOR
C
        K=NNE*(NEL-1)
        D1=D1*PROP(K+1)/2
        D2=D2*PROP(K+2)/2
        D3=D3*PROP(K+3)/2
        AL(N1)=AL(N1)+D1+D3
        AL(N2)=AL(N2)+D1+D2
        AL(N3)=AL(N3)+D2+D3
    999 RETURN
        END
```

Program 22: Routine for calculating the nodal variables' derivatives (RESUL)

The subprogram RESUL now computes the x and y derivatives of the nodal variables.

The variables N1, N2, and N3, and the arrays C2 and C3 have the same meaning as in the previous program. The variable A now contains twice the element area. The derivatives of the nodal unknowns are computed according to the expressions,

$$\frac{\partial \varphi}{\partial x} = \sum_i \varphi_i c(2, i) \qquad \frac{\partial \varphi}{\partial y} = \sum_i \varphi_i c(3, i)$$

where the φ_i are the values of the nodal variables for the three element nodes. The values of C are defined in equations (6.11).

```
      SUBROUTINE RESUL(KON, PROP, RENO, X, Y, AL)
C
C                     PROGRAM 22
C  COMPUTATION OF SECONDARY RESULTS
C
      COMMON NN, NE, NLN, NBN, NDF, NNE, N, MS, IN, IO
      DIMENSION KON(1), PROP(1), RENO(1), X(1), Y(1), AL(1), C2(3), C3(3)
C
C  NEL  = NUMBER OF CURRENT ELEMENT
C  N1, N2, N3 = NUMBERS OF FIRST, SECOND, AND THIRD ELEMENT NODE
C
      DO 100 NEL=1, NE
      L=NNE*(NEL-1)+1
      N1=KON(L)
      N2=KON(L+1)
      N3=KON(L+2)
C
C  COMPUTE SECOND ROW (C2), AND THIRD ROW (C3), OF MATRIX C
C  A    = AREA OF ELEMENT TIMES 2
C
      C2(1)=Y(N2)-Y(N3)
      C2(2)=Y(N3)-Y(N1)
      C2(3)=Y(N1)-Y(N2)
      C3(1)=X(N3)-X(N2)
      C3(2)=X(N1)-X(N3)
      C3(3)=X(N2)-X(N1)
      A=(C2(1)*C3(2)-C2(2)*C3(1))
      DO 5 I=1, 3
      C2(I)=C2(I)/A
    5 C3(I)=C3(I)/A
C
C  COMPUTE DERIVATIVES OF PROBLEM VARIABLE
C  FOR EACH ELEMENT
C
      L=2*(NEL-1)
      RENO(L+1)=AL(N1)*C2(1)+AL(N2)*C2(2)+AL(N3)*C2(3)
      RENO(L+2)=AL(N1)*C3(1)+AL(N2)*C3(2)+AL(N3)*C3(3)
  100 CONTINUE
      RETURN
      END
C
C
```

Program 23: Output program (OUTPT)

The subprogram OUTPT prints the values of the nodal variables and their derivatives according to the following FORTRAN code:

```
      SUBROUTINE OUTPT(AL,RENO)
C
C                  PROGRAM 23
C               OUTPUT OF RESULTS
C
      COMMON NN,NE,NLN,NBN,NDF,NNE,N,MS,IN,IO
      DIMENSION AL(1),RENO(1)
C
C   WRITE VALUES OF PROBLEM VARIABLE AT NODAL POINTS
C
      WRITE(IO,1)
    1 FORMAT(//1X,130('*')//' RESULTS'//' NODAL VARIABLES      '/7X,'NODE'
     *,6X,'VARIABLE')
      WRITE(IO,2) (I,AL(I),I=1,NN)
    2 FORMAT(I10,F15.4)
C
C   WRITE DERIVATIVES OF PROBLEM VARIABLE
C
      WRITE(IO,3)
    3 FORMAT(///' DERIVATIVES OF THE PROBLEM VARIABLE OVER EACH ELEMENT'/
     *4X,'ELEMENT',9X,'X',14X,'Y',14X,'N')
      DO 4 I=1,NE
      K=2*(I-1)
      DN=SQRT(RENO(K+1)**2+RENO(K+2)**2)
    4 WRITE(IO,5) I,RENO(K+1),RENO(K+2),DN
    5 FORMAT(I10,3F15.5)
      WRITE(IO,6)
    6 FORMAT(//1X,130('*'))
      RETURN
      END
```

Example 6.3

As an illustration of the use of the finite element program presented in the previous section, the flow between two plates, changing direction in a 90° angle as shown in Figure 6.28(a) (see p. 196), will be analysed. The stream function formulation will be used first, giving the value $\psi = 4$ to the top side nodes, and $\psi = 0$ to the bottom side nodes. A linear variation of ψ is given to the left nodes, 1 to 5, simulating a flow of velocity equal to 1. The finite element mesh, shown in Figure 6.28(b) (see p. 197), has 46 nodes and 66 triangular elements. The imput data, prepared according to the specification defined in Section 6.9, followed by the program output, are given below.

```
INPUT
46            66            21
 1    -5.          0.
 2    -5.          1.
 3    -5.          2.
 4    -5.          3.
 5    -5.          4.
 6    -3.          0.
 7    -2.875       1.
 8    -2.75        2.
 9    -2.625       3.
10    -2.5         4.
11    -1.8         0.
12    -1.6         0.81
13    -1.365       1.74
14    -1.104       2.784
15    -0.8         4.
16    -0.8         0.
17    -0.433       0.638
18     0.048       1.475
19     0.657       2.534
20     1.5         4.
21     0.          0.
22     0.25        0.25
23     0.5         0.5
```

24	1.25	1.25
25	2.3	2.3
26	4.	4.
27	0.	-0.8
28	0.638	-0.433
29	1.475	0.048
30	2.534	0.657
31	4.	1.5
32	0.	-1.8
33	0.81	-1.6
34	1.74	-1.365
35	2.784	-1.104
36	4.	-0.8
37	0.	-3.
38	1.	-2.875
39	2.	-2.75
40	3.	-2.625
41	4.	-2.5
42	0.	-5.
43	1.	-5.
44	2.	-5.
45	3.	-5.
46	4.	-5.

1	6	2	1
2	2	6	7
3	7	3	2
4	3	7	8
5	8	4	3
6	4	8	9
7	9	5	4
8	5	9	10
9	11	7	6
10	7	11	12
11	12	8	7
12	8	12	13
13	13	9	8
14	9	13	14
15	14	10	9
16	10	14	15
17	16	12	11
18	12	16	17
19	17	13	12
20	13	17	18
21	18	14	13
22	14	18	19
23	19	15	14
24	15	19	20
25	21	17	16
26	17	21	22
27	23	17	22
28	23	18	17
29	18	23	24
30	24	19	18
31	19	24	25
32	25	20	19
33	20	25	26
34	21	27	28
35	28	22	21
36	28	23	22
37	23	28	29
38	29	24	23
39	24	29	30
40	30	25	24
41	25	30	31
42	31	26	25
43	27	32	33
44	33	28	27
45	28	33	34
46	34	29	28
47	29	34	35
48	35	30	29
49	30	35	36

50	36	31	30
51	32	37	38
52	38	33	32
53	33	38	39
54	39	34	33
55	34	39	40
56	40	35	34
57	35	40	41
58	41	36	35
59	37	42	43
60	43	38	37
61	38	43	44
62	44	39	38
63	39	44	45
64	45	40	39
65	40	45	46
66	46	41	40

```
 1
 6
11
16
21
27
32
37
42
43    1.
44    2.
45    3.
46    4.
41    4.
36    4.
31    4.
26    4.
20    4.
15    4.
10    4.
 5    4.
 4    3.
 3    2.
 2    1.
OUTPUT
```

****

INTERNAL DATA

```
NUMBER OF NODES          :    46
NUMBER OF ELEMENTS       :    66
NUMBER OF BOUNDARY NODES:     21
NODAL COORDINATES
```

NODE	X	Y
1	-5.00	0.00
2	-5.00	1.00
3	-5.00	2.00
4	-5.00	3.00
5	-5.00	4.00
6	-3.00	0.00
7	-2.88	1.00
8	-2.75	2.00
9	-2.63	3.00
10	-2.50	4.00
11	-1.80	0.00
12	-1.60	0.81
13	-1.37	1.74
14	-1.10	2.78
15	-0.80	4.00
16	-0.80	0.00
17	-0.43	0.64
18	0.05	1.48
19	0.66	2.53
20	1.50	4.00

21	0.00	0.00
22	0.25	0.25
23	0.50	0.50
24	1.25	1.25
25	2.30	2.30
26	4.00	4.00
27	0.00	-0.80
28	0.64	-0.43
29	1.48	0.05
30	2.53	0.66
31	4.00	1.50
32	0.00	-1.80
33	0.81	-1.60
34	1.74	-1.37
35	2.78	-1.10
36	4.00	-0.80
37	0.00	-3.00
38	1.00	-2.88
39	2.00	-2.75
40	3.00	-2.63
41	4.00	-2.50
42	0.00	-5.00
43	1.00	-5.00
44	2.00	-5.00
45	3.00	-5.00
46	4.00	-5.00

ELEMENT	NODES			QN1	QN2	QN3
1	6	2	1	0.000	0.000	0.000
2	2	6	7	0.000	0.000	0.000
3	7	3	2	0.000	0.000	0.000
4	3	7	8	0.000	0.000	0.000
5	8	4	3	0.000	0.000	0.000
6	4	8	9	0.000	0.000	0.000
7	9	5	4	0.000	0.000	0.000
8	5	9	10	0.000	0.000	0.000
9	11	7	6	0.000	0.000	0.000
10	7	11	12	0.000	0.000	0.000
11	12	8	7	0.000	0.000	0.000
12	8	12	13	0.000	0.000	0.000
13	13	9	8	0.000	0.000	0.000
14	9	13	14	0.000	0.000	0.000
15	14	10	9	0.000	0.000	0.000
16	10	14	15	0.000	0.000	0.000
17	16	12	11	0.000	0.000	0.000
18	12	16	17	0.000	0.000	0.000
19	17	13	12	0.000	0.000	0.000
20	13	17	18	0.000	0.000	0.000
21	18	14	13	0.000	0.000	0.000
22	14	18	19	0.000	0.000	0.000
23	19	15	14	0.000	0.000	0.000
24	15	19	20	0.000	0.000	0.000
25	21	17	16	0.000	0.000	0.000
26	17	21	22	0.000	0.000	0.000
27	23	17	22	0.000	0.000	0.000
28	23	18	17	0.000	0.000	0.000
29	18	23	24	0.000	0.000	0.000
30	24	19	18	0.000	0.000	0.000
31	19	24	25	0.000	0.000	0.000
32	25	20	19	0.000	0.000	0.000
33	20	25	26	0.000	0.000	0.000
34	21	27	28	0.000	0.000	0.000
35	28	22	21	0.000	0.000	0.000
36	28	23	22	0.000	0.000	0.000
37	23	28	29	0.000	0.000	0.000
38	29	24	23	0.000	0.000	0.000
39	24	29	30	0.000	0.000	0.000
40	30	25	24	0.000	0.000	0.000
41	25	30	31	0.000	0.000	0.000
42	31	26	25	0.000	0.000	0.000
43	27	32	33	0.000	0.000	0.000

44	33	28	27	0.000	0.000	0.000
45	28	33	34	0.000	0.000	0.000
46	34	29	28	0.000	0.000	0.000
47	29	34	35	0.000	0.000	0.000
48	35	30	29	0.000	0.000	0.000
49	30	35	36	0.000	0.000	0.000
50	36	31	30	0.000	0.000	0.000
51	32	37	38	0.000	0.000	0.000
52	38	33	32	0.000	0.000	0.000
53	33	38	39	0.000	0.000	0.000
54	39	34	33	0.000	0.000	0.000
55	34	39	40	0.000	0.000	0.000
56	40	35	34	0.000	0.000	0.000
57	35	40	41	0.000	0.000	0.000
58	41	36	35	0.000	0.000	0.000
59	37	42	43	0.000	0.000	0.000
60	43	38	37	0.000	0.000	0.000
61	38	43	44	0.000	0.000	0.000
62	44	39	38	0.000	0.000	0.000
63	39	44	45	0.000	0.000	0.000
64	45	40	39	0.000	0.000	0.000
65	40	45	46	0.000	0.000	0.000
66	46	41	40	0.000	0.000	0.000

---- HALF-BANDWIDTH IS EQUAL TO   8 ----

BOUNDARY CONDITION DATA

NODE	PRESCRIBED VALUES
1	0.0000
6	0.0000
11	0.0000
16	0.0000
21	0.0000
27	0.0000
32	0.0000
37	0.0000
42	0.0000
43	1.0000
44	2.0000
45	3.0000
46	4.0000
41	4.0000
36	4.0000
31	4.0000
26	4.0000
20	4.0000
15	4.0000
10	4.0000
5	4.0000

****

RESULTS

NODAL VARIABLES

NODE	VARIABLE
1	0.0000
2	1.0154
3	2.0224
4	3.0162
5	4.0000
6	0.0000
7	1.0372
8	2.0573
9	3.0430
10	4.0000
11	0.0000
12	0.9011
13	1.9068
14	2.9325

15	4.0000
16	0.0000
17	0.8936
18	1.9824
19	3.0252
20	4.0000
21	0.0000
22	0.7507
23	1.2895
24	2.4316
25	3.4269
26	4.0000
27	0.0000
28	0.8932
29	1.9820
30	3.0249
31	4.0000
32	0.0000
33	0.8998
34	1.9051
35	2.9314
36	4.0000
37	0.0000
38	1.0334
39	2.0524
40	3.0397
41	4.0000
42	0.0000
43	1.0000
44	2.0000
45	3.0000
46	4.0000

DERIVATIVES OF THE PROBLEM VARIABLE OVER EACH ELEMENT

ELEMENT	X	Y	N
1	0.00000	1.01542	1.01542
2	0.01025	1.03591	1.03596
3	0.01025	1.00698	1.00703
4	0.01552	1.01818	1.01830
5	0.01552	0.99380	0.99392
6	0.01127	0.98424	0.98430
7	0.01127	0.98381	0.98387
8	0.00000	0.95704	0.95704
9	0.00000	1.03719	1.03719
10	0.05693	1.09839	1.09987
11	0.04444	1.01456	1.01554
12	0.09004	1.05863	1.06245
13	0.07459	0.97633	0.97917
14	0.06464	0.96638	0.96854
15	0.06221	0.94926	0.95130
16	0.00000	0.87784	0.87784
17	0.00000	1.11245	1.11245
18	0.18437	1.29454	1.30761
19	0.14746	1.04412	1.05448
20	0.26858	1.14656	1.17759
21	0.22717	0.92575	0.95322
22	0.17789	0.88238	0.90013
23	0.17117	0.83505	0.85241
24	0.00000	0.66493	0.66493
25	0.00000	1.40060	1.40060
26	0.95442	2.04835	2.25979
27	0.64731	1.50773	1.64081
28	0.56840	0.97426	1.12794
29	0.55492	0.96801	1.11579
30	0.50381	0.69495	0.85836
31	0.33217	0.61569	0.69958
32	0.31351	0.48465	0.57721
33	0.00000	0.33712	0.33712
34	1.39999	0.00000	1.39999
35	2.04799	0.95478	2.25962
36	1.50737	0.64766	1.64062

37	0.97394	0.56877	1.12785
38	0.96768	0.55526	1.11566
39	0.69493	0.50420	0.85857
40	0.61554	0.33231	0.69952
41	0.48473	0.31368	0.57738
42	0.33712	0.00000	0.33712
43	1.11090	0.00000	1.11090
44	1.29359	0.18497	1.30675
45	1.04347	0.14811	1.05393
46	1.14601	0.26935	1.17723
47	0.92607	0.22810	0.95375
48	0.88230	0.17837	0.90015
49	0.83583	0.17177	0.85329
50	0.66511	0.00000	0.66511
51	1.03342	0.00000	1.03342
52	1.09643	0.05861	1.09800
53	1.01319	0.04621	1.01425
54	1.05761	0.09216	1.06161
55	0.97771	0.07716	0.98075
56	0.96659	0.06605	0.96884
57	0.95225	0.06401	0.95440
58	0.87877	0.00000	0.87877
59	1.00000	0.00000	1.00000
60	1.03146	0.01573	1.03158
61	1.00000	0.01573	1.00012
62	1.01606	0.02329	1.01633
63	1.00000	0.02329	1.00027
64	0.98526	0.01673	0.98540
65	1.00000	0.01673	1.00014
66	0.96025	0.00000	0.96025

****

Regarding the listing shown above, it is interesting to notice that the program output includes the input data, printed in an ordered manner, and the results. These consist of the values of the problem function, in this case the stream function, for each node, and the problem function derivatives, regarding the x and y axes, and the derivative modulus, under the column headers X, Y and N, respectively, for each element. In this formulation the derivatives with the appropirate figure are the fluid velocities, according to expressions (6.40). It can be seen that the velocity u for elements 1 to 8, under column Y, is very approximately equal to 1, the same as the velocity v for elements 59 to 66, under column X, defining a uniform flow. The velocity modulus for elements 25 to 42, indicates the flow perturbation in the corner region.

Finally, it should be mentioned that the program presented above can also be used to solve that type of problem using the potential function formulation, by properly changing the boundary conditions.

6.10 Boundary element solution of potential flow problems

In conventional applications of weighted residual methods, such as Galerkin's, use is made of functions which satisfy the boundary conditions but are approximate in the domain. An alternative scheme can be proposed, using functions which are exact in the domain, but satisfy the boundary conditions only approximately.

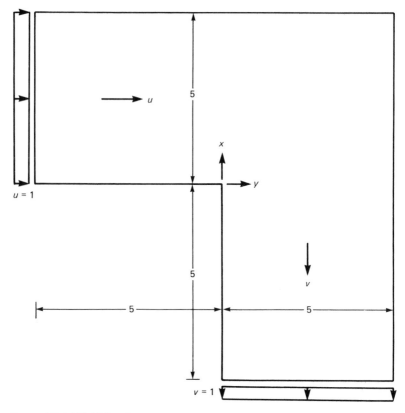

Figure 6.28 (a) Fluid flow for Example 6.3.

6.10.1 Boundary solutions

To introduce the idea of boundary solutions let us consider again the Laplace equation indicated by expression (6.96), subject to boundary conditions (6.97) and (6.98). The weighted residual statement (6.102) can be written in full, as

$$\int_{\Omega}\left(\frac{\partial^2\varphi}{\partial x^2}+\frac{\partial^2\varphi}{\partial y^2}\right)w\,d\Omega+\int_{\Gamma_1}(\varphi-\bar{\varphi})\frac{\partial w}{\partial n}\,d\Gamma+\int_{\Gamma_2}(\bar{q}-q)w\,d\Gamma=0 \quad (6.139)$$

Notice that $w_1=w_3=w$ and $w_2=\partial w/\partial n$. Integrating the first integral in equation (6.139) twice by parts we obtain,

$$\iint\left(\frac{\partial^2 w}{\partial x^2}+\frac{\partial^2 w}{\partial y^2}\right)\varphi\,d\Omega=-\int_{\Gamma_2}\bar{q}w\,d\Gamma-\int_{\Gamma_1}\frac{\partial\varphi}{\partial n}w\,d\Gamma$$

$$+\int_{\Gamma_2}\varphi\frac{\partial w}{\partial n}\,d\Gamma+\int_{\Gamma_1}\bar{\varphi}\frac{\partial w}{\partial n}\,d\Gamma \quad (6.140)$$

We can now assume that the w functions identically satisfy the governing equation $(\partial^2 w/\partial x^2)+(\partial^2 w/\partial y^2)=0$ but not the boundary conditions. This gives

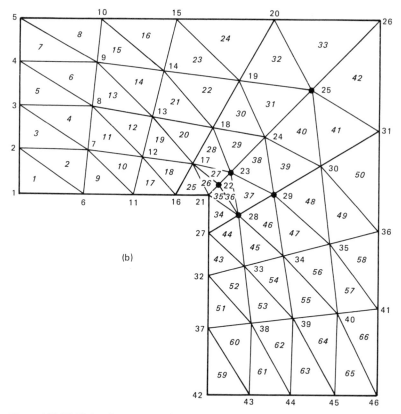

Figure 6.28 (b) Finite element mesh for Example 6.3

$$\int_{\Gamma_2} \bar{q}w \, d\Gamma + \int_{\Gamma_1} \frac{\partial \varphi}{\partial n} w \, d\Gamma = \int_{\Gamma_2} \varphi \frac{\partial w}{\partial n} \, d\Gamma + \int_{\Gamma_1} \bar{\varphi} \frac{\partial w}{\partial n} \, d\Gamma \qquad (6.141)$$

The problem has now been reduced to a boundary problem and expression (6.141) can be the solution of the following:

Example 6.4
Consider the Poisson equation studied in Example 6.2:

$$\frac{\partial^2 \varphi}{\partial x^2} + \frac{\partial^2 \varphi}{\partial y^2} - C = 0 \qquad (a)$$

with boundary conditions $\varphi = 0$ on Γ $(x = \pm 1, \ y = \pm 1)$.
Let us first reduce the problem to a Laplace equation problem. This can be done by defining a new function, v, such that

$$\varphi = \frac{C}{4}(x^2 + y^2) + v \qquad (b)$$

Thus equation (a) becomes,

$$\frac{\partial^2 v}{\partial x^2}+\frac{\partial^2 v}{\partial y^2}=0 \tag{c}$$

with $v=-(C/4)(x^2+y^2)$ on the boundaries $x=\pm 1$ and $y=\pm 1$.

We now approximate v by a trial function that satisfies the Laplace equation, for instance,

$$v=\alpha_1\psi_1 \tag{d}$$

with

$$\psi_1=x^4-6x^2y^2+y^4$$

We now have to satisfy the boundary integrals. Because of symmetry we can consider only $x=1, 0<y<1$. As all the boundary is of type Γ_1, equation (6.141) reduces to,

$$\int_{\Gamma_1}\frac{\partial v}{\partial n}\delta v\,d\Gamma=\int_{\Gamma_1}\bar{v}\frac{\partial\,\delta v}{\partial n}\,d\Gamma \tag{f}$$

or

$$\int_{\Gamma_1}\left(\frac{\partial v}{\partial n}\delta v-\bar{v}\frac{\partial\,\delta v}{\partial n}\right)d\Gamma=0 \tag{g}$$

For the boundary $x=1$, we can write

$$\int_0^1\left(\frac{\partial v}{\partial x}\delta v-\bar{v}\frac{\partial\,\delta v}{\partial x}\right)dy=0 \tag{h}$$

whence

$$\int_0^1 [(4-12y^2)\alpha_1(1-6y^2+y^4)\,\delta\alpha_1+\tfrac{1}{4}c(1+y^2)\,\delta\alpha_1(4-12y^2)]\,dy=0 \tag{i}$$

or

$$\int_0^1 [\tfrac{1}{4}c(1+y^2)+\alpha_1(1-6y^2+y^4)](4-12y^2)\,dy=0 \tag{j}$$

Integrating we have,

$$-\tfrac{1}{5}C+\alpha_1\tfrac{144}{35}=0 \tag{k}$$

and so

$$\alpha_1=\tfrac{7}{144}C \tag{l}$$

This gives

$$v=\alpha_1\psi_1=\tfrac{7}{144}C(x^4-6x^2y^2+y^4) \tag{m}$$

The magnitudes of v and φ may however be displaced from the correct solution by a constant magnitude. In order to determine this constant we can carry out the following integration on the $x=1$ side:

$$\int_0^1 (\bar{v}-v+d)\,dy=0 \tag{n}$$

After integration we find

$$d + \tfrac{1}{3}c - 0.039 = 0 \qquad d = 0.039 - \tfrac{1}{3}c \qquad\qquad (p)$$

Note that the value of v is equal to d at $x = y = 0$.

6.10.2 The boundary element method

In order to develop the formulation of the boundary element method we wrote the Laplace equation using the Laplacian symbol ∇^2, as

$$\frac{\partial^2 w}{\partial x^2} + \frac{\partial^2 w}{\partial y^2} = \nabla^2 w \qquad \text{two dimensions}$$

or $\qquad\qquad\qquad\qquad\qquad\qquad\qquad\qquad\qquad\qquad\qquad\qquad$ (6.142)

$$\frac{\partial^2 w}{\partial x^2} + \frac{\partial^2 w}{\partial y^2} + \frac{\partial^2 w}{\partial z^2} = \nabla^2 w \qquad \text{three dimensions}$$

Our aim is now to find a solution satisfying the Laplace equation. If we assume that a concentrated charge is acting at a point 'i', the governing equation is

$$\nabla^2 w + \Delta_i = 0 \qquad\qquad (6.143)$$

where Δ_i is a Dirac delta function. The solution of this equation is called the fundamental solution. As we have already seen this function has the property that

$$\int_\Omega \varphi(\nabla^2 w + \Delta_i)\, d\Omega = \int_\Omega \varphi \nabla^2 w\, d\Omega + \varphi_i \qquad\qquad (6.144)$$

where φ^i represents the value of the unknown function φ at the point of application of the charge. If equation (6.143) is satisfied by the fundamental solution,

$$\int_\Omega \varphi(\nabla^2 w)\, d\Omega = -\varphi_i \qquad\qquad (6.145)$$

then equation (6.143) becomes,

$$\varphi_i + \int_{\Gamma_2} \varphi \frac{\partial w}{\partial n}\, d\Gamma + \int_{\Gamma_1} \bar{\varphi} \frac{\partial w}{\partial n}\, d\Gamma = \int_{\Gamma_2} \bar{q}\varphi\, d\Gamma + \int_{\Gamma_1} qw\, d\Gamma \qquad (6.146)$$

where $q = \partial \varphi / \partial n$.

For an isotropic three-dimensional medium the fundamental solution of equation (6.140) is

$$w = 1/4\pi r \qquad\qquad (6.147)$$

where r is the distance from the point of application of the unit potential to the point under consideration. Writing the three-dimensional Laplace equation (6.143) in polar coordinates and taking symmetry into consideration we have

$$\frac{\partial^2 w}{\partial r^2} + \frac{2}{r} \frac{\partial w}{\partial r} = \Delta_i \qquad\qquad (6.148)$$

Substituting equation (6.147) into (6.148) we see that the equation is satisfied for any value of r different from zero. To study the case of $r \equiv 0$ we have to carry out the following integration, in a sphere surrounding the point where the load is applied:

$$\int_{\Omega} \nabla^2 w \, d\Omega = - \int_{\Omega} \Delta_i \, d\Omega = -1 \tag{6.149}$$

We can easily prove that the left-hand side of equation (6.149) is also equal to minus one by writing the following expression:

$$\int_{\Omega} \nabla^2 w \, d\Omega = \int_{\Gamma} \frac{\partial w}{\partial n} \, d\Gamma = \int_{\Gamma} \frac{\partial w}{\partial r} \, d\Gamma \tag{6.150}$$

Substituting the fundamental solution (6.147) into (6.150) we obtain,

$$\int_{\Gamma} \frac{\partial w}{\partial r} \, d\Gamma = \frac{1}{4\pi} \int_{\Gamma} \left(-\frac{1}{r^2} \right) d\Gamma = -\frac{1}{4\pi} \left(\frac{4\pi r^2}{r^2} \right) = -1 \tag{6.151}$$

The result in equation (6.151) is independent of r and shows that when $r \to 0$ the left-hand side of equation (6.149) is also equal to -1.

For two dimensions the fundamental solution for the isotropic case is

$$w = \frac{1}{2\pi} \ln \left(\frac{1}{r} \right) \tag{6.152}$$

and similar considerations apply.

Equation (6.146) is valid for any point in the domain, but in order to formulate the problem as a boundary technique we need to take it to the boundary. This will now be done in a simple way. Consider the hemisphere on the boundary of a three-dimensional domain as depicted in Figure 6.29. (The two-dimensional case can also be analysed in the same way.) The boundary point is assumed to be at the centre of the sphere and afterwards the radius 'ε' is reduced to zero. The point will then become a boundary point. The boundary is assumed to be smooth and the point to be on Γ_2 but similar considerations apply if the point is on Γ_1.

To analyse what is happening consider that the Γ_2 boundary is divided into two parts, i.e.

$$\int_{\Gamma_2} \varphi \frac{\partial w}{\partial n} \, d\Gamma = \int_{\Gamma_{2-\varepsilon}} \varphi \frac{\partial w}{\partial n} \, d\Gamma + \int_{\Gamma_\varepsilon} \varphi \frac{\partial w}{\partial n} \, d\Gamma \tag{6.153}$$

We can now substitute the fundamental solution into the second integral on

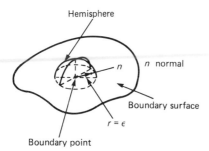

Figure 6.29 Boundary surface assumed to be hemispherical for integration purposes

the right-hand side of equation (6.153) and take it to the limit, i.e. $\varepsilon \to 0$. This gives,

$$\lim_{\varepsilon \to 0}\left(\int_{\Gamma_\varepsilon} \varphi \frac{\partial w}{\partial n}\,d\Gamma\right)=\lim_{\varepsilon \to 0}\left(-\int_{\Gamma_\varepsilon} \varphi \frac{1}{4\pi\varepsilon^2}\,d\Gamma\right)$$

$$=\lim_{\varepsilon \to 0}\left(-\tfrac{1}{2}\varphi\right)=-\tfrac{1}{2}\varphi \qquad\qquad (6.154)$$

Note that as ε is now zero the boundary $\Gamma_{2-\varepsilon}$ again becomes Γ_2. The same result, i.e. $-\tfrac{1}{2}\varphi$, is obtained in two-dimensional problems for a smooth boundary. The subdivision can also be introduced for the right-hand side terms of equation (6.146), i.e.

$$\int qw\,d\Gamma$$

but for this case

$$\lim_{\varepsilon \to 0}\left(\int_{\Gamma_\varepsilon} q\frac{1}{4\pi\varepsilon}\,d\Gamma\right)=0 \qquad\qquad (6.155)$$

and hence this limit does not introduce any new term in equation (6.153). Substituting equation (6.154) into equation (6.146) one has the following equation for a point on the boundary:

$$\tfrac{1}{2}\varphi^i + \int_{\Gamma_2} \varphi \frac{\partial w}{\partial n}\,d\Gamma + \int_{\Gamma_1} \bar\varphi \frac{\partial w}{\partial n}\,d\Gamma = \int_{\Gamma_2} \bar q w\,d\Gamma + \int_{\Gamma_1} qw\,d\Gamma \qquad (6.156)$$

The same result would be obtained if instead of a point on Γ_2 we consider a point on the Γ_1 part of the boundary.

In general equation (6.156) can be written as,

$$\tfrac{1}{2}\varphi^i + \int_{\Gamma} \varphi \frac{\partial w}{\partial n}\,d\Gamma = \int_{\Gamma} qw\,d\Gamma \qquad\qquad (6.157)$$

where $\Gamma=\Gamma_1+\Gamma_2$ and one assumes that $\varphi=\bar\varphi$ on Γ_1 and $\partial\varphi/\partial n=q=\bar q$ on Γ_2.

Equation (6.157) can now be applied on the boundary of the domain under consideration. For simplicity, this will be done for the two-dimensional case only, as suggested in Figure 6.30, where the boundary is divided into n straight segments or boundary elements. The nodal points, where the relevant problem unknowns are considered, will be taken, again for simplicity, in the middle of each segment. This, however, is not the only way to proceed. For instance, nodal points could be taken at the segment intersections, and the segments could be curved, at the cost of some additional complexity in the formulation.

The boundary is discretised into n elements, of which n_1 belong to Γ_1 and n_2

Mid-node

Figure 6.30 Boundary element discretisation

to Γ_2. The values of φ and q are assumed to be constant on each element and equal to the value at the mid-node of the element. Equation (6.157) for a given 'i' point becomes, in discretised form,

$$\tfrac{1}{2}\varphi_i + \sum_{j=1}^{n} \varphi_j \int_{\Gamma_j} \frac{\partial w}{\partial n}\, \mathrm{d}\Gamma = \sum_{j=1}^{n} q_j \int_{\Gamma_j} w\, \mathrm{d}\Gamma \qquad (6.158)$$

This equation applies for a particular node 'i'. The terms

$$\int_{\Gamma_j} \frac{\partial w}{\partial n}\, \mathrm{d}\Gamma$$

relate the 'i' node with the segment 'j' over which the integral is carried out. We shall call these integrals $\hat{H}_{ij}$. The integrals on the right-hand side will be called G_{ij}. Hence we have

$$\tfrac{1}{2}\varphi_i + \sum_{j=1}^{n} \varphi_j \hat{H}_{ij} = \sum_{j=1}^{n} q_j G_{ij} \qquad (6.159)$$

The above integrals are easy to calculate analytically for the constant element case but for higher-order elements they become more difficult to evaluate. For generality the integrals were calculated numerically for all segments except the one corresponding to the node under consideration.

Equation (6.159) relates the value of φ at mid-node 'i' with the value of φ and q at all the boundary elements, including 'i'.

One can write equation (6.159) for each 'i' node, obtaining n equations. Let us now call

$$H_{ij} = \begin{cases} \hat{H}_{ij} & \text{when } i \neq j \\ \hat{H}_{ij} + \tfrac{1}{2} & \text{when } i = j \end{cases} \qquad (6.160)$$

Equation (6.159) can then be written as:

$$\sum_{j=1}^{n} H_{ij}\varphi_j = \sum_{j=1}^{n} G_{ij}q_j \qquad (6.161)$$

The whole set of equations for the n nodes can now be expressed in matrix form as:

$$\mathbf{H}\varphi = \mathbf{G}\mathbf{Q} \qquad (6.162)$$

Note that n_1 values of φ and n_2 values of q are known, hence one has a set of n unknowns in formula (6.162). Reordering the equations in such a way that all the unknowns are on the left-hand side, one can write:

$$\mathbf{A}\mathbf{X} = \mathbf{F} \qquad (6.163)$$

where $\mathbf{X}$ is the vector of unknowns φ and q.

Once the values of φ and q on the whole boundary are known we can calculate the value of φ at any interior point using equation (6.146), which, after discretisation becomes:

$$\varphi^i = \sum_{j=1}^{n} q_j G_{ij} - \sum_{j=1}^{n} \varphi_j \hat{H}_{ij} \qquad (6.164)$$

The internal fluxes q_x $(q_x = \partial\varphi/\partial x)$ or q_y $(q_y = \partial\varphi/\partial y)$ can be calculated by differentiating equation (6.146), i.e.

$$(q_x)_i = \int_\Gamma q \frac{\partial w}{\partial x} \, d\Gamma - \int_\Gamma \varphi \frac{\partial}{\partial x} \left(\frac{\partial w}{\partial n} \right) d\Gamma$$

$$(q_y)_i = \int_\Gamma q \frac{\partial w}{\partial y} \, d\Gamma - \int_\Gamma \varphi \frac{\partial}{\partial x} \left(\frac{\partial w}{\partial n} \right) d\Gamma$$

(6.165)

6.11 Boundary element program for the solution of the Laplace equation

A program similar to the one presented in Section 6.9 will be developed, but following the boundary element formulation, using the simple boundary element type just discussed. Whenever possible the same nomenclature, as in the previous program, will be used, to facilitate understanding.

6.11.1 Data structure

The general integer variables used by the program have the following meanings:

NN   Number of internal points.
NE   Number of boundary elements.

The meaning of the arrays is as follows:

X   One-dimensional array having the x coordinates of the extreme points of the boundary elements.
Y   One-dimensional array of y coordinates of the extreme points of boundary elements.
XM x coordinates of the nodes. XM(I) contains the x coordinate of node I.
YM y coordinate of the nodes. YM(I) contains the y coordinate of node I.
G   Matrix defined in equation (6.162). After application of boundary conditions the matrix **A** is stored in the same location.
H   Matrix defined in equation (6.162).
FI   Prescribed value of boundary conditions. FI(I) contains the prescribed value of the condition at node I.
DFI   Right-hand side vector in equation (6.163). After solution it contains the values of the unknowns φ and q.
IB   One-dimensional integer array of boundary condition data. KODE(I)=0 indicates that the value of the potential is known for node I. KODE(I)=1 indicates that the value of q is known, at boundary node I. The actual values of the prescribed potential and flux are stored in array FI, defined above.
CX x coordinate for internal point where the value of u is required.
CY y coordinate for internal point where the value of u is required.
SOL   Vector of the potential values for internal points.
H   Array containing the matrix **H**, defined in equation (6.162).

Program 24: Main program

After specifying the array dimensions, the basic program parameters are initialised. The program, as presented, allows solution of problems having up to 40 nodes. For computers having enough memory the dimensions can be increased. This modification is only required in the main program, but not in the subroutines, as variable dimensions are used.

The numerical implementation of the boundary element solution is applied as a sequence of subroutine calls.

The subroutine INPUT reads the program input. Subroutine ASBOU forms matrices **H** and **G**, and rearranges them according to the boundary conditions, to form the matrix **A**, defined in equation (6.163). The solution of the system of equations is performed by subroutine SLNPDS. Subroutine RESUL computes the values of the potential at the selected internal points, after reordering the unknown vector. Finally, subroutine OUTPT prints the program output. The listing of the program is the following:

```
C********************************************************************
C
C                         PROGRAM 24
C
C PROGRAM FOR SOLUTION OF TWO DIMENSIONAL POTENTIAL PROBLEMS
C BY THE BOUNDARY ELEMENT METHOD WITH CONSTANT ELEMENTS
C
      COMMON NN, NE, IN, IO
      DIMENSION  X(41),Y(41),XM(40),YM(40),G(40,40),FI(40),DFI(40)
      DIMENSION IB(40),CX(40),CY(40),SOL(40),H(40,40)
C
C INITIALIZATION OF PROGRAM PARAMETERS
C
      NRMX=40
      IN=5
      IO=6
C
C INPUT
C
      CALL INPUT(CX,CY,X,Y,IB,FI)
C
C ASSEMBLE SYSTEM OF EQUATIONS
C
      CALL ASBOU(X,Y,XM,YM,G,H,FI,DFI,IB,NRMX)
C
C SOLUTION OF THE SYSTEM OF EQUATIONS
C
      CALL SLNPD(G,DFI,D,NE,NRMX)
C
C COMPUTE THE POTENTIAL VALUES IN INTERNAL POINTS
C
      CALL RESUL(FI,DFI,IB,CX,CY,X,Y,SOL)
C
C OUTPUT
C
      CALL    OUTPT(XM,YM,FI,DFI,CX,CY,SOL)
C
      CALL EXIT
      END
C
C
```

Program 25: Input program (INPUT)

This subroutine performs all the input required by the program, with the following format:

(1)   *Title card.* One card containing the title of the problem.

(2) *Basic parameters card*. One card containing the number of internal points (NN), and the number of boundary elements (NE). Format (2I5).
(3) *Internal points coordinates cards*. As many cards as internal nodes are required each with the *xy* nodal coordinates. Format (2F10.4).
(4) *Extreme points of boundary elements cards*. Each card defines the coordinates of the extreme of an element, read in counterclockwise direction. Format (2F10.4).
(5) *Boundary condition cards*. As many cards as nodes giving the values of the potential at the node if IB(I) = 0 or the value of the potential derivative if IB(I) = 1 and the corresponding value of φ or q. Format (IS, F10.4).

The listing of this program, which is self-explanatory, is the following:

```
      SUBROUTINE INPUT(CX,CY,X,Y,IB,FI)
C
C                 PROGRAM 25
C         PROGRAM FOR DATA INPUT
C
      COMMON NN,NE,IN,IO
      DIMENSION CX(1),CY(1),X(1),Y(1),IB(1),FI(1),TITLE(18)
C
C N = NUMBER OF BOUNDARY ELEMENTS
C L = NUMBER OF INTERNAL POINTS WHERE THE FUNCTION IS
C     CALCULATED
C
      WRITE(IO,100)
C   READ NAME OF THE PROBLEM
C
  100 FORMAT(' ',120('*'))
      READ(IN,150)TITLE
C
  150 FORMAT(18A4)
      WRITE(IO,250)TITLE
  250 FORMAT(25X,18A4)
C
C   READ BASIC PARAMETERS
C
      READ(IN,200)NE,NN
  200 FORMAT(2I5)
      WRITE(IO,300)NE,NN
  300 FORMAT(//' DATA'//2X,'NUMBER OF BOUNDARY ELEMENTS=',
     1I3/2X,'NUMBER OF INTERNAL POINTS WHERE THE FUNCTION IS
     2CALCULATED=',I3)
C
C   READ INTERNAL POINTS COORDINATES
C
      DO 1 I=1,NN
    1 READ(IN,400)CX(I),CY(I)
  400 FORMAT(2F10.4)
C
C   READ COORDINATES OF EXTREME POINTS OF THE BOUNDARY
C   ELEMENTS IN ARRAY X AND Y
C
      WRITE(IO,500)
  500 FORMAT(//2X,'COORDINATES OF THE EXTREME POINTS OF THE
     1BOUNDARY ELEMENTS',//4X,'POINT',10X,'X',18X,'Y')
      DO 10 I=1,NE
      READ(IN,600)X(I),Y(I)
  600 FORMAT(2F10.4)
   10 WRITE(IO,700)I,X(I),Y(I)
  700 FORMAT(5X,I3,2(5X,E14.7))
C
C   READ BOUNDARY CONDITIONS
C   FI(I)= VALUE OF THE POTENTIAL IN THE NODE I IF IB(I)=0,
C   VALUE OF THE POTENTIAL DERIVATIVE IF IB(I)=1.
C
      WRITE(IO,800)
  800 FORMAT(//2X,'BOUNDARY CONDITIONS'//5X,'NODE',6X,'CODE',
```

```
            15X, 'PRESCRIBED VALUE')
            DO 20 I=1,NE
            READ(IN,900) IB (I),FI(I)
        900 FORMAT(I5,F10. 4)
        20 WRITE(IO,950) I,IB(I),FI(I)
        950 FORMAT (5X,I3,7X,I2,8X,E14. 7)
            RETURN
            END
C
C
```

Program 26: Assembling of the total system of equations and introduction of the boundary conditions (ASBOU)

The objective of this subroutine is to assemble the total system of equations defined by equation (6.162).

The first step is to compute the coordinates of the nodal points, from the boundary element extreme point coordinates, storing them in arrays XM, YM.

Two subroutines, OFFDGT and DIAGT, are called in sequence. The first one computes the off-diagonal terms of matrices **H** and **G**, while subroutine DIAGT computes the corresponding diagonal terms.

In the two final steps the system of equations is rearranged for solution, and the boundary conditions are introduced.

The listing of the subroutine is the following:

```
C
C
        SUBROUTINE ASBOU(X,Y,XM,YM,G,H,FI,DFI,IB,NRMX)
C
C                   PROGRAM 26
C   COMPUTATION OF THE G AND H MATRICES AND ASSEMBLING
C       OF THE TOTAL SYSTEM AX=F
C
        COMMON NN,NE,IN,IO
        DIMENSION X(1),Y(1),XM(1),YM(1),G(NRMX,NRMX),H(NRMX,NRMX),
       *FI(1),IB(1),DFI(1)
C
C COMPUTE THE MID-POINT COORDINATES AND STORE IN ARRAY XM AND YM
C
        X(NE+1)=X(1)
        Y(NE+1)=Y(1)
        DO 10 I=1,NE
        XM(I)=(X(I)+X(I+1))/2
     10 YM(I)=(Y(I)+Y(I+1))/2
C
C COMPUTE G AND H MATRICES
C
        DO 30 I=1,NE
        DO 30 J=1,NE
        IF(I-J)20,25,20
     20 CALL OFFDGT(XM(I),YM(I),X(J),Y(J),X(J+1),Y(J+1),H(I,J),G(I,J))
        GO TO 30
     25 CALL DIAGT(X(J),Y(J),X(J+1),Y(J+1),G(I,J))
        H(I,J)=3. 1415926
     30 CONTINUE
C
C ARRANGE THE SYSTEM OF EQUATIONS READY TO BE SOLVED
        DO 50 J=1,NE
        IF(IB(J))50,50,40
C
     40 DO 50 I=1,NE
        CH=G(I,J)
        G(I,J)=-H(I,J)
        H(I,J)=-CH
     50 CONTINUE
```

```
C
C DFI ORIGINALLY CONTAINS THE INDEPENDENT COEFFICIENTS
C AFTER SOLUTION IT WILL CONTAIN THE VALUES OF THE SYSTEM UNKNOWNS
C
      DO 60 I=1,NE
      DFI(I)=0.
      DO 60 J=1,NE
      DFI(I)=DFI(I)+H(I,J)*FI(J)
   60 CONTINUE
      RETURN
      END
C
C
```

Program 27: Computation of the off-diagonal terms of the H and G matrices (OFFDGT)

This program computes the off-diagonal terms of matrices **H** and **G**, using a four-point Gauss integration formula. The listing of the program is the following:

```
      SUBROUTINE OFFDGT(XP,YP,X1,Y1,X2,Y2,H,G)
C
C                  PROGRAM 27
C THIS SUBROUTINE COMPUTES THE VALUES OF THE H AND G MATRIX
C OFF DIAGONAL ELEMENTS BY MEANS OF NUMERICAL INTEGRATION
C ALONG THE BOUNDARY ELEMENTS
C
C DIST = DISTANCE FROM THE POINT UNDER CONSIDERATION TO THE
C BOUNDARY ELEMENTS
C RA = DISTANCE FROM THE POINT UNDER CONSIDERATION TO THE
C INTEGRATION POINTS IN THE BOUNDARY ELEMENTS
C
      DIMENSION XCO(4),YCO(4),GI(4),OME(4)
      GI(1)=0.86113631
      GI(2)=-GI(1)
      GI(3)=0.33998104
      GI(4)=-GI(3)
      OME(1)=0.34785485
      OME(2)=OME(1)
      OME(3)=0.65214515
      OME(4)=OME(3)
      AX=(X2-X1)/2
      BX=(X2+X1)/2
      AY=(Y2-Y1)/2
      BY=(Y2+Y1)/2
      IF(AX)10,20,10
   10 TA=AY/AX
      DIST=ABS((TA*XP-YP+Y1-TA*X1)/SGRT(TA**2+1))
      GO TO 30
   20 DIST=ABS(XP-X1)
   30 SIG=(X1-XP)*(Y2-YP)-(X2-XP)*(Y1-YP)
      IF(SIG)31,32,32
   31 DIST=-DIST
   32 G=0.
      H=0.
      DO 40 I=1,4
      XCO(I)=AX*GI(I)+BX
      YCO(I)=AY*GI(I)+BY
      RA=SQRT(((XP-XCO(I))**2+(YP-YCO(I))**2)
      G=G+ALOG(1/RA)*OME(I)*SQRT(AX**2+AY**2)
   40 H=H-(DIST*OME(I)*SQRT(AX**2+AY**2)/RA**2)
      RETURN
      END
```

Program 28: Computation of the diagonal terms of matrix H (DIAGT)

This subroutine computes the diagonal terms of matrix **H**, according to the listing given below:

```
C
C
      SUBROUTINE DIAGT(X1,Y1,X2,Y2,G)
C
C               PROGRAM 28
C THIS SUBROUTINE COMPUTES THE VALUES OF THE DIAGONAL
C ELEMENTS OF THE G MATRIX
C
      AX=(X2-X1)/2
      AY=(Y2-Y1)/2
      SR=SQRT(AX**2+AY**2)
      G=2*SR*(ALOG(1/SR)+1)
      RETURN
      END
C
C
```

Program 29: Solution of the system of equations: Non-positive definite case (SLNPD)

The solution of the full system of equations is performed using a standard subroutine for this purpose, which allows for row interchange. The following listing of the subroutine, which allows for row interchanges when zero diagonal coefficients are detected, includes several comment lines, indicating the meaning of the arguments.

```
      SUBROUTINE SLNPD(A,B,D,N,NX)
C
C               PROGRAM 29
C
C SOLUTION OF LINEAR SYSTEMS OF EQUATIONS
C BY THE GAUSS ELIMINATION METHOD PROVIDING
C FOR INTERCHANGING ROWS WHEN ENCOUNTERING A
C ZERO DIAGONAL COEFFICIENT
C
C A SYSTEM MATRIX
C B ORIGINALLY IT CONTAINS THE INDEPENDENT
C   COEFFICIENTS. AFTER SOLUTION IT CONTAINS THE
C   VALUES OF THE SYSTEM UNKNOWNS.
C
C N ACTUAL NUMBER OF UNKNOWNS
C NX ROW AND COLUMN DIMENSION OF A
C
      DIMENSION A(NX,NX),B(NX)
      N1=N-1
      DO 100 K=1,N1
      K1=K+1
      C=A(K,K)
      IF(ABS(C)-0.000001)1,1,3
    1 DO 7 J=K1,N
C
C TRY TO INTERCHANGE ROWS TO GET NON ZERO DIAGONAL COEFFICIENT
C
      IF(ABS(A(J,K))-0.000001)7,7,5
    5 DO 6 L=K,N
      C=A(K,L)
      A(K,L)=A(J,L)
    6 A(J,L)=C
      C=B(K)
      B(K)=B(J)
      B(J)=C
      C=A(K,K)
      GO TO 3
    7 CONTINUE
    8 WRITE(6,2)K
    2 FORMAT('****SINGULARITY IN ROW',I5)
      D=0.
      GO TO 300
```

```
C
C DIVIDE ROW BY DIAGONAL COEFFICIENT
C
    3 C=A(K, K)
      DO 4 J=K1, N
    4 A(K, J)=A(K, J)/C
      B(K)=B(K)/C
C
C ELIMINATE UNKNOWN X(K) FROM ROW I
C
      DO 10 I=K1, N
      C=A(I, K)
      DO 9 J=K1, N
    9 A(I, J)=A(I, J)-C*A(K, J)
   10 B(I)=B(I)-C*B(K)
  100 CONTINUE
C
C COMPUTE LAST UNKNOWN
C
      IF(ABS(A(N, N))-0. 000001)8, 8, 101
  101 B(N)=B(N)/A(N, N)
C
C APPLY BACKSUBSTITUTION PROCESS TO COMPUTE REMAINING UNKNOWNS
C
      DO 200 L=1, N1
      K=N-L
      K1=K+1
      DO 200 J=K1, N
  200 B(K)=B(K)-A(K, J)*B(J)
C
C COMPUTE VALUE OF DETERMINANT
C
      D=1.
      DO 250 I=1, N
  250 D=D*A(I, I)
  300 RETURN
      END
```

Program 30: Computation of internal results (RESUL)

This subroutine first reorders the array FI, containing the boundary condition vector, and array DFI, originally containing the unknown vector, and after solution the results at the nodal points, in such a way that all values of the potential are stored in array FI, and all values of the derivatives are stored in array DFI. It then computes the values of the potential at the internal points. The listing of the subroutine RESUL is the following:

```
      SUBROUTINE RESUL(FI, DFI, IB, CX, CY, X, Y, SOL)
C
C                  PROGRAM 30
C
C THIS SUBROUTINE COMPUTES THE POTENTIAL VALUE FOR INTERNAL
C POINTS.
      COMMON NN, NE, IN, IO
      DIMENSION FI(1), DFI(1), IB(1), CX(1), CY(1), X(1), Y(1), SOL(1)
C
C REORDER FI AND DFI ARRAY TO PUT ALL THE VALUES OF THE POTENTIAL
C IN FI AND ALL THE VALUES OF THE DERIVATIVE IN DFI
C
      DO 20 I=1, NE
      IF (IB(I))20, 20, 10
   10 CH=FI(I)
      FI(I)=DFI(I)
      DFI(I)=CH
   20 CONTINUE
C
C COMPUTE THE POTENTIAL VALUES FOR INTERNAL POINTS
```

```
C
      DO 40 K=1, NN
      SOL (K)=0.
      DO 30 J=1, NE
      CALL OFFDGT(CX(K), CY(K), X(J), Y(J), X(J+1), Y(J+1), A, B)
  30  SOL(K)=SOL(K)+DFI(J)*B-FI(J)*A
  40  SOL(K)=SOL(K)/(2*3.1415926)
      RETURN
      END
C
C
```

Program 31: Output of the results (OUTPT)

The results of the program are printed out by subroutine OUTPT. This subroutine first performs a loop on the boundary nodes, printing the coordinates, the value of the problem function, and the value of its derivative, for each node. It then loops on the internal nodes and for each of them prints the coordinates and the value of the function. The corresponding listing is the following:

```
      SUBROUTINE OUTPT(XM, YM, FI, DFI, CX, CY, SOL)
C
C            PROGRAM 31
C        OUTPUT OF THE RESULTS
      COMMON NN, NE, IN, IO
      DIMENSION XM(1), YM(1), FI(1), DFI(1), CX(1), CY(1), SOL(1)
      WRITE(IO, 100)
 100  FORMAT (' ', 120('*')//1X, 'RESULTS'//2X, 'BOUNDARY NODES'//16X,
     1'X', 23X, 'Y', 19X, 'POTENTIAL', 10X, 'POTENTIAL DERIVATIVE'/)
      DO 10 I=1, NE
  10  WRITE (IO, 200)XM(I), YM(I), FI(I), DFI(I)
 200  FORMAT (4(10X, E14.7))
      WRITE (IO, 300)
 300  FORMAT(//, 2X, 'INTERNAL POINTS',//11X, 'X', 18X, 'Y', 14X,
     1'POTENTIAL',/)
      DO 20 K=1, NN
  20  WRITE(IO, 400)CX(K), CY(K), SOL(K)
 400  FORMAT (3(5X, E14.7))
      WRITE (IO, 500)
 500  FORMAT (' ', 120('*'))
      RETURN
      END
```

Example 6.5
The problem presented in Example 6.3 will now be analysed using the boundary element method. The mesh used, compatible with the finite element mesh of Example 6.3, is shown in Figure 6.31. The input listing and the results obtained are included below:

```
INPUT
FLOW AROUND A CORNER
   24      6
    0.25        0.25
    0.5         0.5
    0.75        0.75
    1.25        1.25
    1.75        1.75
    2.3         2.3
   -5.          0.
   -3.          0.
   -1.8         0.
   -0.8         0.
    0.          0.
    0.         -0.8
```

```
 0.        -1.8
 0.        -3.
 0.        -5.
 1.        -5.
 2.        -5.
 3.        -5.
 4.        -5.
 4.        -2.5
 4.        -0.8
 4.         1.5
 4.         4.
 1.5        4.
-0.8        4.
-2.5        4.
-5.         4.
-5.         3.
-5.         2.
-5.         1.
 0    0.
 0    0.
 0    0.
 0    0.
 0    0.
 0    0.
 0    0.
 0    0.
 1
 1
 1
 1
 0    4.
 0    4.
 0    4.
 0    4.
 0    4.
 0    4.
 0    4.
 0    4.
 0    3.5
 0    2.5
 0    1.5
 0    0.5
 OUTPUT
```

```
*****************************************************************
                    FLOW  AROUND  A  CORNER
```

DATA

NUMBER OF BOUNDARY ELEMENTS= 24
NUMBER OF INTERNAL POINTS WHERE THE FUNCTION IS CALCULATED=   6

COORDINATES OF THE EXTREME POINTS OF THE BOUNDARY ELEMENTS

POINT	X	Y
1	-0.5000000E+01	0.0000000E+00
2	-0.3000000E+01	0.0000000E+00
3	-0.1800000E+01	0.0000000E+00
4	-0.8000000E+00	0.0000000E+00
5	0.0000000E+00	0.0000000E+00
6	0.0000000E+00	-0.8000000E+00
7	0.0000000E+00	-0.1800000E+01
8	0.0000000E+00	-0.3000000E+01
9	0.0000000E+00	-0.5000000E+01
10	0.1000000E+01	-0.5000000E+01
11	0.2000000E+01	-0.5000000E+01
12	0.3000000E+01	-0.5000000E+01
13	0.4000000E+01	-0.5000000E+01
14	0.4000000E+01	-0.2500000E+01
15	0.4000000E+01	-0.8000000E+00

```
16        0.4000000E+01        0.1500000E+01
17        0.4000000E+01        0.4000000E+01
18        0.1500000E+01        0.4000000E+01
19       -0.8000000E+00        0.4000000E+01
20       -0.2500000E+01        0.4000000E+01
21       -0.5000000E+01        0.4000000E+01
22       -0.5000000E+01        0.3000000E+01
23       -0.5000000E+01        0.2000000E+01
24       -0.5000000E+01        0.1000000E+01
```

BOUNDARY CONDITIONS

NODE	CODE	PRESCRIBED VALUE
1	0	0.0000000E+00
2	0	0.0000000E+00
3	0	0.0000000E+00
4	0	0.0000000E+00
5	0	0.0000000E+00
6	0	0.0000000E+00
7	0	0.0000000E+00
8	0	0.0000000E+00
9	1	0.0000000E+00
10	1	0.0000000E+00
11	1	0.0000000E+00
12	1	0.0000000E+00
13	0	0.4000000E+01
14	0	0.4000000E+01
15	0	0.4000000E+01
16	0	0.4000000E+01
17	0	0.4000000E+01
18	0	0.4000000E+01
19	0	0.4000000E+01
20	0	0.4000000E+01
21	0	0.3500000E+01
22	0	0.2500000E+01
23	0	0.1500000E+01
24	0	0.5000000E+00

***1

RESULTS

BOUNDARY NODES

X	Y	POTENTIAL	POTENTIAL DERIVATIVE
-0.4000000E+01	0.0000000E+00	0.0000000E+00	-0.1037593E+01
-0.2400000E+01	0.0000000E+00	0.0000000E+00	-0.1066041E+01
-0.1300000E+01	0.0000000E+00	0.0000000E+00	-0.1180589E+01
-0.4000000E+00	0.0000000E+00	0.0000000E+00	-0.1970099E+01
0.0000000E+00	-0.4000000E+00	0.0000000E+00	-0.1970401E+01
0.0000000E+00	-0.1300000E+01	0.0000000E+00	-0.1181272E+01
0.0000000E+00	-0.2400000E+01	0.0000000E+00	-0.1068007E+01
0.0000000E+00	-0.4000000E+01	0.0000000E+00	-0.1037986E+01
0.5000000E+00	-0.5000000E+01	0.4943445E+00	0.0000000E+00
0.1500000E+01	-0.5000000E+01	0.1513807E+01	0.0000000E+00
0.2500000E+01	-0.5000000E+01	0.2519698E+01	0.0000000E+00
0.3500000E+01	-0.5000000E+01	0.3529423E+01	0.0000000E+00
0.4000000E+01	-0.3750000E+01	0.4000000E+01	0.9846837E+00
0.4000000E+01	-0.1650000E+01	0.4000000E+01	0.9066683E+00
0.4000000E+01	0.3500000E+00	0.4000000E+01	0.6876949E+00
0.4000000E+01	0.2750000E+01	0.4000000E+01	0.2104455E+00
0.2750000E+01	0.4000000E+01	0.4000000E+01	0.2104695E+00
0.3500000E+00	0.4000000E+01	0.4000000E+01	0.6879585E+00
-0.1650000E+01	0.4000000E+01	0.4000000E+01	0.9065224E+00
-0.3750000E+01	0.4000000E+01	0.4000000E+01	0.9996083E+00
-0.5000000E+01	0.3500000E+01	0.3500000E+01	-0.3840605E-01
-0.5000000E+01	0.2500000E+01	0.2500000E+01	-0.7807081E-02
-0.5000000E+01	0.1500000E+01	0.1500000E+01	-0.1323907E-01
-0.5000000E+01	0.5000000E+00	0.5000000E+00	0.1666080E-01

INTERNAL POINTS

X	Y	POTENTIAL
0.2500000E+00	0.2500000E+00	0.9533993E+00
0.5000000E+00	0.5000000E+00	0.1437491E+01
0.7500000E+00	0.7500000E+00	0.1839047E+01
0.1250000E+01	0.1250000E+01	0.2491796E+01
0.1750000E+01	0.1750000E+01	0.3002077E+01
0.2300000E+01	0.2300000E+01	0.3432488E+01

****

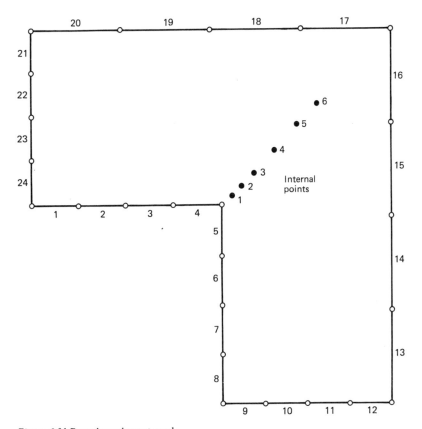

Figure 6.31 Boundary element mesh

Figure 6.32 shows the streamline results for boundary elements versus finite elements along the diagonal. The boundary element results are higher near the corner, due to the possibility of representing better rapid variations in the stream function using boundary elements. Because of this boundary elements are used in many problems presenting singularities.

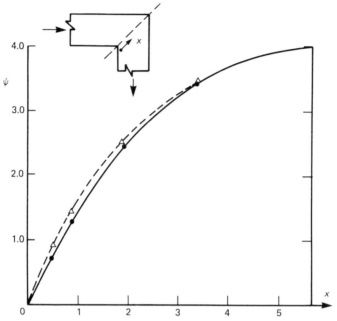

Figure 6.32 Results for the stream function along the diagonal: —△—, boundary elements; ●, finite elements

Bibliography

BREBBIA, C.A. *The Boundary Element Method for Engineers*, 2nd edn, Pentech Press, London, Halsted Press, New York (1980)
BREBBIA, C.A. and FERRANTE, A. *Computational Methods for the Solution of Engineering Problems*, 2nd edn, Pentech Press, London, Crane and Russak, New York (1980)
MASSEY, B.S. *Mechanics of Fluids*, 2nd edn, Van Nostrand Reinhold, London (1970)

Exercises

6.1 Consider an incompressible, steady flow with a stream function $\psi = x^2 + y^2$. Determine if the velocity potential for this flow exists.

6.2 Plot the streamlines corresponding to the velocity potentials: (a) $\varphi = -xy$; and (b) $\varphi = -x^3 + 3xy^2$.

6.3 Consider a two-dimensional source of strength $q = 2\pi\mu$ per unit length and a sink of the same strength, both separated by a distance $2l$. Prove that the streamlines are all circles passing through the source and sink.

6.4 Assume there is a flow around a rectangular corner as shown in Figure 6.33. This flow is represented by the following potential:

$$\varphi = -Ar^2 \cos(2\theta)$$

Now assume that a source is located at the corner with a strength of q per unit depth. Sketch the resulting streamlines and the line dividing the two flows. How strong does the source q need to be to have a divisor streamline at a distance l from the corner where the source is applied?

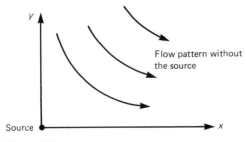

Figure 6.33

6.5 Consider that a source of strength q per unit length is located at a distance l from two rectangular walls as shown in Figure 6.34. Applying the method of images find the source distribution which will make the corner a streamline. Then find the velocities and pressure along the walls assuming that the pressure at infinity is known.

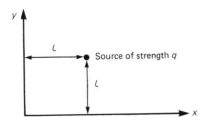

Figure 6.34

6.6 Consider a sink of strength $-q$ per unit length at the origin and that the incompressible, irrotational fluid is parallel to the wall with pressure p_∞ and velocity V, at infinity (Figure 6.35). Find and sketch the values of pressure along the wall.

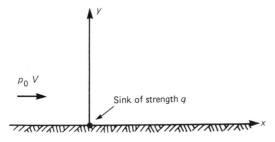

Figure 6.35

Chapter 7

Navier–Stokes equations

7.1 Introduction

In some previous chapters we have considered that the fluids under study were inviscid or frictionless. Real fluids, however, possess viscosity which produces shear stresses in the moving fluid leading to losses of energy. In this chapter we will consider the case of laminar flow, and then turbulent flows for real fluids.

The equations of motion of real fluids are called Navier–Stokes equations and can easily be deduced from considerations of equilibrium for a differential element of volume. Their solution, however, is more difficult, and can only be obtained analytically for a few special cases. Considerable effort is currently being put into devising numerical solutions using computers.

Viscosity has two important effects on bodies in a fluid. Depending on the shape of the body it can produce wakes behind the obstruction resulting in a *pressure drag*. This drag is sometimes called 'form drag'. The other component of drag, produced by the skin friction, is due to the resistance offered by the viscous forces. Hence, form drag predominates at high Reynolds numbers, and viscous drag is important at low Reynolds numbers.

The formation of a wake behind an obstruction is due to the separation of the boundary layer. This produces turbulence and, consequently, reduction in the pressure behind the obstruction, which increases the pressure drag. If the shape of the body is such that separation tends to move downstream, the wake is small, and the pressure drag is also small. For this type of body shape, skin friction may contribute more to drag than the form drag. Bodies of this type are called streamlined; on the other hand, if separation occurs over much of the perimeter, the body is said to be bluff and presents a large wake. For bluff bodies, pressure drag is much larger than skin friction.

Differentiation between the two types of drag is usually difficult in experiments or calculations, and the drag is expressed in terms of a drag coefficient C_D which takes into consideration the two components. The drag force is then

$$F_D = \tfrac{1}{2} C_D \rho V^2 \Omega \tag{7.1}$$

where C_D is the total drag coefficient, ρ the fluid density, V the upstream velocity, and Ω usually represents the frontal area of the body, i.e. the area projected in the direction of the incoming flow, although sometimes it is defined as the external surface of the body. Note that the term $\frac{1}{2}\rho V^2$ is the dynamic pressure, and hence C_D is the ratio of drag to dynamic forces, and will be the same for two dynamically similar flows. C_D is considered to be independent of the size of the body and related only to Re. In piles and other infinitely long bodies F_D is given as force per unit length and Ω is replaced by the diameter, or the transverse dimensions.

Figure 7.1 shows some bodies and their corresponding wakes. The streamlined body of Figure 7.1(a) presents a very small wake, but the wake increases for a cylinder (b) and becomes very large for a plate perpendicular to the main flowstream (c). For the latter, the drag, when the plate is held in this position, is up to 100 times its value when the plate is parallel to the main stream.

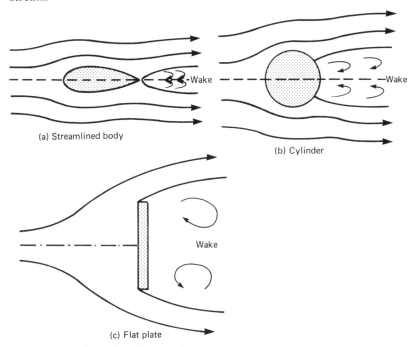

(a) Streamlined body

(b) Cylinder

(c) Flat plate

Figure 7.1 Drag forces in different sections

The wake will depend on the Reynolds number of the flow. For instance, for the cylindrical obstruction of Figure 7.2, the streamlines follow the body as shown in (a) for very low Reynolds numbers with negligible inertia forces. When Re increases, the boundary layer will separate from the body, as shown in (b), and two symmetric eddies form in the wake. With an increase in Re, the length of the wake increases, and the eddies lengthen. This arrangement is unstable, and for a cylinder at $Re = 40$ to 70 a periodic oscillation of the wake occurs. Then at around $Re = 90$, the eddies start to break off, alternately, from each side of the cylinder and are carried downstream. These eddies continue to be shed and form what is called the vortex street. This shedding of vortex produces circulation over the cylinder and lift forces which tend to cause

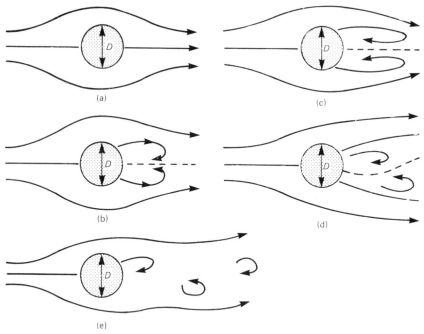

(a)

(b)

(c)

(d)

(e)

Figure 7.2 Cylinder

vibrations. The frequency f of the vortex street is given by

$$fD/V \simeq 0.20 \tag{7.2}$$

for $250 < Re < 2 \times 10^5$. The ratio of expression (7.2) is known as the Strouhal number. At a large Reynolds number, the regularity of the wake is destroyed by the turbulence.

Undesirable oscillations have damaged masts, chimneys, piles in rivers, and even large suspension bridges. A way of preventing such oscillation is to attach fins to the section, oriented in the direction of the flow.

Figure 7.3 presents the variation of C_D with Re for a cylinder. At low Re, of the order of $Re < 0.5$, inertia forces are negligible and viscous forces dominate. Hence the drag is proportional to the velocity V or inversely proportional to Re. Most of the drag is due to skin friction. When separation occurs, the pressure drag contribution increases, and the shape of the C_D curve decreases with V or Re. At $Re = 200$, the von Karman street is acting, and pressure drag accounts for about $3/4$ of total drag. C_D reaches a value of around 0.95 at $Re \simeq 2000$ and then increases to 1.2 for $Re = 3 \times 10^4$. This increase is due to the turbulence of the wake and the change in position of the separation point which now moves upstream.

At $Re \simeq 2 \times 10^5$, the boundary layer becomes turbulent before separation, the separation point moves downstream and the wake narrows. The drag coefficient is reduced to about 0.3 and increases again to 0.7 for $5 \times 10^5 < Re < 3 \times 10^6$. Since viscous effects are small, C_D becomes independent of Re from there on.

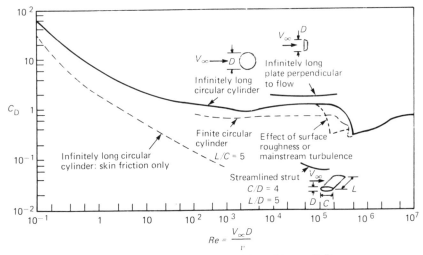

Figure 7.3 Drag coefficient versus Reynolds number. (From Massey, B. S., *Mechanics of Fluids*, 2nd printing, Van Nostrand Reinhold (1970).)

To reduce drag, we can induce the transition from laminar to turbulent boundary layer to occur earlier. Drag is in many cases reduced by increasing surface roughness.

7.2 Equilibrium equations

We can consider a specific fluid volume at time t as shown in Figure 7.4. The external actions are represented by distributed surface loadings ($\vec{b}$) app.ied on the boundaries of the domain, and given per unit surface area, and a distributed body force ($\vec{b}$) per unit mass.

For equilibrium, the time rate of change of total momentum equals the sum of all external forces. The change in momentum can be written as

$$\rho \frac{D\vec{v}}{Dt} = \rho \vec{a} \qquad (7.3)$$

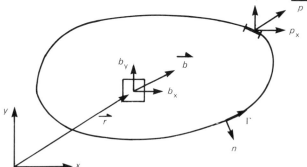

Figure 7.4 Two-dimensional definitions

For the total domain, we can write Newton's law, considering the two-dimensional case for simplicity, as

$$\iint \rho \vec{b}\, d\Omega + \int \vec{p}\, d\Gamma = \iint \rho \frac{D\vec{v}}{Dt}\, d\Omega \tag{7.4}$$

Similarly, the time rate of change of the total moment of momentum is equal to the vector of the moments of external forces, i.e.

$$\iint \rho(\vec{r} \times \vec{b})\, d\Omega + \int (\vec{r} \times \vec{p})\, d\Gamma = \iint \rho \left(\vec{r} \times \frac{D\vec{v}}{Dt} \right) d\Omega \tag{7.5}$$

where the integrals apply to the position at time t, and $D\vec{r}/Dt$ is the acceleration vector. The differential equilibrium equations can now be obtained by expanding the surface integral involving $\vec{p}$ in terms of the stress vectors, and then applying Gauss's integration by parts. Alternatively, we can consider equilibrium of the small incompressible fluid element shown in Figure 7.5. Equilibrium for this element, according to Newton's law, gives

$$\frac{\partial \sigma_{xx}}{\partial x} + \frac{\partial \tau_{xy}}{\partial y} + \rho b_x = \rho \frac{Du}{Dt}$$

$$\frac{\partial \sigma_{yy}}{\partial y} + \frac{\partial \tau_{xy}}{\partial x} + \rho b_y = \rho \frac{Dv}{Dt} \tag{7.6}$$

Expanding them, we obtain

$$\frac{\partial \sigma_{xx}}{\partial x} + \frac{\partial \tau_{xy}}{\partial y} + \rho b_x = \rho \left(\frac{\partial u}{\partial t} + u \frac{\partial u}{\partial x} + v \frac{\partial u}{\partial y} \right)$$

$$\frac{\partial \sigma_{yy}}{\partial y} + \frac{\partial \tau_{xy}}{\partial x} + \rho b_y = \rho \left(\frac{\partial v}{\partial t} + u \frac{\partial v}{\partial x} + v \frac{\partial v}{\partial y} \right) \tag{7.7}$$

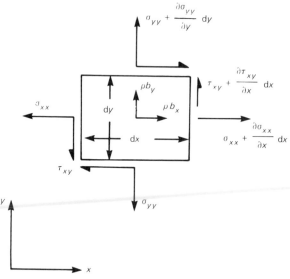

Figure 7.5 Differential element in equilibrium

These expressions are called momentum equations.

The stress components consist of pressure and viscous terms. We can write,

$$\sigma_{xx} = \tau_{xx} - p$$
$$\sigma_{yy} = \tau_{yy} - p \tag{7.8}$$
$$\tau_{xy} = \tau_{xy}$$

where τ denotes the viscous components and the pressure $p = -\frac{1}{2}(\sigma_{xx} + \sigma_{yy})$. Later, we shall include additional dissipative terms due to turbulence, in τ.

The momentum equations are now

$$-\frac{\partial p}{\partial x} + \frac{\partial \tau_{xx}}{\partial x} + \frac{\partial \tau_{xy}}{\partial y} + \rho b_x = \rho \frac{Du}{Dt}$$
$$\tag{7.9}$$
$$-\frac{\partial p}{\partial y} + \frac{\partial \tau_{yy}}{\partial y} + \frac{\partial \tau_{xy}}{\partial x} + \rho b_y = \rho \frac{Dv}{Dt}$$

Note that if the τ terms are neglected, the fluid is said to be frictionless, as in Chapter 3, and cannot resist any tangential force.

7.3 Constitutive equations: Newtonian fluids

We consider here the relationship between stress and strain rates. The term 'Newtonian' refers to a fluid for which the viscous stress–strain rate relations are linear.

We can write the relationship between τ and strain rates e as a function of only two parameters, for *isotropic* fluids, i.e. similar to isotropic solids:

$$\tau_{xx} = \lambda e_v + 2\mu e_{xx}$$
$$\tau_{yy} = \lambda e_v + 2\mu e_{yy} \tag{7.10}$$
$$\tau_{xy} = 2\mu e_{xy}$$

where λ is bulk viscosity and μ the viscosities previously defined. The strain rates are:

$$e_{xx} = \frac{\partial u}{\partial x} \qquad e_{yy} = \frac{\partial v}{\partial y} \qquad e_{xy} = \frac{1}{2}\left(\frac{\partial u}{\partial y} + \frac{\partial v}{\partial x}\right)$$

$$e_v = \frac{\partial u}{\partial x} + \frac{\partial v}{\partial y}$$

Note that e_v is the volumetric deformation rate of the fluid and for incompressible fluids $e_v = 0$. Hence

$$\tau_{xx} = 2\mu e_{xx} = 2\mu \frac{\partial u}{\partial x}$$

$$\tau_{yy} = 2\mu e_{yy} = 2\mu \frac{\partial v}{\partial y} \tag{7.11}$$

$$\tau_{xy} = 2\mu e_{xy} = \mu\left(\frac{\partial u}{\partial y} + \frac{\partial v}{\partial x}\right)$$

Note that,

$$\sigma_{xx} = 2\mu \frac{\partial u}{\partial x} - p$$

$$\sigma_{yy} = 2\mu \frac{\partial v}{\partial y} - p \qquad (7.12)$$

7.3.1 Deformation rate measures

The quantities e_{xx} and e_{yy} are the extensional strain rates defining the relative change in length of a differential line element per unit time. The e_{xy} quantity is the shearing strain rate, i.e. the decrease in the angle between two orthogonal line elements, and is equal to the sum of θ_{xy} and θ_{yx} angles shown in Figure 7.6, divided by 2, i.e.

$$2e_{xy} = \theta_{xy} + \theta_{yx} = \frac{\partial v}{\partial x} + \frac{\partial u}{\partial y}$$

$$e_{yx} = e_{xy} \qquad (7.13)$$

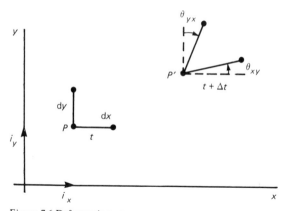

Figure 7.6 Deformation measures

For three-dimensional problems we also have the following components

$$e_{xz} = \frac{1}{2}\left(\frac{\partial u}{\partial z} + \frac{\partial w}{\partial x}\right) = e_{zx}$$

$$e_{yt} = \frac{1}{2}\left(\frac{\partial v}{\partial z} + \frac{\partial w}{\partial y}\right) = e_{zy} \qquad (7.14)$$

and the volumetric strain rate is

$$e_v = \frac{\partial u}{\partial x} + \frac{\partial v}{\partial y} + \frac{\partial w}{\partial z} = 0 \qquad (7.15)$$

When $e_{xy} = 0$ the line elements of Figure 7.6 remain orthogonal and

$$\theta_{xy} = \omega_z \qquad \theta_{yx} = -\omega_z \qquad (7.16)$$

when ω_z is the angular velocity with respect to the z axis. This suggests that the difference between θ_{xy} and θ_{yx} can be taken as measure of the 'average' angular velocity about z. We introduce

$$\omega_z = \frac{1}{2}\left(\frac{\partial v}{\partial x} - \frac{\partial u}{\partial y}\right) \tag{7.17}$$

For three-dimensional cases, we also compute the angular velocity about the other two axes, i.e.

$$\omega_x = \frac{1}{2}\left(\frac{\partial w}{\partial y} - \frac{\partial v}{\partial z}\right)$$
$$\omega_y = \frac{1}{2}\left(\frac{\partial u}{\partial t} - \frac{\partial w}{\partial x}\right) \tag{7.18}$$

The set of ω can be arranged in the vorticity vector $\vec{\omega}$, such that,

$$\vec{\omega} = \omega_x \vec{i}_x + \omega_y \vec{i} + \omega_z \vec{i}$$
$$= \tfrac{1}{2}\,\mathrm{curl}\,\vec{v} = \tfrac{1}{2}\vec{\nabla} \times \vec{v} \tag{7.19}$$

The flow is irrotational when the average angular velocities are zero, i.e.

$$\vec{\omega} = \vec{0} \tag{7.20}$$

Equation (7.20) requires the velocity vector to be the gradient of a continuous function φ, such that,

$$\vec{v} = \vec{\nabla}\varphi \tag{7.21}$$

One can interpret φ as the velocity potential discussed in Chapter 6.

7.4 Navier–Stokes equations for incompressible Newtonian fluid

The equilibrium equations (7.9) can now be written taking into consideration expression (7.11) as,

$$-\frac{\partial p}{\partial x} + 2\mu\frac{\partial^2 u}{\partial x^2} + \mu\left(\frac{\partial^2 u}{\partial y^2} + \frac{\partial^2 v}{\partial x\,\partial y}\right) + \rho b_x = \rho\frac{Du}{Dt}$$
$$-\frac{\partial p}{\partial y} + 2\mu\frac{\partial^2 v}{\partial y^2} + \mu\left(\frac{\partial^2 u}{\partial x\,\partial y} + \frac{\partial^2 v}{\partial x^2}\right) + \rho b_y = \rho\frac{Dv}{Dt} \tag{7.22}$$

Noting that for continuity,

$$\partial u/\partial x = -\partial v/\partial y \tag{7.23}$$

equations (7.9) can be written as,

$$-\frac{\partial p}{\partial x} + \mu\left(\frac{\partial^2 u}{\partial x^2} + \frac{\partial^2 u}{\partial y^2}\right) + \rho b_x = \rho\frac{Du}{Dt}$$
$$-\frac{\partial p}{\partial y} + \mu\left(\frac{\partial^2 v}{\partial x^2} + \frac{\partial^2 v}{\partial y^2}\right) + \rho b_y = \rho\frac{Dv}{Dt} \tag{7.24}$$

or

$$-\frac{\partial p}{\partial x}+\mu\nabla^{2}u+\rho b_{x}=\rho\frac{Du}{Dt}$$

$$-\frac{\partial p}{\partial y}+\mu\nabla^{2}v+\rho b_{y}=\rho\frac{Dv}{Dt}$$

(7.25)

Friction is neglected by setting $\mu=0$. For the case of 'creeping' flow, the convective terms on the right-hand side of expression (7.25) are assumed to be zero, and we obtain,

$$-\frac{\partial p}{\partial x}+\mu\nabla^{2}u+\rho b_{x}=\rho\frac{\partial u}{\partial t}$$

$$-\frac{\partial p}{\partial y}+\mu\nabla^{2}v+\rho b_{y}=\rho\frac{\partial v}{\partial t}$$

(7.26)

This assumption neglects the inertia terms which are small by comparison with the friction terms. Note that a third equation is supplied by the incompressibility requirement.

7.5 Turbulence

At this stage, we can divide the flow into two general categories, *laminar* and *turbulent* flow. If the flow particles follow streamlines which do not intersect each other, the flow is laminar. Viscous flow, for which the inertial forces are small or can be neglected by comparison with the viscous forces, are an example of laminar flow normally for $10^{-2}<Re<0$. For Reynolds numbers between 10^{-2} and 10^{3}, we need to consider both forces, and for $Re>10^{3}$ the viscous forces are negligible.

If the Reynolds number is large, the flow is no longer laminar as the particles tend to move in a random manner. Such flows are called turbulent flows and, although random in nature, they can be analysed in terms of average velocities and pressure, using statistical concepts as suggested in Figure 7.7.

Turbulent flows are accounted for by interpreting the instantaneous flow variables as the source of an average and a random deviation. We can write,

$$u=u'+u''$$

$$v=v'+v''$$

$$p=p'+p''$$

(7.27)

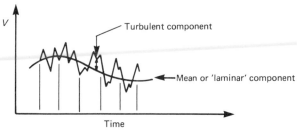

Figure 7.7 Velocity distribution at a given point

Notice that turbulence is eminently a three-dimensional problem. We will continue working in two dimensions, however, to illustrate the problem better.

A prime on a variable denotes an ensemble average and a double prime denotes a deviation. Introducing expression (7.27) into the previously deduced instantaneous momentum equations results in additional terms relating the deviations.

Consider first the equilibrium equations (7.9) taking into account incompressibility:

$$-\frac{\partial p}{\partial x}+\rho b_x+\frac{\partial \tau^f_{xx}}{\partial x}+\frac{\partial \tau^f_{xy}}{\partial y}=\rho\left(\frac{\partial u}{\partial t}+u\frac{\partial u}{\partial x}+v\frac{\partial u}{\partial y}\right)=\rho\left(\frac{\partial u}{\partial t}+\frac{\partial(uu)}{\partial x}+\frac{\partial(uv)}{\partial y}\right)$$

$$-\frac{\partial p}{\partial y}+\rho b_y+\frac{\partial \tau^f_{yy}}{\partial y}+\frac{\partial \tau^f_{xy}}{\partial x}=\rho\left(\frac{\partial v}{\partial t}+u\frac{\partial v}{\partial x}+v\frac{\partial v}{\partial y}\right)=\rho\left(\frac{\partial v}{\partial t}+\frac{\partial(uv)}{\partial x}+\frac{\partial(vv)}{\partial y}\right)$$

$$(7.28)$$

where τ^f denotes the frictional stresses. Substituting for u, v and p and averaging over the total ensemble results in

$$-\frac{\partial p'}{\partial x}+\langle \rho b_x\rangle+\frac{\partial}{\partial x}(\tau^f_{xx}-\rho\langle u''u''\rangle)+\frac{\partial}{\partial y}(\tau^f_{xy}-\rho\langle u''v''\rangle)$$

$$=\rho\frac{\partial(u')}{\partial t}+\rho\frac{\partial(u'u')}{\partial x}+\rho\frac{\partial(v'u')}{\partial y} \qquad (7.29)$$

and similarly for the second equation. The symbol $\langle\ \rangle$ represents the ensemble average. Note that by definition

$$\langle f'g\rangle=f'\langle g\rangle \qquad \langle f''\rangle=0 \qquad (7.30)$$

We can interpret the second-order velocity deviation terms as equivalent stresses, generally called Reynolds stresses and write

$$\tau=\tau^f+\tau^t \qquad (7.31)$$

where

$$\langle\tau^t_{xx}\rangle=-\rho\langle u''u''\rangle$$

$$\langle\tau^t_{xy}\rangle=-\rho\langle u''v''\rangle=\langle\tau^t_{yx}\rangle \qquad (7.30)$$

$$\langle\tau^t_{yy}\rangle=-\rho\langle v''v''\rangle$$

If the fluid is Newtonian, the final result is similar to the Navier–Stokes equations seen previously, with the instantaneous variables replaced by ensemble average values, i.e.

$$-\frac{\partial p'}{\partial x}+\rho b'_x+\mu\nabla^2 u'+\frac{\partial \tau^t_{xx}}{\partial x}+\frac{\partial \tau^t_{xy}}{\partial y}=\frac{\partial(u'u')}{\partial x}+\frac{\partial(v'u')}{\partial y}+\frac{\partial u'}{\partial t} \qquad (7.33)$$

and similarly for the second equation.

It is easy to prove that continuity gives

$$\frac{\partial u'}{\partial x}+\frac{\partial v'}{\partial y}=0 \qquad (7.34)$$

A frequent choice for the Reynolds stresses is

$$\tau^t_{xx}=2\eta e_{xx} \qquad \tau^t_{yy}=2\eta e_{yy} \qquad \tau^t_{xy}=2\eta e_{xy}=\tau^t_{yx} \qquad (7.35)$$

when η is an 'eddy' viscosity determined experimentally. Another possibility is to use the Prandtl mixing length model.

7.6 Applications

7.6.1 Flow between two plates

An interesting application of the Navier–Stokes equation is to determine the velocity distribution for flow between two parallel plates, indicated in Figure 7.8. We can assume that the vertical component is zero ($v=0$).

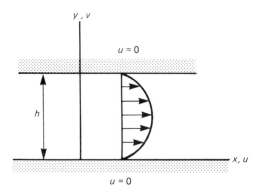

Figure 7.8 Flow between two plates

The continuity equation is

$$\frac{\partial u}{\partial x}+\frac{\partial v}{\partial y}=0 \tag{7.36}$$

where u is the velocity component in the x direction and for $v=0$, we have $u=u(y)$ only.

For confined time-independent laminar flow and forced convection, the momentum equation in the x direction can be written as

$$\rho\left(u\frac{\partial u}{\partial x}+v\frac{\partial u}{\partial y}\right)=-\frac{\partial p}{\partial x}+\mu\frac{\partial^2 u}{\partial y^2} \tag{7.37}$$

As $u=u(y)$ and $v=0$, this equation becomes,

$$0=-\frac{\partial p}{\partial x}+\mu\frac{\partial^2 u}{\partial y^2} \tag{7.38}$$

Integrating equation (7.38) twice,

$$u=\frac{1}{2\mu}\frac{\partial p}{\partial x}y^2+c_1 y+c_2 \tag{7.39}$$

Taking into consideration the boundary conditions $u=0$ at $y=(0, h)$, we obtain

$$u = \frac{h^2}{2\mu}\left(\frac{\partial p}{\partial x}\right)\left(\frac{y^2}{h^2} - \frac{y}{h}\right) \tag{7.40}$$

Equation (7.40) represents Poiseuille flow solution between parallel plates.

7.6.2 Laminar flow in a pipe

Consider now a circular pipe of constant section as in Figure 7.9. The equilibrium equation in the x direction can be written in cylindrical coordinates by considering equilibrium in an annular segment.

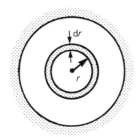

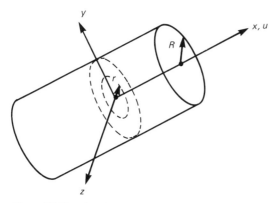

Figure 7.9 Circular pipe

The momentum equation in the x direction can be written as,

$$\frac{1}{\mu}\frac{\partial p}{\partial x} = \nabla^2 u \tag{7.41}$$

where

$$\nabla^2 u = \frac{\partial^2 u}{\partial y^2} + \frac{\partial^2 u}{\partial z^2}$$

To transform coordinates we have to take into account that u is a function of r only, i.e.

$$u = u(r) \qquad r^2 = y^2 + z^2$$

Hence,

$$\frac{\partial u}{\partial y} = \frac{du}{dr}\left(\frac{\partial r}{\partial y}\right) = \frac{y}{r}\left(\frac{du}{dr}\right)$$

and

$$\frac{\partial^2 u}{\partial y^2} = \frac{\partial}{\partial y}\left[\frac{y}{r}\left(\frac{du}{dr}\right)\right] = \frac{1}{r}\frac{du}{dr} + y\frac{d}{dr}\left(\frac{1}{r}\frac{du}{dr}\right)\frac{\partial r}{\partial y}$$

$$= \frac{1}{r}\frac{du}{dr} + \frac{y^2}{r}\frac{d}{dr}\left(\frac{1}{r}\frac{du}{dr}\right)$$

Similarly,

$$\frac{\partial^2 u}{\partial z^2} = \frac{1}{r}\frac{du}{dr} + \frac{z^2}{r}\frac{d}{dr}\left(\frac{1}{r}\frac{du}{dr}\right)$$

Whence,

$$\nabla^2 u = \frac{\partial^2 u}{\partial y^2} + \frac{\partial^2 u}{\partial z^2} = \frac{2}{r}\frac{du}{dr} + r\frac{d}{dr}\left(\frac{1}{r}\frac{du}{dr}\right)$$

Thus, in cylindrical coordinates, the Laplacian becomes

$$\nabla^2 u = \frac{\partial^2 u}{\partial r^2} + \frac{1}{r}\frac{\partial u}{\partial r}$$

$$= \frac{1}{r}\frac{\partial}{\partial r}\left(r\frac{\partial u}{\partial r}\right) \tag{7.42}$$

Hence the momentum equation can be written,

$$\frac{1}{\mu}\frac{\partial p}{\partial x} = \frac{1}{r}\frac{\partial}{\partial r}\left(r\frac{\partial u}{\partial r}\right) \tag{7.43}$$

Integrating this equation once we have

$$\frac{r^2}{2\mu}\frac{\partial p}{\partial x} + c_1 = r\frac{\partial u}{\partial r} \tag{7.44}$$

Dividing by r and integrating again gives,

$$u = \frac{r^2}{4\mu}\frac{\partial p}{\partial x} + \frac{c_1}{\mu}\ln r + c_2 \tag{7.45}$$

We know that the velocity is zero at $r=R$. From considerations of symmetry we know that $du/dr=0$ at $r=0$. Hence $c_1 \equiv 0$, and the value of c_2 is given by

$$0 = \frac{R^2}{4\mu}\frac{\partial p}{px} + c_2 \qquad \text{at } r=R \tag{7.46}$$

and so

$$c_2 = -\frac{R^2}{4\mu}\frac{\partial \dot{p}}{\partial x} \tag{7.47}$$

Hence,

$$u = \frac{r^2}{4\mu}\left(\frac{\partial p}{\partial x}\right) - \frac{R^2}{4\mu}\left(\frac{\partial p}{\partial x}\right) = \frac{1}{4\mu}\left(\frac{\partial p}{\partial x}\right)(r^2 - R^2) \qquad (7.48)$$

or

$$u = -\frac{R^2}{4\mu}\left(\frac{\partial p}{\partial x}\right)\left[1 - \left(\frac{r}{R}\right)^2\right] \qquad (7.49)$$

The volumetric flow rate can now be calculated, i.e.

$$Q = \int u \, d\Omega = \int_0^R 2\pi r u \, dr$$

$$= \int_0^R \frac{1}{4\mu}\left(\frac{\partial p}{\partial x}\right)(r^2 - R^2) 2\pi r \, dr$$

$$= -\frac{\pi R^4}{8\mu}\left(\frac{\partial p}{\partial x}\right)$$

The *average velocity* is

$$\bar{U} = \frac{Q}{\Omega} = \frac{Q}{\pi R^2} = -\frac{R^2}{8\mu}\left(\frac{\partial p}{\partial x}\right) \qquad (7.50)$$

The point of maximum velocity is at $r=0$ and gives

$$U_{max} = -\frac{R^2}{4\mu}\left(\frac{\partial p}{\partial x}\right) = 2\bar{U} \qquad (7.51)$$

Stresses over the section are given by

$$\tau = \mu \frac{\partial u}{\partial r} = \frac{1}{2}\left(\frac{\partial p}{\partial x}\right)r \qquad (7.52)$$

The results agree with those used in Chapter 4.

Bibliography

BATCHELOR, G.K. *An Introduction to Fluid Dynamics*, Cambridge University Press, Cambridge (1970)
CONNOR, J.J. and BREBBIA, C.A. *Finite Element Techniques for Fluid Flow*, 2nd edn, Butterworths, London (1977)
MASSEY, B.S. *Mechanics of Fluids*, 2nd edn, Van Nostrand Reinhold, London (1970)
MILNE-THOMSON, L.M. *Theoretical Hydrodynamics*, Macmillan, London (1938)

Exercises

7.1 Find the vorticity for a flow defined by the following two velocity components: $u=0$, $v=cy$.

7.2 Consider a velocity field with $u=f(y)$ only and $v=0$. If body forces are neglected in equation (7.22), what is the form of the Navier–Stokes equations?

7.3   Consider a viscous fluid with a velocity field given by

$$u = -cx \qquad v = cy$$

Determine whether the field is rotational, compute the stresses and find the acceleration field. Neglecting body forces write the Navier–Stokes equations and the expression for the pressure taking a reference pressure $p = p_0$.

7.4   Assume that a vehicle as shown in Figure 7.10 contains an inviscid fluid. The vehicle has a constant acceleration in the x direction. Calculate the angle of inclination θ of the free surface.

Figure 7.10

7.5   Consider a circular pile which has been driven into a river bed. The length of the pile and the depth of the river is 20 m, the diameter of the pile is 0.40 m. Compute first the velocity for which vortex shedding of frequency 0.5 s^{-1} (natural frequency of the pile) occurs and then with that velocity compute drag forces on the pile. Assume that the velocity is constant over depth. Notice that when vortex shedding frequency reaches the frequency of the pile (0.5 s^{-1}) the pile may break.

7.6   Given an incompressible fluid with viscosity $\mu = 2 \times 10^{-5}$ N s m^{-2} and velocity field

$$u = x^2 - y^2 \qquad v = -2xy$$

compute at a point $x = 1$, $y = 2$, in the x direction:

(a)   the excess of the total normal compressive stress over the pressure p;
(b)   the magnitude of the shearing stress.

7.7   Consider that an offshore structure can be approximated by the column–superstructure system shown in Figure 7.11 with the following dimensions: column length, $l = 75$ m; column diameter, $D = 10$ m.

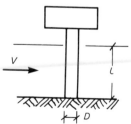

Calculate the total drag forces for the column assuming that the water velocity is $V = 1$ m s^{-1} and $\rho = 10^3$ kg m^{-3}; then compute the vortex shedding frequency.

Figure 7.11

Chapter 8

Turbomachinery

8.1 Introduction

Turbomachinery, which includes turbines, aims to convert the energy of a fluid into torque on a rotating shaft. Pumps work in the opposite way, transmitting mechanical energy to the fluid. The torque produced in turbines is usually transformed into electric energy by an alternator.

A hydroelectric power station is a complex and expensive installation, but once the initial capital cost is incurred, its maintenance cost is insignificant and it provides an inexhaustible source of energy. The output of a hydroelectric plant can be varied unlike nuclear and thermal plants which run at constant output levels—thermal plants for reasons of efficiency and atomic plants as a question of design. Hence, hydroelectric plants are in many cases used to meet the oscillations in demand present in the grid.

It is improbable that an engineer will be required to design a pump or turbine as they are manufactured by a few firms with considerable experience in the field. However, he will need to know a few basic principles since he may be required to select an appropriate machine and to understand the main differences between various machines.

8.2 Basic theory

Consider the velocities at the exit of a pump impeller as shown in Figure 8.1(a), knowing that the same conditions apply to a turbine. The parameters shown in Figure 8.1(a) are defined as follows:

β_2 = blade angle
v_2 = velocity of fluid relative to blade at outlet
u_2 = peripheral speed of the impeller (tangential)
V_2 = absolute velocity of fluid leaving the blade
V_{r2} = radial component of V_2
α_2 = angle between absolute velocity V_2 and the direction of u_2

The subscript 2 indicates that the quantity refers to its value at the outlet.

We can define a similar vector at the inlet, as shown in Figure 8.1(b), with a subscript 1 to indicate that it applies at the inlet. The variables are defined as follows:

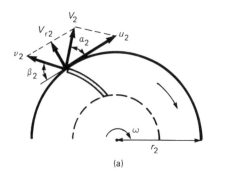
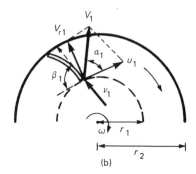

Figure 8.1 Velocity vectors at (a) the outlet and (b) the inlet

β_1 = blade angle
v_1 = velocity of fluid relative to blade at inlet
u_1 = peripheral speed of the impeller (tangential)
V_1 = absolute velocity of fluid entering the blade
V_{r1} = radial component of V_1
α_1 = angle between absolute velocity V_1 and the direction of u_1

We can now apply the equation of moment of momentum, seen in Chapter 7, to determine the torque required or exerted on the axis. Note that the effect of pressures can be neglected as pressures act radially, and that we will also neglect frictional effects. Under these assumptions, torque T will be given by

$$T = \int r_2 V_2 \cos \alpha_2 \, dm - \int r_1 V_1 \cos \alpha_1 \, dm \tag{8.1}$$

where dm is an infinitesimal mass of water that circulates in unit time.

The work per unit time is given by the product of the torque T and the angular velocity ω, i.e.

$$\text{work} = T\omega = \left(\int r_2 V_2 \cos \alpha_2 \, dm - \int r_1 V_1 \cos \alpha_1 \, dm \right) \omega \tag{8.2}$$

But $r_2 \omega = u_2$ and $r_1 \omega = u_1$. Hence

$$\text{work} = T\omega = \int u_2 V_2 \cos \alpha_2 \, dm - \int u_1 V_1 \cos \alpha_1 \, dm \tag{8.3}$$

If u, V and m are measured in SI units then the units of work are N m. If we want the head H we have to divide expression (8.3) by the weight W of the liquid circulating per unit time:

$$H = \frac{1}{W} \left(\int u_2 V_2 \cos \alpha_2 \, dm - \int u_1 V_1 \cos \alpha_1 \, dm \right) \tag{8.4}$$

where $W = gM$, with M being the mass of the fluid per unit time. The above expression is valid for a pump. For a turbine, we have to change the signs as the flow occurs in the opposite direction, i.e.

$$(\text{work})_{\text{turbine}} = \int u_1 V_1 \cos \alpha_1 \, dm - \int u_2 V_2 \cos \alpha_2 \, dm \tag{8.5}$$

In order to use the above equations, we must assume that the distribution of velocities is uniform, which approximates to reality as the number of blades increases. For this case,

$$H = \frac{u_2 V_2 \cos \alpha_2 - u_1 V_1 \cos \alpha_1}{g} \qquad (8.6)$$

This equation is of fundamental importance and is applied to all turbomachines. We can transform this equation following Figure 8.2, into

$$H = \frac{u_2^2 - u_1^2}{2g} + \frac{V_2^2 - V_1^2}{2g} - \frac{v_2^2 - v_1^2}{2g} \qquad (8.7)$$

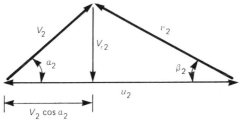

Figure 8.2 Vector diagram:

$$V_2 \cos \alpha_2 = \frac{V_2^2 + u_2^2 - v_2^2}{2u_2}$$

The first term represents the increase in pressure head due to the forced vortex centrifugal force for the case of a pump, the second represents the gain in kinetic energy, and the third is the change in the pressure head due to the variation of the relative velocity.

We can see that the piezometric head generated by the pump will be equal to $(u_2^2 - u_1^2)/2g$, although in practice it is taken equal to $u_2^2/2g$, i.e. a bit larger, due to recirculatory flow.

Normally, water enters the pump in the radial direction, hence in expression (8.6) $\cos \alpha_1 \equiv 0$, leading to,

$$H = \frac{u_2 V_2 \cos \alpha_2}{g} \qquad (8.8)$$

Note that the term $V_2 \cos \alpha_2$ is the tangential component of the velocity at the outlet.

Equation (8.8) applies for a pump. For a turbine, the head is given by the relationship

$$H = \frac{u_1 V_1 \cos \alpha_1}{g} \qquad (8.9)$$

and the angle α_2 is made equal to $90°$ in order to minimise losses due to turbulence in the discharge tube.

To study the influence of the blade angle β_2, we can write equation (8.8) as

$$H = \frac{u_2}{g} (u_2 - V_{r2} \cot \beta_2) \qquad (8.10)$$

by noting that from Figure 8.2 we can establish the equality $V_2 \cos \alpha_2 = u_2 - V_{r_2} \cot \beta_2$. We can also express equation (8.10) in terms of the discharge Q, which is equal to V_{r_2} multiplied by the section at point r_2, called Γ_2. Hence

$$\Gamma_2 H = \Gamma_2 \frac{u_2^2}{g} - Q \frac{u_2}{g} \cot \beta_2 \qquad (8.11)$$

with $Q = \Gamma_2 V_{r_2}$.

Here Q and H are linearly related, i.e.

$$H = a - bQ \qquad (8.12)$$

where a and b are constants, provided that we know the value of u_2 and the characteristics of the runner, i.e. given β_2 and Γ_2. The above relationship is shown in Figure 8.3(a). The optimum blade angle for a centrifugal pump is around $25°$. Note that if $\beta_2 > 90°$, the head required increases.

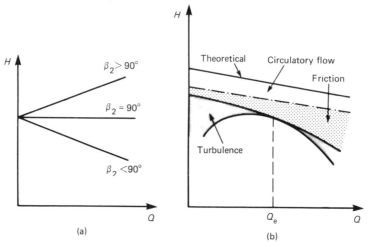

Figure 8.3 Head discharge curves: (a) theoretical; (b) experimental results

These theoretical considerations are not fully valid as we have not taken into consideration losses in the machine due to a series of reasons and, more specifically, we have assumed that the pressures are equal on the two faces of a blade, by assuming the velocities are a function of the radial distance only. This hypothesis is of course not true, as it would not allow movement of the runner. However, the approximate results are of practical value if we multiply the theoretical head H by an empirical correction coefficient which varies from 0.7 to 0.85. The differences are larger in pumps than in turbines as in the latter the inlet velocity is much more uniform, which is a characteristic of convergent fluids. The actual head discharge curves look like those shown in Figure 8.3(b). The circulatory flow effect is due to the inability of the finite number of blades to give a perfect β_2 angle to the flow, and it produces an angle β_2' smaller than β_2. Note also that pumps or turbines are designed for a given discharge, for which the velocity is tangential to the blade. This is the point of best efficiency, indicated in Figure 8.3(b) as Q_e. There are also other mechanical losses to be taken into consideration as well as internal leakages; for instance, fluid that has passed through the impeller in a pump, which may leak through clearance, may flow back into the suction side and give rise to mechanical loss.

Note that the mass per unit time is given by the discharge Q multiplied by the density ρ. To obtain the power, we have to multiply the mass per unit time by H and by the gravitational acceleration g. This gives

$$\text{power} = g\rho QH \tag{8.13}$$

The SI unit of power is the watt (W) which is equivalent to 1 joule of work completed per second, i.e. $1\,\text{W} = 1\,\text{J s}^{-1} = 1\,\text{N m s}^{-1}$. If the head H is a linear function of the discharge Q, from equation (8.13) the power will be a quadratic function. Particularly, from equation (8.11), the power P is given by

$$P = \gamma \left[\left(\Gamma_2 \frac{u_2^2}{g} \right) Q - \left(\frac{u_2}{g} \cot \beta_2 \right) Q^2 \right] \tag{8.14}$$

The relationship between discharge and power is shown in Figure 8.4. For instance, we can see that for $\beta_2 > 90°$ the power needed will increase very rapidly, which is not a desirable feature.

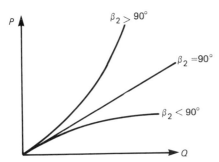

Figure 8.4 Relationship between P and Q for different blade angles β_2

The *efficiency* of a machine is defined as the ratio of output of useful power created by the machine to the input of power supplied. In the case of a pump or turbine the efficiency is the ratio of the power at the inlet to that at the outlet.

For a *pump* efficiency η is

$$\eta = \frac{\gamma QH}{P} \tag{8.15}$$

where P is the power given at the pump axis.

For a *turbine* the efficiency is

$$\eta = \frac{P}{\gamma QH} \tag{8.16}$$

where now P is the power resultant at the axis of the turbine.

In pumps the efficiency is never more than 80% while in turbines it is always greater than 90%.

The losses of energy in a turbine or pump are mechanical, hydraulic, and volumetric losses.

Mechanical losses are due to friction between solid surfaces or solid–fluid interfaces. Mechanical efficiency η_m is given by

$$\eta_m = \frac{\gamma(Q+Q^*)H}{P} \quad \text{(pump)}$$

$$\frac{P}{\gamma(Q-Q^*)H} \quad \text{(turbine)} \tag{8.17}$$

where the terms Q^* are due to mechanical losses. The mechanical efficiency of well designed machines is high, of the order of 95 to 98%.

Hydraulic losses are due to turbulence and frictional effects within the fluid. Hence

$$H^* = \begin{cases} H - \text{losses} & \text{(pump)} \\ H + \text{losses} & \text{(turbine)} \end{cases} \tag{8.18}$$

The losses tend to be proportional to Q^2 and produce the following hydraulic efficiency:

$$\eta_h = \begin{cases} H^*/H & \text{(pumps)} \\ H/H^* & \text{(turbine)} \end{cases} \tag{8.19}$$

which gives up to 95% efficiency, being a bit higher in turbines than in pumps.

Volumetric loss is due to losses of discharge from the high pressure to the low pressure regions through the clearances existing between the mechanical components. If the loss volume is Q^*, the volumetrical efficiency is

$$\eta_v = \frac{Q}{Q+Q^*} \quad \text{(pump)}$$

$$\frac{Q-Q^*}{Q} \quad \text{(turbine)} \tag{8.20}$$

In large machines, this efficiency may be around 98%.

The total efficiency is, in principle,

$$\eta = \eta_m \eta_h \eta_v \tag{8.21}$$

The above theory applies to pumps and reaction turbines. *Reaction turbines* are those in which the energy of the fluid is converted into kinetic energy. The turbine runner is always surrounded by water and, hence, the static pressure difference is zero. The work done is due to the conversion of the kinetic energy.

In the reaction turbine, the kinetic energy is appreciable as the fluid leaves the runner and enters the draft tube. This tube is designed in such a way that the pressure upstream is less than atmospheric pressure, thus increasing the effective head across the runner.

There are two types of reaction turbines: one is the Francis turbine shown in Figure 8.5 and the other is the Kaplan turbine shown in Figure 8.6. In both cases the power is obtained by using the moment of momentum of the fluid.

The Francis turbine is well suited for 25 to 180 m head installations and has an efficiency of around 93% for the larger installations. In Kaplan turbines, the fluid moves as a free vortex, and the radial component of flow changes to an axial component. The moment of momentum is constant, and the tangential

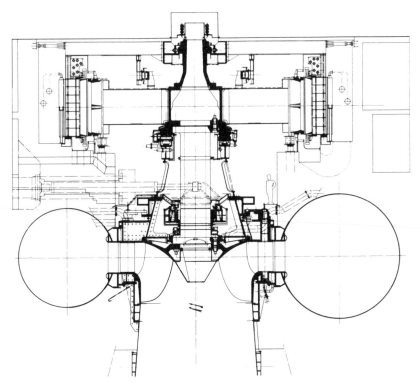

Figure 8.5 Francis turbine, Cabora Bassa, Mozambique. This unit has three
vertical shafts. Output, 485 MW; head, 127 m. Illustration shows a vertical
turbine cross-section (courtesy of Neyrpic Industries)

component of velocity is increased with a reduction in radius. There are flow
blades with little curvature, and the flow is directed tangentially to the blades.
The velocity diagram of Figure 8.7 shows how the tangential component of the
absolute velocity is reduced. The blade angles can be adjusted to account for
changes in head. Kaplan turbines are used for very low heads, from a few
metres to 30 m, and have an efficiency of around 94%.

Conventional propeller or Kaplan turbines with special casing and curved
draft tubes have been proved very costly for low head sites. Work on tidal
energy has resulted in the so-called bulb turbines. They are horizontal shaft
turbines with fixed or adjustable blades and guide vanes. They are considered
axial turbines as their centre line coincides with that of the flow, as indicated in
Figure 8.8. They are very efficient and require less structural work than a
Kaplan turbine. Their range of application is from very low heads up to about
15 m. The most interesting application of these turbines is in the tidal power
plant at Rance, France, shown in Figure 8.9. They can be used for small plants
in channels and rivers. The blades of Kaplan turbines can pivot, which permits
adjustment of the blade angle for different openings and changes in head.

Designs for pumps (for liquids) or for blowers (for gases) are based on the
same equations as those used for turbines. They can be divided into radial
flow, axial flow, or mixed flow machines indicated in Figure 8.10. For high

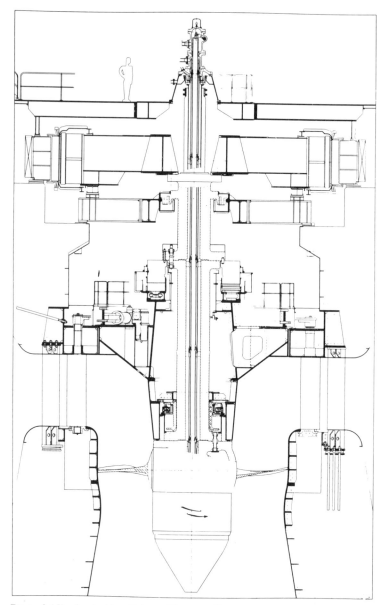

Figure 8.6 Kaplan turbine, Palmar, Uruquay. Illustration shows general
turbine assembly. Output, 112 MW; head, 32 m (courtesy of Neyrpic
Industries)

heads one uses the radial or centrifugal pumps, frequently with two or more
impellers in series. For large discharges with small heads, one can use the axial
flow pump. Medium head and medium discharge problems can be solved
using the mixed flow pump. A chart defining the types of pumps for best
efficiency is given in Figure 8.11.

A new type of machine is the pump–turbine. This is a machine developed to

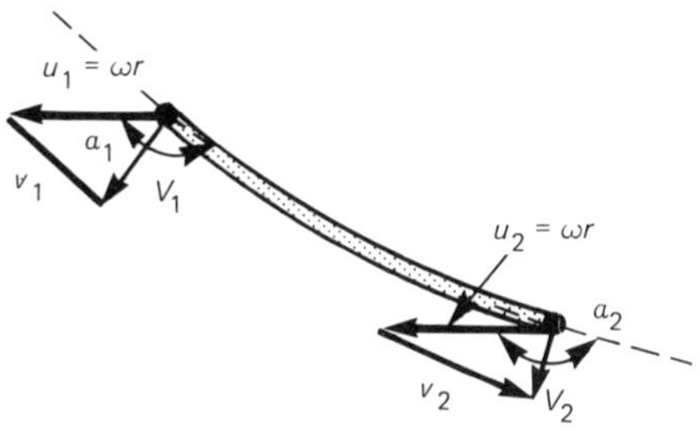

Figure 8.7 Velocity vector diagram for Kaplan turbine; radius r is constant

cope with the fluctuating demand for electric power, by using pumped storage as a means of storing energy from the grid and delivering it at peak demand periods. An example of such a machine is shown in Figure 8.12. The main difficulty with this type of machine is that the respective pump and turbine optimum operating points do not occur at the same pressure on the flow versus pressure characteristic curve as indicated in Figure 8.13. In addition, notice that the turbine operates under static head minus losses in the duct, and the pump operates under static head plus those losses. Hence the delivery head of the pump needs to be greater than the net head driving the turbine. This situation requires a compromise. The design of these machines can be based on a conventional Francis turbine or one with adjustable blades or a modified runner, a sort of compromise between a turbine runner and a pump impeller, such as in the case of the Torrejón scheme, shown in Figure 8.12.

Problem 8.1
Consider a centrifugal pump with an impeller of dimensions $r_1 = 7.5$ cm, $r_2 = 15$ cm and a thickness of 5 cm at r_1 and 2 cm at r_2. Calculate (i) the speed in rpm; (ii) the head; (iii) the torque; (iv) the power and (v) the pressure rise across the impeller for a discharge of 100 l/s. Consider $\beta_1 = \beta_2 = 30°$, neglect losses and assume $\alpha_1 = 90°$.

(a) The velocity of the fluid entering the impeller is given by

$$V_1 = V_{r1} = \frac{Q}{2\pi r_1 b_1} = \frac{100}{2\pi \times 0.075 \times 0.05 \times 1000} = 0.318 \text{ m s}^{-1}$$

where b_1 is the impeller thickness at r_1. Then peripheral speed will be

$$u_1 = \frac{V_1}{\tan \beta_1} = \frac{0.318}{\tan 30°} = 0.55 \text{ m s}^{-1}$$

from which one can compute the speed in rpm, as

$$N = \frac{u_1}{r_1} \frac{60}{2\pi} = \frac{0.55}{0.075} \frac{60}{2\pi} = 70.13 \text{ rpm}$$

(b) The radial component of the velocity leaving the blade is

$$V_{r2} = \frac{Q}{2\pi b_2 r_2} = \frac{r_1 b_1}{r_2 b_2} V_1 = \frac{0.075 \times 0.05}{0.15 \times 0.02} \times 0.318 = 0.397 \text{ m s}^{-1}$$

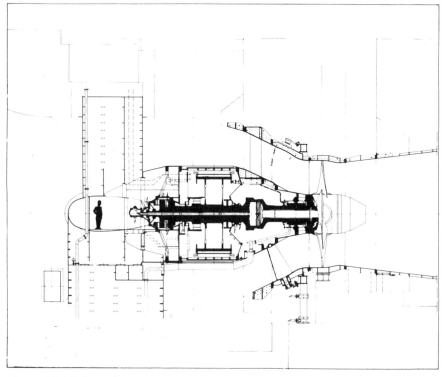

Figure 8.8(a) Bulb turbines: transverse cross-section

where b_2 is the impeller thickness at r_2. Then

$$\frac{u_2}{u_1}=\frac{r_2}{r_1}=\frac{0.15}{0.075}=2$$

and

$$u_2=2u_1=1.10 \text{ m s}^{-1}$$

Therefore

$$V_2 \cos \alpha_2=u_2-V_2 \cot \beta_2=1.10-0.397 \cot 30°=0.412 \text{ m s}^{-1}$$

and, from equation (8.8) ($\alpha_2=0$)

$$H=\frac{u_2 V_2 \cos \alpha_2}{g}=\frac{1.10 \times 0.412}{9.81}=0.046 \text{ m s}^{-1}$$

(c) The torque can now be calculated

$$T=\rho Q(r_2 V_2 \cos \alpha_2)=1000 \frac{100}{1000}(0.15 \times 0.412)=6.18 \text{ N m}$$

(d) The power is computed from the torque as,

KAPLAN TYPE

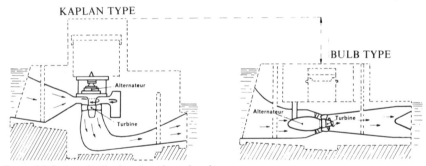

BULB TYPE

Figure 8.8 (b) Longitudinal section through unit

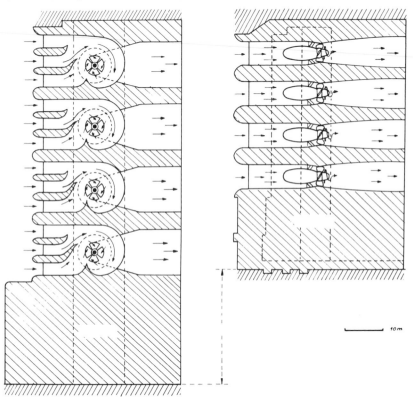

Figure 8.8 (c) Comparison between the structural requirements for a 75 500 kW plant with four bulb turbines and one with four Kaplan units—plan and cross-sectional views (courtesy of Neyrpic Industries)

$$P = T\omega = T\frac{u_1}{r_1} = 6.18\frac{0.55}{0.075} = 45.3 \text{ W}$$

(e) The velocities of the fluid relative to the blade computed at inlet and outlet are

$$v_1 = \frac{u_1}{\cos \beta_1} = \frac{0.55}{\cos 30°} = 0.635 \text{ m s}^{-1}$$

$$v_2 = V_{r_2} \cot \beta_2 = 0.397 \cot 30° = 0.687 \text{ m s}^{-1}$$

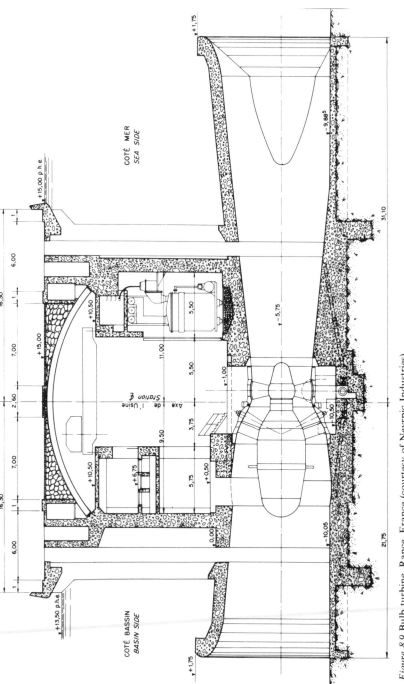

Figure 8.9 Bulb turbine, Rance, France (courtesy of Neyrpic Industries)

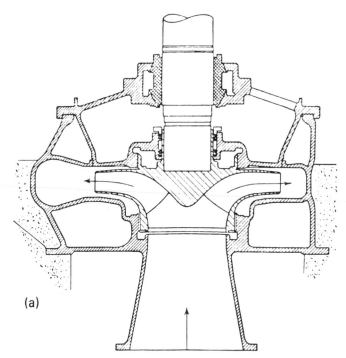

(a)

Sectional elevation of Eagle Mountain and Hay-
field pumps, Colorado River Aqueduct.
(*Worthington Corp.*)

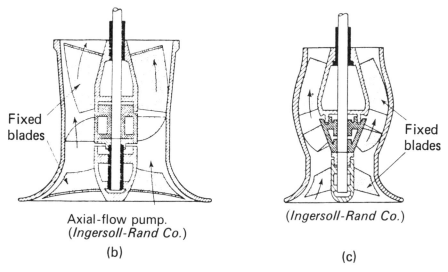

Fixed
blades

Fixed
blades

Axial-flow pump.
(*Ingersoll-Rand Co.*)

(*Ingersoll-Rand Co.*)

(b)

(c)

Figure 8.10 Pumps: (a) radial flow; (b) mixed flow; (c) axial flow (*After V.L. Streeter and E.B. Wylie*,
'*Fluid Mechanics*', 6th edn, McGraw-Hill, New York, 1975)

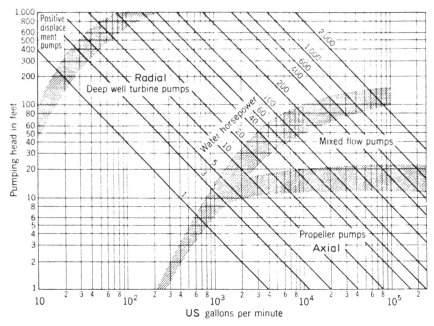

Figure 8.11 Chart for selection of pump type (After V. L. Streeter and E. B. Wylie 'Fluid Mechanics' 6th edn, McGraw-Hill, New York (1975))

Applying Bernouilli's equation gives

$$H = \left(\frac{V_2^2}{2g} + \frac{p_2}{\gamma} + Z_2\right) - \left(\frac{V_1^2}{2g} + \frac{p_1}{\gamma} + Z_1\right)$$

which is equivalent to equation (8.7), i.e.

$$\Delta H = \frac{u_2^2 - u_1^2}{2g} + \frac{V_2^2 - V_1^2}{2g} - \frac{v_2^2 - v_1^2}{2g}$$

Hence the pressure rise across the impeller is

$$\Delta H = \frac{p_2 - p_1}{\gamma} + Z_2 - Z_1 = \frac{u_2^2 - u_1^2}{2g} - \frac{v_2^2 - v_1^2}{2g}$$

$$= \frac{1.10^2 - 0.55^2}{2 \times 9.81} - \frac{0.687^2 - 0.635^2}{2 \times 9.81} = 0.84 \text{ m of } H_2O$$

8.3 Impulse turbines

In the case of impulse turbines, all the fluid energy is converted into kinetic energy at atmospheric pressure. The turbine blades have the shapes described in Figure 8.14 and the system is described in Figure 8.15. At the nozzle the total head is given by

$$H = \frac{p_1}{\gamma} + \frac{V_1^2}{2g}.$$ \hspace{1cm} (8.22)

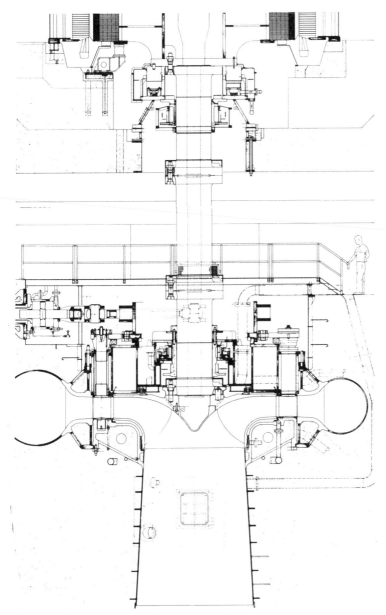

Figure 8.12 Pump–turbine, Le Cheylas, France. Illustration shows four vertical-shaft Francis turbines (cross-section). Turbine output, 250 MW; head, 260 m. These units can also be run as pumps discharging $83 \, \text{m}^3 \text{s}^{-1}$ at 260 m

If C_V is the nozzle coefficient, we find that the jet velocity is given by

$$V = C_V(2gH)^{1/2} = C_V \left[2g \left(\frac{p_1}{\gamma} + \frac{V_1^2}{2g} \right) \right]^{1/2} \tag{8.23}$$

The jet with velocity V will strike the buckets as shown in Figure 8.16. Notice

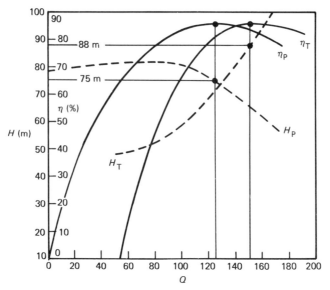

Figure 8.13 Operating curves for a reversible pump–turbine.
Maximum turbine efficiency occurs at 88 m head; maximum pump
efficiency occurs at 75 m head (courtesy of Neyrpic Industries)

that the double-cupped buckets will split the flow stream at an angle β. The
velocity of the runner is u, and hence the velocity V can be decomposed into a
component v_r and the runner velocity u. The velocity at the exit of the bucket is
assumed to be equal to v_r but in general it is around 90% less due to friction
losses.

The component of momentum changes by

$$F = \rho Q(v_r - v_r \cos \beta) \tag{8.24}$$

and the power exerted on the bucket is

$$P = Fu = \rho Q u v_r (1 - \cos \beta) \tag{8.25}$$

Note that to maximise the power one must take $\beta = 180°$, and the term uv_r
should be a maximum, but this is not practical as the water must clear away
from the next blade. In practice β is taken to be approximately equal to $165°$.
For the maximum condition we have

$$\frac{\mathrm{d}}{\mathrm{d}u}(uv_r) = \frac{\mathrm{d}}{\mathrm{d}u}[u(V-u)] = V - 2u = 0$$

and so

$$u = V/2 \tag{8.26}$$

In practice, the tangential runner speed is around $0.47V$ to $0.47V$.
Substituting this result in expression (8.25) and taking $\cos \beta \simeq -1$, we find

$$P = \rho Q \frac{V}{2}\left(V - \frac{V}{2}\right)(1 + 1) = \gamma Q \frac{V^2}{2g} \tag{8.27}$$

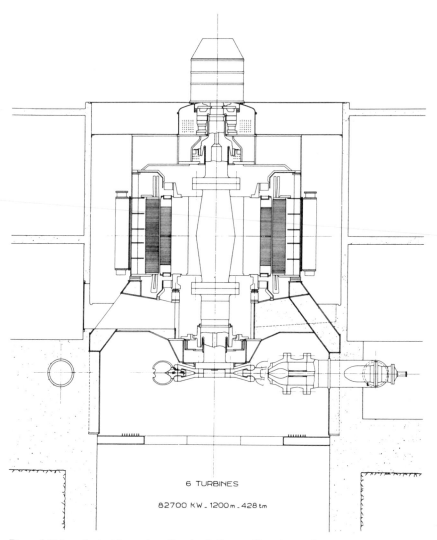

6 TURBINES

82700 KW _ 1200 m _ 428 tm

Figure 8.14 Impulse turbine system, Roseland, France. Six twin-nozzle
single-runner vertical-shaft Pelton turbines. Output, 82 600 kW; head 1.18 m;
speed, 428 rpm; runner diameter, 3.250 m. Illustration shows vertical turbine
cross-section (courtesy of Neyrpic Industries)

In many installations only one jet is used, which discharges horizontally.
The efficiency of Pelton turbines drops off rapidly with change in head as
shown by equation (8.27), and because of this they are employed for large
heads, say from 200 m to 1000 m. For these heads we can always ensure the
design head is operative and in these conditions the efficiency of such a turbine
may be around 80%. Multiple nozzle turbines are nowadays very popular and
two examples are shown in Figure 8.17.

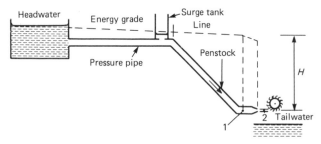

Figure 8.15 Pelton turbine

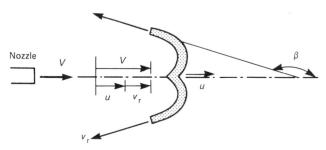

Figure 8.16 Flow through bucket

8.4 Characteristic curves

Extensive experimental facilities exist to study the characteristics of turbines and pumps on models or prototypes; the characteristics studied are defined as follows.

8.4.1 Pumps

In this case, the characteristic curves are: (a) the head; (b) the power in the axis; and (c) the efficiency curves; all with reference to the discharge.

Figure 8.18 shows the characteristic curves for two types of pump: a centrifugal and an axial flow pump. These curves are for a given mechanical configuration. For instance, by varying blade angle β_2, we can obtain another, different set of curves. If the H–Q curve has a horizontal part, it is said to be *unstable*, as the pump can take different discharges Q for the same value of the head H. This must be avoided.

The equal efficiency curves are obtained by testing the pump for different discharges Q and different heads as shown in Figure 8.19. Within a certain range, the efficiency is approximately constant. We can say that the hydraulic efficiency at several points, from equations (8.8) and (8.19), is equal to

$$\eta_h = \frac{H^* g}{u_2 V_2 \cos \beta_2} \tag{8.28}$$

This equation applies to several points for which η is approximately constant. As β_2 is constant, we find that the vector diagram for any of these

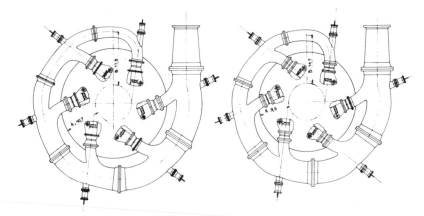

Figure 8.17 Multiple-nozzle Pelton turbine. Illustration shows six-nozzle distribution manifolds 270 (Sharavathi) and 307. Note that dimensions *A* and *B* depend on nozzle diameter (courtesy of Neyrpic Inudstries)

points must be of similar shape, i.e. that

$$\frac{u^2}{V_2 \cos \beta_2} = \text{constant} \qquad (8.29)$$

Hence, for any of these positions, the velocities in the vector diagram can be expressed as,

$$\text{velocity} = \text{constant} \times \sqrt{H} \qquad (8.30)$$

or in revolutions per unit time,

$$N = \text{constant} \times \sqrt{H} \qquad (8.31)$$

Hence for a given pump and in the range of values described,

$$\frac{H_{N_1}}{H_{N_2}} = \left(\frac{N_1}{N_2}\right)^2$$

$$\frac{Q_{N_1}}{Q_{N_2}} = \frac{V_{N_1}}{V_{N_2}} = \frac{H_{N_1}^{1/2}}{H_{N_2}^{1/2}} = \frac{N_1}{N_2} \qquad (8.32)$$

$$\frac{P_{N_1}}{P_{N_2}} = \frac{(QH)_{N_1}}{(QH)_{N_2}} = \left(\frac{N_1}{N_2}\right)^3$$

8.4.2 Turbines

The power given by the turbine will generally vary with the demand, and hence turbines are projected in such a way that they give optimum efficiency for a wide range around normal conditions.

Figure 8.20 shows the characteristic curves for a Pelton turbine. Usually the efficiency and power are given with reference to velocity for a constant head.

By contrast, the curves for a Francis turbine, given by Figure 8.21, present a larger drop in the efficiency when we move away from the optimum. We can draw curves of equal efficiency similar to those for pumps.

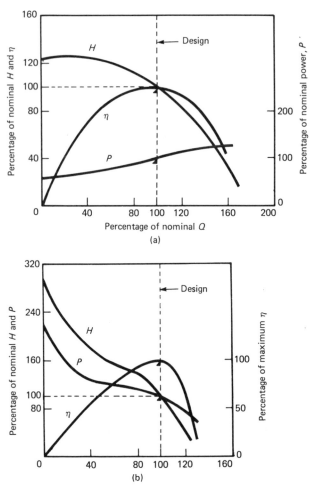

Figure 8.18 Characteristic curves for pumps: (a) centrifugal; (b) axial. (From Webber, N., *Fluid Mechanics for Civil Engineers*, E. & F. N. Spon, London (1965).)

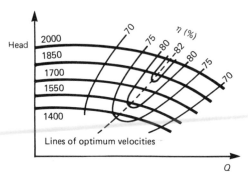

Figure 8.19 Curves of equal efficiency for a centrifugal pump. (From Webber, N., *Fluid Mechanics for Civil Engineers*, E. & F. N. Spon, London (1965).)

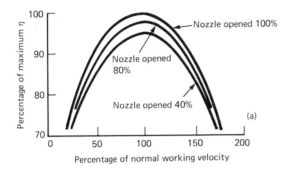

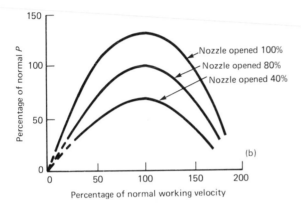

Figure 8.20 Characteristic curves for Pelton turbines: (a) velocity–η; (b) P–velocity. (From Webber, N., *Fluid Mechanics for Civil Engineers*, E. & F. N. Spon, London (1965).)

8.5 Specific speed

The specific speed is a constant widely used to select and compare types of units. It is defined differently for pumps and turbines, as follows:

(a) The specific speed of a *pump* is the velocity required for a pump geometrically similar to the one under consideration to deliver a unit discharge at unit head.

(b) The specific speed of a *turbine* geometrically similar to the one under consideration is defined as the speed required to produce unit power under unit head.

The specific speed will be denoted N_s, and its definition can be obtained by consideration of dimensionality.

The ratio between the discharge of the unit—pump or turbine—under consideration and the one that defines the specific speed, is

$$\frac{Q}{Q_s} = \frac{\Omega V}{\Omega_s V_s} \tag{8.33}$$

where Ω is the perimeter area and V is the flow velocity in the radial direction.

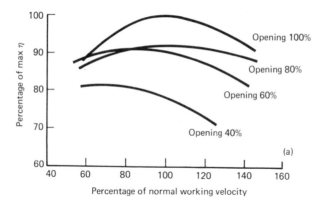

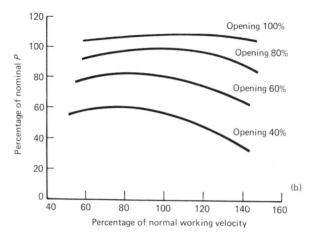

Figure 8.21 Characteristic curves for Francis turbines: (a) velocity–η; (b) P–velocity. (From Webber, N., *Fluid Mechanics for Civil Engineers*, E. & F. N. Spon, London (1965).)

If there is similarity of geometric shape and hydraulic behaviour,

$$\frac{\Omega}{\Omega_s} = \left(\frac{D}{D_s}\right)^2 \tag{8.34}$$

where D is the diameter. Then,

$$\frac{V}{V_s} = \left(\frac{H}{H_s}\right)^{1/2} \tag{8.35}$$

Hence,

$$\frac{Q}{D^2 H^{1/2}} = \frac{Q_s}{D_s^2 H_s^{1/2}} \tag{8.36}$$

Note that the tangential velocities are related as follows:

$$\frac{u}{u_s} = \frac{DN}{D_s N_s} = \left(\frac{H}{H_s}\right)^{1/2} \tag{8.37}$$

Hence, we have

$$\frac{Q}{D^3 N} = \frac{Q_s}{D_s^3 N_s} \tag{8.38}$$

From equations (8.36) and (8.38), we can eliminate D to obtain

$$N_s = N \left(\frac{Q}{Q_s}\right)^{1/2} \left(\frac{H_s}{H}\right)^{3/4} \tag{8.39}$$

For the specific pump we put H_s and Q_s equal to unity and have

$$N_s = \frac{NQ^{1/2}}{H^{3/4}} \tag{8.40}$$

This is the specific speed for pumps.

For a *turbine*, since power is proportional to the term QH, equation (8.12) can be written as

$$\frac{P}{QH} = \frac{P_s}{Q_s H_s} \tag{8.41}$$

Hence, using equations (8.36) and (8.38), we eliminate D to give

$$\left(\frac{Q}{Q_s}\right)^{1/2} = \frac{N_s}{N} \left(\frac{H}{H_s}\right)^{3/4} \tag{8.42}$$

Substituting this result into equation (8.41), we have

$$N_s = N \left(\frac{P}{P_s}\right)^{1/2} \left(\frac{H_s}{H}\right)^{5/4} \tag{8.43}$$

If we now put P_s and H_s equal to unity, we obtain the specific speed for a turbine:

$$N_s = N \frac{P^{1/2}}{H^{5/4}} \tag{8.44}$$

Note that the specific speed is independent of the dimensions but depends on the shape of the machine. All machines with the same form will have the same N_s.

The specific speed is proportional to the rotational velocity and inversely proportional to the head. It is an important parameter in choosing the appropriate type of machine. Figures 8.22 and 8.23 show diagrams of head against specific speed for pumps and turbines respectively.

Figure 8.24 compares the efficiency curves for some turbines. Note that the efficiency remains constant over a large range for the case of Kaplan and Pelton turbines. The fixed blade, bulb-type turbine, is particularly inefficient outside a small range.

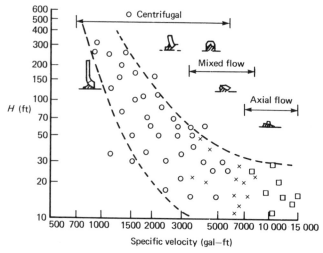

Figure 8.22 Head *v.* specific speed for pumps. (From Webber, N.,
Fluid Mechanics for Civil Engineers, E. & F. N. Spon, London (1965).)

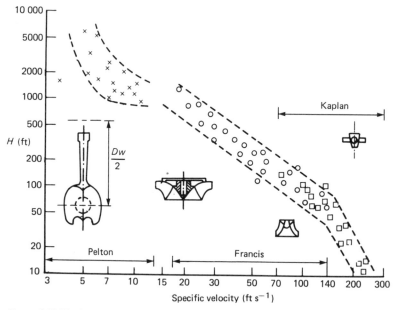

Figure 8.23 Head *v.* specific speed for turbines. (From Webber, N.,
Fluid Mechanics for Civil Engineers, E. & F. N. Spon, London (1965).)

8.6 Cavitation

One of the main problems in turbomachinery is *cavitation*. This happens when
the water reaches a region of such low pressure that it can vaporise. The
bubbles created in this way are carried out by the flow to a region of higher

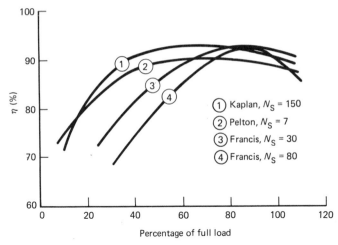

Figure 8.24 Efficiency curves for some turbines. (From Webber, N., *Fluid Mechanics for Civil Engineers*, E. & F. N. Spon, London (9165).)

pressure where they suddenly collapse. If the bubbles collapse against solid surfaces, they produce large forces which can cause pitting of the surface. In addition, noise and vibration occur which can damage other mechanical parts.

Cavitation introduces severe restrictions in the specific speed of pumps and turbines and their heads. Low pressures on the low pressure side of blades can produce cavitation which eventually destroys the blades. Furthermore, bubbles will result in a lower efficiency for the machine as the expanded vapour will result in a lower volume of water passing through the machine. The cavitation parameter σ is useful to define the tendency of the machine to cavitate; it is written as

$$\sigma = \frac{p - p_v}{\rho(V^2/2)} \qquad (8.45)$$

where p is the absolute pressure at the point under consideration, p_v is the vapour pressure, and V is the undisturbed velocity.

When $\sigma = 0$, the pressure is reduced to vapour pressure, and cavitation occurs. Two geometrically similar systems with the same cavitation parameter σ will behave similarly regarding cavitation.

The best solution to the problem of cavitation is to avoid the low pressures that produce it. Sometimes, however, cavitation-resistant materials or special coatings have to be used.

Problem 8.2
A 8 km long penstock (diameter 1 m) carries water from a reservoir to an impulse turbine. Calculate the power that can be produced by the turbine if the machine is 80% efficient and the reservoir is at an elevation of 500 m over the turbine. Assume that $\lambda = 0.015$ for the penstock, neglect losses in the nozzle and take the jet diameter to be 0.1 m. Calculate the diameter of the turbine wheel to achieve an angular velocity of 360 rpm. Assume ideal conditions for the bucket design (i.e. $V_{bucket} = \frac{1}{2} V_{jet}$).

Using Bernoulli's equation gives

$$\frac{p_1}{\gamma} + \frac{V_1^2}{2g} + Z_1 = \frac{p_2}{\gamma} + \frac{V_2^2}{2g} + Z_2 + h_L$$

and so

$$0 + 0 + 500 = 0 + \frac{V_{jet}^2}{2g} + 0 + \frac{\lambda L}{D}\frac{V_{jet}^2}{2g}$$

where the left-hand side corresponds to the reservoir and the right-hand side to the turbine jet.

For continuity

$$V_{pipe}\Omega_{pipe} = V_{jet}\Omega_{jet}$$

Then

$$V_{pipe} = V_{jet}\left(\frac{\Omega_{jet}}{\Omega_{pipe}}\right) = V_{jet}\left(\frac{0.10}{1.00}\right)^2 = 0.01\,V_{jet}$$

Therefore

$$\frac{V_{jet}^2}{2g}\left(1 + \frac{\lambda L}{D}0.01^2\right) = 500 \text{ m}$$

Thus

$$V_{jet} = 98.3 \text{ m s}^{-1}$$

The power is

$$P = Q\gamma V_{jet}^2\eta = 98.3\frac{\pi}{4}(0.10)^2 \times 9810 \times \frac{98.3^2 \times 0.80}{2 \times 9.81}$$

$$= 2982 \text{ W} \simeq 2.98 \text{ kW}$$

Finally

$$V_{bucket} = \tfrac{1}{2}V_{jet} = \tfrac{1}{2}D\omega = 49.15$$

so that

$$D = \frac{49.15 \times 2}{360 \times \pi/30} = 2.61 \text{ m}$$

Bibliography

ROBERTSON, J.A. and CROWE, C.T. *Engineering Fluid Mechanics*, 2nd edn, Houghton Mifflin Co., Boston (1976)

SABERSKY, R.H., ACOSTA, A.J. and HAUPTMANN, E.G. *Fluid Flow. A First Course in Fluid Mechanics*, 2nd edn, Macmillan, New York (1971)

WEBBER, N., *Fluid Mechanics for Engineers*, E. & F.N. Spon, London (1965)

Exercises

8.1 Consider a centrifugal pump rotating at 2000 rpm with an impeller of 1.00 m diameter. The α_1 angle at the inlet is 90° and at the exit $\alpha_2 = 60°$.

Find the hydraulic efficiency of the pump for $V_2 = 10 \text{ m s}^{-1}$ if the head produced by the machine is $H = 47.5 \text{ m}$.

8.2 A centrifugal pump with an impeller diameter of 1.50 m rotates at 2600 rpm. The inlet angle is $\alpha_1 = 90°$ and at the exit $\beta_2 = 20°$. The discharge of the pump is $Q = 1000 \text{l s}^{-1}$ and the head $H = 1200 \text{ m}$. Considering that the loss of head in the river is 1 m and the pipe diameter 0.50 m, calculate the total head produced by the runner (equation (8.8)) and the head difference between inlet and outlet. The section of flow is considered to be the same at the inlet and outlet and is 0.2. Note that if the same flow section is assumed $V_1 = V_{r_1} = V_{r_2}$.

8.3 A turbine has $H = 100 \text{ m}$ and discharge $Q = 12 \text{ m}^3 \text{ s}^{-1}$, and has to operate a generator with speed $N = 300 \text{ rpm}$. Compute the tangential component to be given to the water for $r = 2 \text{ m}$ and fixed vanes, the torque exerted on the impeller and the power required. Assume that $\alpha_2 = 90°$ and neglect any losses.

8.4 Draw the theoretical head–discharge curve for a centrifugal pump of the following dimensions:

$r_1 = 4 \text{ cm} \qquad r_2 = 8 \text{ cm}$

b_1 (thickness at r_1) = 2 cm

b_2 (thickness at r_2) = 1.5 cm

The speed of the pump is $N = 1500 \text{ rpm}$ and $\beta_2 = 30°$.

8.5 Determine the power that can be achieved by a Pelton turbine with an efficiency of 80% if the elevation of the reservoir (see Figure 8.25) is 1800 m and the elevation at the penstock is 800 m. The diameter of the pipe is 0.60 m and it has a length of 10 km. The Pelton turbine has a diameter of 4 m and the penstock resistance coefficient is $\lambda = 0.02$. Neglect losses in the nozzle and assume that the speed of the results from the condition $V_{jet} = 2V_{bucket}$. Determine the angular speed of the wheel and the torque on the turbine shaft.

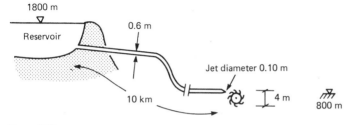

1800 m
Reservoir
0.6 m
Jet diameter 0.10 m
10 km
4 m
800 m

Figure 8.25

8.6 A Pelton turbine has a 15 km long penstock with a diameter of 3 m. The jet diameter is 0.30 m and the elevation of the reservoir over the turbine is 1200 m. Compute losses in the penstock with $\lambda = 0.015$ and a 90%

efficiency. Calculate the power produced by the turbine neglecting losses in the nozzle.

8.7 Consider a centrifugal pump with the characteristics curves and dimensions shown in Figure 8.26. If the pump is doubled in size and halved in speed, what will be the head and discharge of the new pump at maximum efficiency?

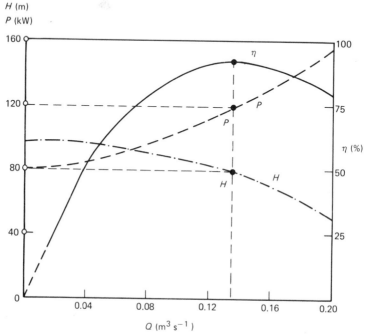

Figure 8.26 H, P and η versus *Q*. Pump characteristics: $D_1 = 40\,\text{cm}$, $N_1 = 2400\,\text{rpm}$

8.8 Consider that an impulse turbine is needed to drive a generator with 4 pairs of poles and 60 Hz. The head is 1000 m and the discharge 1 m³ s⁻¹. Take a nozzle coefficient $C_V = 0.90$, neglect losses at the nozzle and assume that the efficiency of the turbine is 85%. Determine the diameter and the speed of the wheel required.

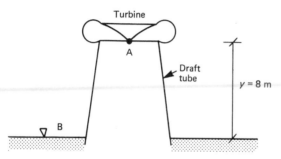

Figure 8.27

8.9 Consider a Francis turbine with a velocity of 10 m s⁻¹ at the entrance of the draft tube and a velocity of 1 m s⁻¹ at the exit. If the tail water is 8 m below the starting of the draft tube, and the losses in this tube are 1 m find the pressure head at A (Figure 8.27) and determine if cavitation can occur.

Solutions

Chapter 2.

2.1 The flow is:

$$Q = \Omega_1 \left\{ \frac{2g \, \Delta h}{\left(\frac{\Omega_1}{\Omega_2}\right)^2 - 1} \right\}^{1/2}$$

$$= (10 \times 2.50) \left(\frac{2 \times 9.81 \times 0.40}{((10 \times 2.50)/(9 \times 2.10))^2 - 1} \right)^{1/2} = 80.88 \text{ m}^3 \text{ s}^{-1}$$

2.2 $\quad p_s = \gamma H + \frac{1}{2}\rho v_0^2 \qquad \rho = 1026 \text{ kg m}^{-3}$

$$= 1206 \times 9.81 \times 20 + \frac{1026}{2} \times \left(\frac{10 \times 1000}{3600} \right)^2 = 240 \text{ kN m}^{-2}$$

2.3 For a Venturi meter, ignoring frictional effects, equation (2.21) gives

$$Q = \Omega_1 \left(\frac{2gh}{(\Omega_1/\Omega_2)^2 - 1} \right)^{1/2}$$

where

$$h = h_m \left(\frac{\rho_m - \rho}{\rho} \right)$$

with $\rho_m = 13.6 \text{ g cm}^{-3}$ and $\rho = 1.0 \text{ g cm}^{-3}$. Thus

$$Q = \frac{\pi D_1^2}{4} \left(\frac{2gh_m(\rho_m/\rho - 1)}{(D_1/D_2)^2 - 1} \right)^{1/2} = \frac{\pi(0.03)^2}{4} \left(\frac{2 \times 9.81 \times 0.012 \times 12.6}{(0.03/0.01)^2 - 1} \right)^{1/2}$$

$$= 0.00043 \text{ m}^3 \text{ s}^{-1} = 0.43 \text{ l s}^{-1}$$

2.4 In this problem $\Omega = \pi R^2 = \pi(0.05)^2 = 7.85 \times 10^{-3} \text{ m}^3$, and so

$$Re = \frac{\rho L V}{\mu} = \frac{900}{0.040} \times 0.10 \left(\frac{5 \times 10^{-3}}{7.85 \times 10^{-3}} \right)$$

$$= 1433$$

2.5   We write the Bernouilli equation for this problem as

$$\frac{p_1}{\gamma} + \frac{V_1^2}{2g} + y_1 = \frac{p_2}{\gamma} + \frac{V_2^2}{2g} + y_2 + h_l + h_t$$

where h_l is the head loss and h_t is the head absorbed by the turbine. Notice that we can assume that at the reservoir,

$$p_1 = 0, \ V_1 = 0, \ y_1 = 1000 \text{ m}$$

and at the discharge of the pump,

$$p_2 = 0, \ V_2 = 0, \ y_2 = 100 \text{ m}$$

Hence:

$$h_t = (y_1 - y_2) - h_l = 900 - 10 = 890 \text{ m}$$

The power P is the rate of work, given by

$$P = Qlgh_t = 50 \times 9810 \times 890$$
$$= 436 \times 10^6 \text{ N m s}^{-1}$$
$$= 436 \times 10^6 \text{ W} = 436 \text{ MW}$$

Chapter 3

3.1   First we determine whether the flow is laminar or turbulent. To do this we write

$$V = \frac{Q}{\Omega} = \frac{0.01}{\frac{1}{4}\pi(0.10)^2} = 1.27 \text{ m s}^{-1}$$

and so

$$Re = \frac{VD}{v} = \frac{1.27 \times 0.10}{5 \times 10^{-4}} = 254$$

Thus Re ($= 254$) is less than 2000 and the flow is *laminar*.
    The head loss for a pipe of length L is given by equation (3.14) as

$$h_f = \frac{32\,\mu V}{\rho g D^2} L = \frac{32 v V}{g D^2} L$$
$$= \frac{32 \times 5 \times 10^{-4} \times 1.27}{9.81 \times 0.10^2} \times 100 = 20.71 \text{ m}$$

i.e. the head loss is 20.71 m for 100 m of pipe.

3.2   For this problem we first determine whether the flow is laminar or turbulent:

$$V = \frac{Q}{\Omega} = \frac{0.04}{\pi/4 \times 0.15^2} = 1.59 \text{ m s}^{-1}$$

$$Re = \frac{VD}{v} = \frac{1.59 \times 0.15}{10^{-6}} = 2.38 \times 10^5$$

Therefore the flow is *turbulent*.

From Figure 3.5:

$$k/D = \begin{cases} 0.0012 & \text{galvanised pipe} \\ 0.006 & \text{concrete pipe} \end{cases}$$

Then we can calculate the friction factor λ from Figure 3.6 using these values of k/D.

To calculate the loss per kilometre, we can use the Darcy–Weisbach formula, i.e.

$$h_f = \lambda \frac{L}{D}\left(\frac{V^2}{2g}\right) = \begin{cases} 0.016 \dfrac{1000}{0.15}\dfrac{(1.59)^2}{2\times9.81} = 13.74 \text{ m km}^{-1} & \text{galvanised pipe} \\[2mm] 0.032 \dfrac{1000}{0.15}\dfrac{(1.59)^2}{2\times9.81} = 27.49 \text{ m km}^{-1} & \text{concrete pipe} \end{cases}$$

3.3   In this problem

$$V = \frac{Q}{\Omega} = \frac{10^{-6}}{\pi/4(0.02)^2} = 0.0032 \text{ m s}^{-1}$$

$$Re = \frac{VD}{v} = \frac{0.0032 \times 0.02}{2.2 \times 10^{-4}} = 0.29$$

Hence the flow is *laminar*.

The pressure drop can be calculated as,

$$\Delta p_f = h_f \rho g = \frac{32\,\mu L V}{D^2}$$

$$= \frac{32 \times 0.40 \times 100 \times 0.0032}{(0.02)^2}$$

$$= 10.240 \times 10^3 \text{ N m}^{-2} \text{ per 100 m}$$

3.4

$$Re = \frac{VD}{v} = \frac{0.20 \times 0.05}{2.2 \times 10^{-4}} = 45.5$$

Thus the flow is *laminar*. Hence,

$$\frac{h_f}{L} = \frac{32v}{gD^2}V = \frac{32 \times 2.2 \times 10^{-4} \times 0.20}{9.81 \times (0.05)^2}$$

$$= 0.057$$

Then

$$\frac{dh}{ds} = \frac{d}{ds}\left(\frac{p}{\gamma}+y\right) = -0.057$$

$$\gamma = \rho g = 1818 \times 9.81 = 17836 \text{ N m}^{-3}$$

If the flow is *upwards* $dy/ds = +1$ and

$$dp/ds = \gamma(-1-0.057)$$

$$= 17836(-1.057) = -18.853 \text{ N m}^{-3}$$

The pressure *decreases* upwards. The shear stress is

$$\tau = \frac{r}{2}\left(\gamma \frac{\partial h}{\partial s}\right) = r\left(\frac{17836}{2} \times 0.057\right)$$

$$= r(508.32)$$

At the wall $r = R = 0.025$ m and so

$$\tau = 0.025 \times 508.32 = 12.70 \text{ N m}^{-2}$$

At the centre $r = 0$ and so $\tau = 0$.

3.5

$$Re = \frac{VD}{\nu} = \frac{2 \times 0.04}{1 \times 10^{-6}} = 8 \times 10^4$$

Thus the flow is *turbulent*. Hence,

$$h_f = 1(2-1) = 1 \text{ m}$$

At the same time,

$$h_f = \lambda \frac{LV^2}{2dD}$$

Therefore

$$\lambda = h_f \frac{2gD}{LV^2} = \frac{1 \times 2 \times 9.81 \times 0.04}{5 \times 4}$$

$$= 0.039$$

3.6   For water at 10°C, $\nu = 1.31 \times 10^{-6} \text{ m}^2 \text{ s}^{-1}$

$$V = \frac{Q}{\Omega} = \frac{0.1}{\pi/4(0.5)^2} = 0.509 \text{ m s}^{-1}$$

$$Re = \frac{VD}{\nu} = \frac{0.509 \times 0.5}{1.31 \times 10^{-6}} = 0.19 \times 10^6$$

Hence the flow is *turbulent*. From Figure 3.8 we have a rugosity $k/D = 0.006$ and a friction factor $\lambda = 0.032$. Hence

$$h_f = \lambda \frac{L}{D}\left(\frac{V^2}{2g}\right)$$

$$= 0.032 \frac{1000}{0.50}\left(\frac{(0.509)^2}{2 \times 9.81}\right)$$

$$= 0.845 \text{ m}$$

The power required is given by

$$P = \gamma Q h_f = 9810 \times 0.10 \times 0.845$$

$$= 828.9 \text{ W}$$

3.7   For this case, $v = 10^{-6}$ m^2 s^{-1} and $\gamma = 9810$ N m^{-3}. Also

$$V = \frac{Q}{\Omega} = \frac{10}{\pi/4 \times 4} = 3.18 \text{ m s}^{-1}$$

and so

$$Re = \frac{VD}{v} = \frac{3.18 \times 2}{10^{-6}} = 6.36 \times 10^6$$

Hence the flow is *turbulent*. We select (Figures 3.7 and 3.8)

$$k/D = 0.00005 \qquad \lambda = 0.012$$

One can now set up Bernouilli's equation at the pump intake at the river and at the canal. It gives,

$$\overbrace{\frac{p_1}{\gamma} + \frac{V_1^2}{2g} + y_1 + h_p}^{\text{pump intake}} = \overbrace{\frac{p_2}{\gamma} + \frac{V_2^2}{2g} + y_2 + h_f}^{\text{canal}}$$

where h_p is the head at the pump end and h_f the canal losses. Therefore

$$0 + 0 + 0 + h_p = 0 + 0 + 100 + \lambda \frac{L}{D}\left(\frac{V^2}{2g}\right)$$

and so

$$h_p = 100 + 0.012 \times \frac{10000}{2} \frac{(3.18)^2}{2(9.81)}$$

$$= 100 + 30.92 = 130.92 \text{ m}$$

The power needed at 80% efficiency is:

$$P = \frac{1}{0.80} Q\gamma h_p$$

$$= \frac{10 \times 9810 \times 130.92}{0.80}$$

$$= 16.05 \times 10^6 \text{ W} = 16050 \text{ kW}$$

3.8   The change in pressure is

$$\frac{dp}{ds} = \frac{(p_{10} + \gamma y) - (p_0 + \gamma y_0)}{\Delta x}$$

Also

$$\gamma_{\text{oil}} = 0.90 \times 9810 = 8830 \text{ N m}^{-3}$$

and so

$$\frac{dp}{ds} = \left(\frac{(100 + 8.83 \times 10) - 150}{10}\right) \times 10^3 \text{ N m}^{-3}$$

$$= \left(\frac{188 - 150}{10} \right) \times 10^3 \text{ N m}^{-3}$$

$$= \frac{38}{10} \times 10^3 \text{ N m}^{-3} = 3.8 \text{ kN m}^{-2} \text{ per metre}$$

The *pressure* in this case is upwards, hence the direction of the flow is downwards. The *mean* velocity is

$$V = -\frac{R^2}{8\mu} \left(\frac{dp}{ds} \right)$$

$$= -\frac{(0.05)^2}{8 \times 0.4} (3800) = 2.97 \text{ m s}^{-1}$$

3.9

$$Re = \frac{VD\rho}{\mu} = \frac{1 \times 0.10 \times 0.800}{0.1} = 800$$

and so the flow is *laminar*. We now have a force at the support (F_s), the weight of the pipe F_w) and the frictional forces on the walls, F_f) (see Figure S.1). Hence:

$$F_s = F_w + F_f = 500 \text{ N} + F_f$$

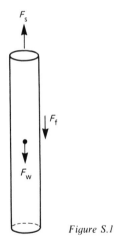

Figure S.1

The frictional forces are computed by knowing the shear stress on the pipe wall, where Ω_s is the shear cross-section, i.e.

$$F_f = \Omega_s \tau = \Omega_s \gamma \frac{r}{2} \left(\frac{\partial h}{\partial s} \right)$$

$$= (2\pi R \times 10 \text{ m}) \gamma \frac{R}{2} \left(\frac{32 \, \mu V}{\gamma D^2} \right)$$

$$= (2\pi \times 10) \times 64 \, \mu V = 4021 \, \mu V$$

$$= 4021 \times 0.12 \times 1 = 482 \text{ N}$$

Hence the force at the support is,

$$F_s = 500 + 482 = 982 \text{ N}$$

Chapter 4

4.1 For each element

$$\left\{ \begin{matrix} Q_j \\ Q_k \end{matrix} \right\}^i = k^i \begin{bmatrix} 1 & -1 \\ -1 & 1 \end{bmatrix} \left\{ \begin{matrix} H_j \\ H_k \end{matrix} \right\}^i$$

and so

$$\left\{ \begin{matrix} Q_1^1 \\ Q_2^1 \end{matrix} \right\} = k^1 \begin{bmatrix} 1 & -1 \\ -1 & 1 \end{bmatrix} \left\{ \begin{matrix} H_1 \\ H_2 \end{matrix} \right\} \quad \text{element 1}$$

$$\left\{ \begin{matrix} Q_1^2 \\ Q_2^2 \end{matrix} \right\} = k^2 \begin{bmatrix} 1 & -1 \\ -1 & 1 \end{bmatrix} \left\{ \begin{matrix} H_1 \\ H_2 \end{matrix} \right\} \quad \text{element 2}$$

Also, we have

$$k^i = \frac{\pi}{128} \frac{\rho g D^4}{\mu L} = \frac{\pi}{128} \frac{g D^4}{\nu L}$$

and so

$$k^1 = 24 \times 10^{-3} \text{ m}^2 \text{ s}^{-1}$$

$$k^2 = 192 \times 10^{-3} \text{ m}^2 \text{ s}^{-1}$$

The system of equations can be written as

$$10^{-3} \begin{bmatrix} 24 + 192 & -24 - 192 \\ -24 - 192 & +24 + 192 \end{bmatrix} \left\{ \begin{matrix} H_1 \\ H_2 \end{matrix} \right\} = \left\{ \begin{matrix} -C_1 \\ -C_2 \end{matrix} \right\}$$

which reduces to

$$10^{-3} \begin{bmatrix} 216 & -216 \\ -216 & 216 \end{bmatrix} \left\{ \begin{matrix} H_1 \\ H_2 \end{matrix} \right\} = \left\{ \begin{matrix} -C_1 \\ -C_2 \end{matrix} \right\}$$

Now for $H_1 = 10$ m we have

$$10^{-3} \times 216 H_2 = -C_2 + 2160 \times 10^{-3}$$
$$= -2 + 2160 \times 10^{-3}$$
$$= -2 + 2.16 = 0.16$$

and so

$$H_2 = \frac{0.16}{0.216} = 0.74 \text{ m}$$

Hence:

$$Q^1 = k^1 (H_1 - H_2) = 24 \times 10^{-3} \times 9.26 = 0.222 \text{ m}^3 \text{ s}^{-1}$$
$$Q^2 = k^2 (H_1 - H_2) = 192 \times 10^{-3} \times 9.26 = 1.778 \text{ m}^3 \text{ s}^{-1}$$

and the total discharge is 2.00 m³ s⁻¹.

4.2   In this case the system matrix is given by

$$k = \frac{\pi}{128}\frac{gD^4}{\gamma L} = 24 \times 10^{-3} \text{ m}^2 \text{ s}^{-1}$$

$$k\begin{bmatrix} 1+1 & -1 & -1 \\ -1 & +1+1 & -1 \\ -1 & -1 & +1+1 \end{bmatrix}\begin{Bmatrix} H_1 \\ H_2 \\ H_3 \end{Bmatrix} = \begin{Bmatrix} -C_1 \\ -C_2 \\ -C_3 \end{Bmatrix}$$

Note $H_2 = H_3$ for symmetry and $H_1 = 10$ m. Thus we can write

$$k\begin{bmatrix} 2 & -1 \\ -1 & 2 \end{bmatrix}\begin{Bmatrix} H_2 \\ H_3 \end{Bmatrix} = \begin{Bmatrix} -C_2 \\ -C_3 \end{Bmatrix} + k\begin{Bmatrix} 1 \\ 1 \end{Bmatrix} \times 10 \text{ m}$$

and so

$$24 \times 10^{-3}\begin{bmatrix} 2 & -1 \\ -1 & 2 \end{bmatrix}\begin{Bmatrix} H_2 \\ H_3 \end{Bmatrix} = \begin{Bmatrix} -1 \\ -1 \end{Bmatrix} + 24 \times 10^{-1}\begin{Bmatrix} 1 \\ 1 \end{Bmatrix}$$

As $H_2 = H_3$ we have

$$24 \times 10^{-3} \times H_3 = -1 + 2.40$$
$$= -1 + 2.40 = 1.40$$

$$H_3 = \frac{1.40}{24 \times 10^{-3}} = \frac{1.400}{0.024} = 58.33 \text{ m}$$

$$Q_1 = Q_3 = 24 \times 10^{-3} \times 41.77 = 1.00 \text{ m}^3 \text{ s}^{-1}$$

Also, note that

$$Q_2 \equiv 0$$

We can now write

$$\begin{bmatrix} +6.79 & -0.25 & -0.38 \\ -0.25 & +6.79 & -0.38 \\ -0.38 & -0.38 & 1.01 \end{bmatrix}\begin{Bmatrix} H_2 \\ H_3 \\ H_4 \end{Bmatrix} = \begin{Bmatrix} -20 \\ -20 \\ +40 \end{Bmatrix} + \begin{Bmatrix} 61.6 \\ 61.6 \\ 2.5 \end{Bmatrix}$$

$$\begin{bmatrix} +6.79 & -0.25 & -0.38 \\ -0.25 & +6.79 & -0.38 \\ -0.38 & -0.38 & 1.01 \end{bmatrix}\begin{Bmatrix} H_2 \\ H_3 \\ H_4 \end{Bmatrix} = \begin{Bmatrix} 41.6 \\ 41.6 \\ 42.5 \end{Bmatrix}$$

Note that $H_2 = H_3$ here and so

$$\begin{bmatrix} +6.54 & -0.38 \\ -0.76 & 1.01 \end{bmatrix}\begin{Bmatrix} H_3 \\ H_4 \end{Bmatrix} = \begin{Bmatrix} 41.6 \\ 42.5 \end{Bmatrix}$$

Therefore

$$H_1 = 10 \text{ m}$$
$$H_2 = H_3 = 9.208 \text{ m}$$
$$H_4 = 49.00 \text{ m}$$
$$Q^1 = Q^2 = 6.16 \times 0.792 = 4.88 \text{ m}^3 \text{ s}^{-1}$$

$$Q^3 = 0.25 \times 39.00 = 9.75 \text{ m}^3 \text{ s}^{-1} \qquad Q^4 = 0$$
$$Q^5 = Q^6 = 0.38 \times 39.792 = 15.12 \text{ m}^3 \text{ s}^{-1}$$

The system is shown in Figure S.2.

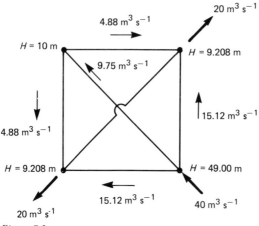

Figure S.2

4.3

$$k^1 = k^2 = \frac{\pi}{128} \frac{2D^4}{vL} = \frac{\pi}{128} \left(\frac{9.81}{10^{-6}}\right) \left(\frac{4^4 \times 10^{-4}}{1000}\right) = 6.16 \text{ m}^2 \text{ s}^{-1}$$

$$k^3 = k^4 = \frac{\pi}{128} \left(\frac{9.81}{10^{-6}}\right) \left(\frac{2^4 \times 10^{-4}}{1500}\right) = 0.25 \text{ m}^2 \text{ s}^{-1}$$

$$k^5 = k^6 = \frac{\pi}{128} \left(\frac{9.81}{10^{-6}}\right) \left(\frac{2^4 \times 10^{-4}}{1000}\right) = 0.38 \text{ m}^2 \text{ s}^{-1}$$

System matrix:

$$
\begin{bmatrix}
\begin{pmatrix} 6.16 \\ +6.16 \\ +0.25 \end{pmatrix} & -6.16 & -6.16 & -0.25 \\
-6.16 & \begin{pmatrix} 6.16 \\ +0.25 \\ +0.38 \end{pmatrix} & -0.25 & -0.38 \\
-6.16 & -0.25 & \begin{pmatrix} +6.16 \\ +0.25 \\ +0.38 \end{pmatrix} & -0.38 \\
-0.25 & -0.38 & -0.38 & \begin{pmatrix} 0.25 \\ +0.38 \\ +0.38 \end{pmatrix}
\end{bmatrix}
\begin{Bmatrix} H_1 \\ H_2 \\ H_3 \\ H_4 \end{Bmatrix}
=
\begin{Bmatrix} -C_1 \\ -20 \\ -20 \\ +40 \end{Bmatrix}
$$

$$\begin{bmatrix} +12.57 & -6.16 & -6.16 & -0.25 \\ -6.16 & +6.79 & -0.25 & -0.38 \\ -6.16 & -0.25 & +6.79 & -0.38 \\ -0.25 & -0.38 & -0.38 & +1.01 \end{bmatrix} \begin{pmatrix} H_1 \\ H_2 \\ H_3 \\ H_4 \end{pmatrix} = \begin{pmatrix} -C_1 \\ -20 \\ -20 \\ +40 \end{pmatrix}$$

4.4   Notice that

$$k^1 = \frac{\pi g D^4}{128 \gamma L} = \frac{\pi}{128} \left(\frac{9.81}{10^{-6}} \right) \left(\frac{5^4 \times 10^{-4}}{1000} \right) = 15.04 \text{ m}^2 \text{ s}^{-1}$$

$$k^2 = \frac{\pi}{128} \left(\frac{9.81}{10^{-6}} \right) \left(\frac{8^4 \times 10^{-4}}{2000} \right) = 49.28 \text{ m}^2 \text{ s}^{-1}$$

$$k^3 = \frac{\pi}{128} \left(\frac{9.81}{10^{-6}} \right) \left(\frac{2^4 \times 10^{-4}}{500} \right) = 0.77 \text{ m}^2 \text{ s}^{-1}$$

System matrix:

$$\begin{bmatrix} 15.04 & -15.04 & 0 & 0 \\ -15.04 & (15.04+49.28) & -49.28 & 0 \\ 0 & -49.28 & (49.28+0.77) & -0.77 \\ 0 & 0 & -0.77 & 0.77 \end{bmatrix}$$

Hence:

$$\begin{bmatrix} 64.32 & -49.28 \\ -49.28 & 50.05 \end{bmatrix} \begin{Bmatrix} H_2 \\ H_3 \end{Bmatrix} = \begin{Bmatrix} 601.6 \\ 7.70 \end{Bmatrix}$$

$H_3 = 38.19 \text{ m}$ $H_2 = 38.60 \text{ m}$

$Q^1 = 15.04(1.40) = 21.06 \text{ m}^3 \text{ s}^{-1}$

$Q^2 = 49.28(0.41) = 20.20 \text{ m}^3 \text{ s}^{-1}$

$Q^3 = 0.77(28.19) = 21.70 \text{ m}^3 \text{ s}^{-1}$

4.5

$$k^1 = \frac{\pi g D^4}{128 \gamma L} = \frac{\pi}{128} \left(\frac{9.81}{10^{-6}} \right) \left(\frac{10^{-4}}{100} \right) = 0.240 \text{ m}^2 \text{ s}^{-1}$$

$$k^2 = \frac{\pi}{128} \left(\frac{9.81}{10^{-6}} \right) \left(\frac{2^4 \times 10^{-4}}{120} \right) = 3.208 \text{ m}^2 \text{ s}^{-1}$$

$$k^3 = \frac{\pi}{128} \left(\frac{9.81}{10^{-6}} \right) \left(\frac{2^4 \times 10^{-4}}{120} \right) = 3.208 \text{ m}^2 \text{ s}^{-1}$$

$$k^4 = \frac{\pi}{128} \left(\frac{9.81}{10^{-6}} \right) \left(\frac{10^{-4}}{100} \right) = 0.240 \text{ m}^2 \text{ s}^{-1}$$

$$k^5 = \frac{\pi}{128} \left(\frac{9.81}{10^{-6}} \right) \left(\frac{2^4 \times 10^4}{160} \right) = 2.406 \text{ m}^2 \text{ s}^{-1}$$

System matrix:

$$
\begin{bmatrix}
\begin{pmatrix} 0.240 \\ +3.208 \end{pmatrix} & -0.240 & -3.208 & 0 \\
-0.240 & \begin{pmatrix} -0.240 \\ +3.208 \\ +2.406 \end{pmatrix} & -2.406 & -3.208 \\
-3.208 & -2.406 & \begin{pmatrix} +3.208 \\ +0.240 \\ +2.406 \end{pmatrix} & -0.240 \\
0 & -3.208 & -0.240 & \begin{pmatrix} +3.208 \\ +0.240 \end{pmatrix}
\end{bmatrix}
$$

$$
\begin{bmatrix}
3.448 & -0.240 & -3.208 & 0 \\
-0.240 & +5.854 & -2.406 & -3.208 \\
-3.208 & -2.406 & +5.654 & -0.240 \\
0 & -3.208 & -0.240 & +3.548
\end{bmatrix}
$$

$$
\begin{bmatrix}
5.854 & -2.406 \\
-2.406 & 5.654
\end{bmatrix}
\begin{Bmatrix} H_2 \\ H_3 \end{Bmatrix}
= \begin{Bmatrix} 73.76 \\ 133.12 \end{Bmatrix}
$$

$H_3 = 35.05$ m $H_2 = 27.00$ m

One can then calculate the fluxes.

4.6   For each element

$$
\begin{Bmatrix} Q_j \\ Q_k \end{Bmatrix}^i = k^i \begin{bmatrix} 1 & -1 \\ -1 & 1 \end{bmatrix} \begin{Bmatrix} H_j \\ H_k \end{Bmatrix}^i
$$

$$
k^j = \frac{\pi}{128}\left(\frac{\rho g D^4}{\mu L}\right) = \frac{\pi}{128}\left(\frac{g D^4}{\nu L}\right) = 0.24 \times 10^6 \left(\frac{D^4}{L}\right)
$$

Element	Length (m)	Diameter (m)	D^4/L (m^3)	k^i (m^2 s^{-1})
1	1000	0.4	25.6×10^{-6}	6.144
2	1000	0.2	1.6×10^{-6}	0.384
3	2000	0.283	3.33×10^{-6}	0.800
4	2000	0.283	3.33×10^{-6}	0.800
5	2000	0.573	53.3×10^{-6}	12.800

System matrix:

6.144 +0.384	−6.144	−0.384	
−6.144	6.144 −0.8+0.8	−0.8	−0.8
−0.384	−0.8	+0.384 +0.8 +12.8	−12.8
	−0.8	+12.8	+0.8 +12.8

$$\begin{bmatrix} +6.528 & -6.144 & -0.384 & 0 \\ -6.144 & +7.744 & -0.80 & -0.80 \\ -0.384 & -0.80 & +13.984 & -12.8 \\ 0 & -0.80 & -12.8 & +13.6 \end{bmatrix} \begin{pmatrix} H_1 \\ H_2 \\ H_3 \\ H_4 \end{pmatrix} = \begin{pmatrix} -C_1 \\ +10 \\ +10 \\ -C_4 \end{pmatrix}$$

Notice that $H_1 = 20$ m and $H_4 = 10$ m.

$$\begin{bmatrix} 7.744 & -0.80 \\ -0.80 & +13.984 \end{bmatrix} \begin{Bmatrix} H_2 \\ H_3 \end{Bmatrix} = \begin{Bmatrix} 10 \\ 10 \end{Bmatrix} + 20 \begin{Bmatrix} 6.144 \\ 0.384 \end{Bmatrix} + 10 \begin{Bmatrix} 0.80 \\ 12.8 \end{Bmatrix}$$

$$= \begin{Bmatrix} 10 \\ 10 \end{Bmatrix} + \begin{Bmatrix} 122.88 \\ 7.68 \end{Bmatrix} + \begin{Bmatrix} 8.0 \\ 128.0 \end{Bmatrix}$$

$$\begin{bmatrix} 7.744 & -0.80 \\ -0.80 & +13.984 \end{bmatrix} \begin{Bmatrix} H_2 \\ H_3 \end{Bmatrix} = \begin{Bmatrix} 140.88 \\ 145.68 \end{Bmatrix}$$

$$\begin{aligned} H_2 - 0.1033 H_3 &= 18.192 \\ -H_2 + 17.48 H_3 &= 182.10 \end{aligned}$$

$$0 + 17.376 H_3 = 200.292$$

$$H_3 = 11.526 \text{ m}$$

$$H_2 = 18.192 + 0.1033 \times 11.526 = 19.382 \text{ m}$$
$$C_1 = -6.528 \times 20 + 6.144 \times 19.382 + 0.384 \times 11.526$$
$$= -7.05 \text{ m}^3 \text{ s}^{-1}$$

$$C_4 = 0.80H_2 + 12.8H_3 - 13.6H_4$$
$$= 0.80 \times 19.382 + 12.8 \times 11.526 - 13.6 \times 10$$
$$= 27.0384 \text{ m}^3 \text{ s}^{-1} \simeq 27.05 \text{ m}^3 \text{ s}^{-1}$$

Check:

$$\sum_i C_i = -7.05 - 10 - 10 + 27.05 = 0$$
$$Q^1 = k^1(H_1 - H_2) = 6.144 \times 0.618 = 3.797 \text{ m}^3 \text{ s}^{-1}$$
$$Q^2 = k^2(H_1 - H_3) = 0.384 \times 8.474 = 3.254 \text{ m}^3 \text{ s}^{-1}$$
$$Q^3 = k^3(H_2 - H_3) = 0.80 \times 7.856 = 6.285 \text{ m}^3 \text{ s}^{-1}$$
$$Q^4 = k^4(H_2 - H_4) = 0.80 \times 9.382 = 7.50 \text{ m}^3 \text{ s}^{-1}$$
$$Q^5 = k^5(H_3 - H_4) = 12.80 \times 1.526 = 19.33 \text{ m}^3 \text{ s}^{-1}$$

Notice that equilibrium is satisfied at all nodes.

Chapter 5

5.1   The depth can be calculated from $V_c^2 = gh_c$ and so

$$h_c = \frac{V_c^2}{g} = \frac{9}{9.81} = 0.917 \text{ m}$$

5.2   The speed of the wave is given by

$$V = \sqrt{(gh)} = \sqrt{(9.81 \times 0.20)} = 1.40 \text{ m s}^{-1}$$

5.3   The energy for a rectangular channel is,

$$E = h + \frac{q^2}{2gH^2}$$

where

$$q = \frac{Q}{b} = \frac{20 \text{ m}^3 \text{ s}^{-1}}{8 \text{ m}} = 2.5 \text{ m}^2 \text{ s}^{-1}$$

Therefore

$$E = h + \frac{(2.5)^2}{2gh^2} = h + \frac{0.318}{h^2}$$

We can then plot the E versus h curve (Figure S.3) using the following table:

h (m)	3.83	2.38 1.77	1.48 1.35	1.29 1.29	1.32 1.42	1.54 1.72	1.90 2.08
E (m)	0.30	0.40 0.50	0.60 0.70	0.80 0.90	1.00 1.20	1.40 1.60	1.80 2.00

The conjugate depth to $h = 0.50$ m is $h \simeq 1.65$ m.

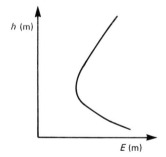

h (m)

E (m)   *Figure S.3*

5.4   Notice that for critical flow,

$q = (gh_c^3)^{1/2}$

The total discharge is,

$Q = L(gh_c^3)^{1/2}$

where L is the width of the weir. The energy is,

$E_c = h_c + \dfrac{V_c^2}{2g}$

and from formula (5.47), for a wide channel,

$\tfrac{1}{2}h_c = V_c^2/2g$

Hence

$E_c = h_c + \tfrac{1}{2}h_c = \tfrac{3}{2}h_c$ and so $h_c = \tfrac{2}{3}E_c$

For high weirs $E_c \simeq H$, and

$Q = Lg^{1/2}(\tfrac{2}{3}E_c)^{3/2} \simeq 0.545 g^{1/2}LH^{3/2}$

Hence,

$Q \simeq 0.545(9.81)^{1/2} \times 18 \times (0.8)^{3/2} = 21.98 \text{ m}^3 \text{ s}^{-1}.$

5.5   The velocity of the water in the reservoir can be neglected. Hence at the channel entrance we have the same situation as for a broad-crested weir, i.e.

$Q = 0.545 g^{1/2}LH^{3/2}$

In this case $L = 6$ m and $H = 4$ m, thus

$Q = 0.545(9.81)^{1/2} \times 6 \times 4^{3/2} = 70.95 \text{ m}^3 \text{ s}^{-1}.$

5.6

$$F_1 = \dfrac{q}{(gh_1^3)^{1/2}} = \left\{ \dfrac{1}{8} \left[\left(2\dfrac{h_2}{h_1} + 1 \right)^2 - 1 \right] \right\}^{1/2}$$

Thus

$$q = \left\{ gh_1^3 \times \frac{1}{8} \left[\left(2\frac{h_2}{h_1} + 1 \right)^2 - 1 \right] \right\}^{1/2}$$

$$= \left\{ 9.81 \times (0.4)^3 \times \frac{1}{8} \left[\left(2\frac{1.6}{0.4} + 1 \right)^2 - 1 \right] \right\}^{1/2}$$

$$= 2.50 \ \text{m}^2 \ \text{s}^{-1}.$$

5.7 Manning's equation gives

$$Q = \frac{1}{n} R^{2/3} S^{1/2} \Omega$$

where $n = 0.015$. Also since

$$\Omega = 64 \ \text{m}^2 \qquad \Gamma = 24 \ \text{m}$$

we have

$$R = 64/24 = 2.66 \ \text{m} \qquad R^{2/3} = 1.92 \ \text{m}^{2/3}$$

and

$$S = 0.0012 \qquad S^{1/2} = 0.0346$$

Hence

$$Q = \frac{1}{0.015} (1.92)(0.0346)(64) = 283 \ \text{m}^3 \ \text{s}^{-1}.$$

Chapter 6

6.1 Note that

$$\omega = \frac{1}{2} \left\{ \frac{\partial v}{\partial x} - \frac{\partial u}{\partial y} \right\} = -\frac{1}{2} \nabla \psi$$

and

$$\nabla^2 \psi = 2 + 2 = 4$$

Hence $\omega \neq 0$ and the velocity potential cannot exist as the flow is *rotational*.

6.2 (a) $\varphi = -xy$,

$$u = -\frac{\partial \varphi}{\partial x} = y = \frac{\partial \psi}{\partial y}$$

Hence

$$\psi = \tfrac{1}{2}y^2 + f(x)$$

$$v = -\frac{\partial \varphi}{\partial y} = x - \frac{\partial \psi}{\partial x}$$

and

$$\psi = -\tfrac{1}{2}x^2 + g(y)$$

We can then write,

$$\psi = \tfrac{1}{2}(y^2 - x^2)$$

The streamlines can be plotted as shown in Figure S.4.

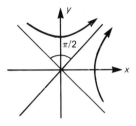

Figure S.4

(b) $\varphi = -x^2 + 3xy^2$,

$$u = -\frac{\partial \varphi}{\partial x} = 3(x^2 - y^2) + \frac{\partial \psi}{\partial y}$$

Thus

$$\psi = 3x^2 y - y^3 + f(x)$$

$$v = -\frac{\partial \varphi}{\partial y} = -6xy = -\frac{\partial \psi}{\partial x}$$

and so

$$\psi = 3x^2 y + g(y)$$

We can deduce,

$$\psi = 3x^2 y - y^3$$

These streamlines can be plotted as shown in Figure S.5.

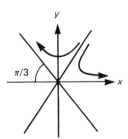

Figure S.5

6.3   The stream function is (equation (6.72))

$$\psi = \frac{q}{2\pi} \tan^{-1}\left(\frac{2ly}{x^2 - l^2 + y^2}\right)$$

Hence a *streamline* is defined by

$$\frac{2ly}{x^2 - l^2 + y^2} = \text{constant} = c$$

or,

$$x^2 + \left(y - \frac{l}{c}\right)^2 = l^2\left(\frac{1}{c^2} + 1\right)$$

which demonstrates that the streamlines are circles. Notice that if c is given, we have $x = \pm l$ for $y = 0$, which means that the circles pass through source and sink (Figure S.6).

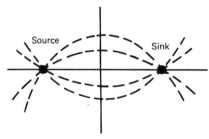

Figure S.6

6.4   Given the flow represented by

$$\varphi_f = -Ar^2 \cos(2\theta)$$

and a source represented by

$$\varphi_s = -\frac{q}{2\pi} \ln r$$

The total potential can be written as,

$$\varphi = -Ar^2 \cos(2\theta) - \frac{q}{2\pi} \ln r$$

The radial velocity is

$$v_r = -\frac{\partial \varphi}{\partial r} = 2Ar \cos(2\theta) + \frac{q}{2\pi r}$$

For $x = 0$ we have $\theta = \pi/2$ and $v_r = 0$; thus

$$2Ar = \frac{q}{2\pi r}$$

If $r = l$ is given q needs to be $q = 4l^2\pi A$.
Figure S.7 shows the streamlines for this problem.

6.5   In this case we can consider three images of the zone as shown in Figure S.8. Hence the total potential at P is given by the superposition of the four sources:

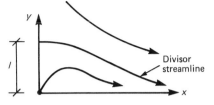

Figure S.7

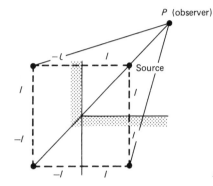

Figure S.8

$$-\varphi = \frac{q}{2\pi} \{\ln [(x-l)^2 + (y-l)^2]^{1/2} + \ln [(x+l)^2 + (y-l)^2]^{1/2}$$

$$+ \ln [(x-l)^2 + (y+l)^2]^{1/2} + \ln [(x+l)^2 + (y+l)^2]^{1/2}\}$$

This distribution will make the corner a streamline. The velocity on $y=0$ for instance is,

$$u = -\frac{\partial \varphi}{\partial x} = \frac{q}{\pi} \left(\frac{x-l}{(x-l)^2 + l^2} + \frac{x+l}{(x+l)^2 + l^2} \right) \tag{a}$$

The pressure can be found as,

$$\Delta p = p_\infty - p = \rho u^2 / 2$$

whence u is calculated using equation (a). The distribution of Δp along x is as shown in Figure S.9.

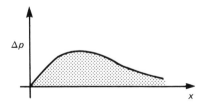

Figure S.9

6.6   Notice that the flow can be represented as the superposition of the velocity potential without the source, i.e.

$$\varphi_f = -Vx$$

and the one for the source,

$$\varphi_s = \frac{q}{2\pi}\ln r$$

Hence:

$$\varphi = -Vx + \frac{q}{2\pi}\ln r$$

The velocity in the x direction is

$$u = -\frac{\partial\varphi}{\partial x} = V - \frac{q}{2\pi}\left(\frac{x}{x^2+y^2}\right)$$

along x, $y=0$ and so

$$u = V - \frac{q}{2\pi x}$$

and the pressure is

$$p = p_\infty + \tfrac{1}{2}\rho(V^2 - u^2)$$

Notice that

$$(V-u)^2 = \frac{q^2}{4\pi^2 x^2} = V^2 - 2Vu + u^2$$

Hence:

$$\Delta p = p - p_\infty = \frac{\rho q}{2\pi}\left(\frac{V}{x} - \frac{q}{4\pi x^2}\right)$$

which can be represented as in Figure S.10.

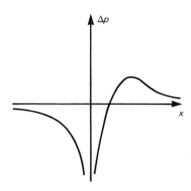

Figure S.10

Chapter 7

7.1   For $u=0$ and $v=cy$ we have

$$\omega = \frac{1}{2}\left(\frac{\partial v}{\partial x} - \frac{\partial u}{\partial y}\right) = \tfrac{1}{2}c$$

7.2

$$-\frac{\partial p}{\partial x}+\mu\frac{\partial^2 f}{\partial y^2}=0$$

Thus

$$\frac{\partial^2 f}{\partial y^2}=\frac{1}{\mu}\frac{dp}{dx}$$

7.3   The field is irrotational since

$$\omega=\frac{1}{2}\left(\frac{\partial v}{\partial x}-\frac{\partial u}{\partial y}\right)=0 \tag{a}$$

The stresses are

$$\sigma_{xx}=-p+2\mu\frac{\partial u}{\partial x}=-p-2\mu c \tag{b}$$

$$\sigma_{yy}=-p+2\mu\frac{\partial v}{\partial y}=-p+2\mu c \tag{c}$$

$$\tau_{xy}=2\mu\left(\frac{\partial u}{\partial y}+\frac{\partial v}{\partial x}\right)=0 \tag{d}$$

Therefore

$$f=\rho gy+\text{constant} \tag{e}$$

$$p=-a\rho x+\rho gy+\text{constant} \tag{f}$$

The constant can be taken to be the atmospheric pressure in the free surface. Hence in the free surface $p=p_0$ and,

$$\rho gy=\rho ax \tag{g}$$

$$y=\frac{a}{g}x \tag{h}$$

$$\tan\theta=\frac{dy}{dx}=\frac{a}{g} \tag{i}$$

which gives the inclination of the free surface. The accelerations are

$$a_x=u\frac{\partial u}{\partial x}+v\frac{\partial u}{\partial y}=+c^2 x$$

$$a_y=u\frac{\partial v}{\partial x}+v\frac{\partial v}{\partial y}=+c^2 y$$

The Navier–Stokes equations are (cf equation (7.22))

$$-\frac{\partial p}{\partial x}=\rho c^2 x \Rightarrow p=-\tfrac{1}{2}\rho c^2 x^2+\text{constant}$$

$$-\frac{\partial p}{\partial y}=\rho c^2 y \quad \therefore p = -\tfrac{1}{2}\rho c^2 y^2 + \text{constant}$$

Hence

$$p = -\tfrac{1}{2}\rho c^2(x^2 + y^2) + p_0$$

7.4   The equations of motion in the x and y directions are

$$\rho a = -\frac{\partial p}{\partial x} \tag{a}$$

$$0 = -\frac{\partial p}{\partial y} + \rho g \tag{b}$$

where a is the horizontal acceleration. Hence from equation (a)

$$p = -\rho a x + f(y) \tag{c}$$

From equations (b) and (c)

$$\frac{\partial p}{\partial y} = \rho g = \frac{\partial f}{\partial y} \tag{d}$$

7.5 $S = fD/V = 0.2,\ f = 2\pi/T.$
Critical velocity:

$$V = 5fD = 5 \times \tfrac{1}{2} \times 0.4 = 1 \text{ m s}^{-1}$$

Drag:

$$P_D = \tfrac{1}{2}\rho D C_D V^2$$

where P_D is force per unit length. Thus

$$P_D = \tfrac{1}{2} \times 10^3 \text{ kg m}^{-3} \times 0.40 \text{ m} \times 1.0 \times 1.0 \text{ m}^2 \text{ s}^{-2}$$
$$= 200 \text{ N m}^{-1}$$

Total force: $F_D = P_D \times 20 \text{ m} = 4 \times 10^3$ N.

7.6   We know that

(a)

$$\sigma_{xx} = -p + 2\mu\frac{\partial u}{\partial x}$$

$$-\sigma_{xx} - p = 2\mu\frac{\partial u}{\partial x}$$

$$\frac{\partial u}{\partial x} = +2x$$

Hence $x = 1$ and so

$$-\sigma_{xx} - p = +2(2 \times 10^{-5})(2) = +8 \times 10^{-5} \text{ N m}^{-2}$$

(b)

$$\tau_{xy} = 2\mu \times \frac{1}{2}\left(\frac{\partial u}{\partial y} + \frac{\partial v}{\partial x}\right)$$

$$\frac{\partial u}{\partial y} + \frac{\partial v}{\partial x} = -2y - 2y = -4y$$

Thus

$$\tau_{xy} = 2(2 \times 10^{-5})\tfrac{1}{2}(-4y)$$

and at $y = 2$ we have

$$\tau_{xy} = -16 \times 10^{-5} \text{ N m}^{-2}$$

Chapter 8

8.1

$$H = \frac{u_2 V_2 \cos \alpha_2}{g}$$

$$= \frac{2000 \times 2 \times \pi \times 0.50 \times 0.50 \times 10}{60 \times 9.81} = 53.37 \text{ m}$$

$$\eta = 100 \times \frac{47.5}{53.37} \simeq 89\%$$

8.2   Figure S.11 shows the pump outlet blade.

$$Q = 1000 \text{ l s}^{-1} = 1 \text{ m}^3 \text{ s}^{-1}$$

$$V_{\text{d}} = \frac{Q}{\Omega} = \frac{1}{\pi(0.25)^2} = 5.09 \text{ m s}^{-1}$$

$$u_2 = \frac{1600}{60} \times 1.50 \times \pi = 125.66 \text{ m s}^{-1}$$

$$V_{r2} = \frac{1}{0.2} = 5 \text{ m s}^{-1} = V_1 = V_{r1}$$

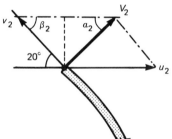

Figure S.11

$$V_2^2 = V_{r2}^2 + \left(u_2 - \frac{V_{r2}}{\tan 20°}\right)^2$$

$$= 25 + \left(125.66 - \frac{5}{0.36}\right)^2 = 12519.76 \text{ m}^2 \text{ s}^{-2}$$

$$V_2 = 111.89 \text{ m s}^{-1}$$

$$V_2 \cos \alpha_2 = u_2 - V_{r2}/\tan 20° = 111.78 \text{ m s}^{-1}$$

$$H = \frac{u_2 V_2 \cos \alpha_2}{g} = \frac{125.66 \times 111.78}{9.81} = 1431.83 \text{ m}$$

Apply Bernouilli's equation at inlet and outlet:

$$\frac{p_1}{\gamma} + \frac{V_1^2}{2g} = \frac{p_2}{\gamma} + \frac{V_2^2}{2g} - H + H_1$$

where H_1 represents losses. Thus

$$\frac{p_2 - p_1}{\gamma} = H - H_1 + \frac{V_1^2 - V_2^2}{2g}$$

$$= 1431.83 - 1 + \frac{25 - 12519.76}{2 \times 9.81}$$

$$= 1430.83 - 636.81 = 793.99 \text{ m}$$

Hence the head difference between inlet and outlet is

$$H_d = H - H_1 - H_{discharge}$$

$$= 1431.83 - 1 - 1200 = 230.83 \text{ m}$$

We can apply Bernouilli's equation again to obtain the total head, i.e.

$$\frac{p_d}{\gamma} + \frac{V_d^2}{2g} + H_d = \frac{p_2}{\gamma} + \frac{V_2^2}{2g}$$

and so

$$\frac{p_d - p_2}{\gamma} = \frac{V_2^2 - V_d^2}{2g} - H_d$$

$$= \frac{(111.89)^2 - (5.09)^2}{2 \times 9.81} - 230.83$$

$$= 432.94 \text{ m}$$

which is the total head produced by the runner.

8.3

$$H = \frac{u_1 V_1 \cos \alpha_1}{g}$$

Thus

$$V_1 \cos \alpha_1 = \frac{Hg}{u_1} = \frac{100 \times 9.81}{300 \times 2\pi \times 2/60}$$

$$= 15.61 \text{ m s}^{-1}$$

The torque is

$$T = \rho Q(rV_1 \cos \alpha_1)$$

$$= 1000 \times 12 \times 2 \times 15.61 = 374640 \text{ N m}$$

and the power is

$$P = \gamma QH = 9810 \times 12 \times 100 = 11772 \text{ kW}$$

8.4 From equation (8.10)

$$H = \frac{u_2^2}{g} - \frac{u_2 Q \cot \beta_2}{2\pi r_2 b_2 g}$$

where

$$u_2 = N \frac{2\pi}{60} r_2 = 1600 \frac{2\pi}{60} 0.08 = 13.40 \text{ m s}^{-1}$$

$$H = \frac{(13.404)^2}{9.81} - \frac{13.404 \cot 30°}{2\pi \times 0.08 \times 0.015 \times 9.81} Q$$

$$= 18.315 - 313.88Q$$

The theoretical head–discharge relationship is then a straight line, which can be drawn as in Figure S.12.

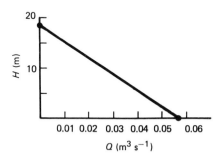

Figure S.12

8.5 We can compute the velocity at the penstock by continuity, i.e.

$$V_p = V_j \left(\frac{\Omega_j}{\Omega_p} \right) = 0.0278 V_j$$

where the subscripts p and j stand for penstock and jet respectively. The losses in the penstock are,

$$h_1 = \frac{\lambda L}{D}\left(\frac{V_p^2}{2g}\right) = \frac{0.02 \times 10000}{0.6}\frac{(0.0278)^2}{2 \times 9.81}V_j^2$$

$$= 0.257\left(\frac{V_j^2}{2g}\right) = 0.0131V_j^2$$

From Bernouilli's equation

reservoir   jet

$$\frac{p_1}{\gamma} + \frac{V_1^2}{2g} + Z_1 = \frac{p_j}{\gamma} + \frac{V_j^2}{2g} + Z_j + h_1$$

$$0 + 0 + 1800 = 0 + \frac{V_j^2}{2g} + 800 + h_1$$

Thus

$$V_j = \left(\frac{2g \times 1000}{1.257}\right)^{1/2} = 124.93 \text{ m s}^{-1}$$

One can now calculate the ideal power produced by this jet:

$$P = Q\gamma\frac{V_j^2}{2g} = \frac{\gamma\Omega_j V_j^3}{2g}$$

$$= \frac{9810(\pi/4)(0.10)^2(124.93)^3}{2 \times 9.81}$$

$$= 7657 \text{ kW}$$

Because of losses the real power of the turbine is,

$$P = 7657 \times 0.80 = 6125 \text{ kW}$$

The speed of the bucket V_b is,

$$V_b = \tfrac{1}{2}V_j = \frac{124.93}{2} = 62.46 \text{ m s}^{-1}$$

$$= r\omega$$

Hence

$$\omega = \frac{62.46}{2.0} = 31.23 \text{ rad s}^{-1}$$

The speed of the wheel can now be calculated as,

$$N = 31.23 \times \frac{1}{2\pi} \times 60 = 298 \text{ rpm}$$

and the torque is given by

$$P = T\omega$$

and so

$$T = \frac{P}{\omega} = \frac{6125}{298} = 20 \text{ kN m}$$

8.6 We can first apply Bernouilli's equation:

$$\overbrace{\frac{p_1}{\gamma}+\frac{V_1^2}{2g}+Z_1}^{\text{reservoir}}=\overbrace{\frac{p_2}{\gamma}+\frac{V_2^2}{2g}+Z_2+h_l}^{\text{jet}}$$

$$0+0+1000=0+\frac{V_j^2}{2g}+0+\frac{\lambda L}{D}\left(\frac{V_p^2}{2g}\right)$$

Thus

$$\frac{V_j^2}{2g}\left[1+\frac{\lambda L}{D}\left(\frac{V_p}{V_{jet}}\right)^2\right]=1000 \text{ m}$$

For continuity,

$$V_p=V_j\left(\frac{\Omega_j}{\Omega_p}\right)=V_j\left(\frac{0.09}{9.00}\right)$$

$$=0.01V_j$$

Hence,

$$V_j^2=\frac{1000\times 2\times 9.81}{1+\frac{1}{3}(0.015\times 15000)(0.01)^2}$$

$$=\frac{19620}{1.0075}=19473.94$$

Therefore

$$V_j=139.55 \text{ m s}^{-1}$$

The power is

$$P=Q\gamma V^2\eta$$

$$=139.55\times\left(\frac{\pi}{4}\right)\times(0.30)^2\times 9810\times\frac{(139.55)^2}{2\times 9.81}\times 0.90$$

$$=86444 \text{ kW}=86 \text{ MW}$$

$$(Q=V_j\Omega_j)$$

8.7 For this problem we have

$$D_1=0.40 \text{ m} \qquad D_2=0.40\times 2=0.80 \text{ m}$$

$$N_1=2400 \text{ rpm}=40 \text{ rps}$$

$$N_2=1200 \text{ rpm}=20 \text{ rps}$$

Note that at main efficiency

$$H_{N_1}=80 \text{ m}$$

$$Q_{N_1}=0.135 \text{ m}^3 \text{ s}^{-1}$$

From equation (8.37)

$$H_{N_2} = H_{N_1} \left(\frac{D_2}{D_1}\right)^2 \left(\frac{N_2}{N_1}\right)^2 = H_{N_1} \left(\frac{2D_1}{D_1}\right)^2 \left(\frac{N_1}{2N_1}\right)^2 = H_{N_1}$$

Thus

$$H_{N_2} = 80 \text{ m} = H_{N_1}$$

and for the discharge, from equation (8.36),

$$Q_{N_2} = Q_{N_1} \left(\frac{D_2}{D_1}\right)^3 \left(\frac{N_2}{N_1}\right) = Q_{N_1} \left(\frac{2D_1}{D_1}\right)^3 \left(\frac{N_1}{2N_1}\right)$$

$$= 4Q_{N_1}$$

Thus

$$Q_{N_2} = 4 \times 0.135 = 0.54 \text{ m}^3 \text{ s}^{-1}$$

8.8   The power required is

$$P = \gamma Q H \eta = 9810 \times 1 \times 1000 \times 0.85$$

$$= 8338.5 \text{ kW}$$

The specific speed, where the units of N, P, H are rpm, kW, m respectively, is

$$N_S = N \frac{P^{1/2}}{H^{5/4}} = N \frac{19.31}{5623.41} = 0.0162N$$

The speed N for 60 and four p9les is

$$N = 3600/4 = 900 \text{ rpm}$$

Hence the required N_S is

$$N_S = 900 \times 0.0162 \simeq 15$$

The velocity of the jet is

$$V_j = C_V (2gH)^{1/2} = 0.9(2 \times 9.81 \times 1000)^{1/2} = 126 \text{ m s}^{-1}$$

$$V_{bucket} = 126/2 = 63 \text{ m s}^{-1}$$

The angular speed is

$$\omega = \frac{900}{60} 2\pi = 94.2 \text{ rad s}^{-1}$$

Hence the velocity is

$$u = \omega D / 2$$

$$D = \frac{2u}{\omega} = \frac{2 \times 63}{94.2} = 1.33 \text{ m}$$

and so

(Note that D is the diameter of the wheel at the centre of the buckets.)

8.9   From Bernouilli's equation

$$y_A + \frac{V_1^2}{2g} + \frac{p_1}{\gamma} = y_B + \frac{V_2^2}{2g} + \frac{p_2}{2g} + h_1$$

and so

$$\frac{p_1}{\gamma} = -8 - \frac{10^2}{2 \times 9.81} + \frac{1^2}{2 \times 9.81} + 1$$

$$= -12.04 \text{ m}$$

Notice that this is a suction pressure and that the barotropic pressure is ~ 10.5 m. As the vapour pressure at 20°C is around 0.25 m cavitation can occur.

Index

mL

before